CONTEMPORARY CONTINENTAL THEOLOGY

CONTEMPORARY CONTINENTAL THEOLOGY

An Interpretation for Anglo-Saxons

WALTER MARSHALL HORTON
OBERLIN COLLEGE

STUDENT CHRISTIAN MOVEMENT PRESS
58, BLOOMSBURG STREET,
LONDON, W.C.1

FIRST PUBLISHED NOVEMBER 1938

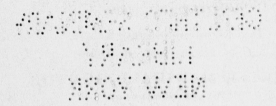

Printed in the United States of America

To

EMILE BAUDIN (*Strasbourg*)
who first introduced me to Continental
Catholic thought

and

GEORG WÜNSCH (*Marburg*)
who first introduced me to Continental
Protestant thought

Two whom I honor as teachers,
fear as critics, love as friends.

TABLE OF CONTENTS

PREFACE

THIS book is a sequel and an act of atonement.

Contemporary English Theology, which I published in 1936, gave rise to much sharper criticism than I had expected. In our world of rampant nationalism, to praise and recommend the work of any nation in any field, even theology, and to compare it with the work of other nations, is evidently equivalent to throwing out the apple of discord. Ever since I ventured to recommend the reading of English theology to my American compatriots, I have been dodging missiles from many different angles. Americans asked why American theology was not good enough for Americans; Scotsmen, why I had chosen to write on "English" rather than "British" theology; Continentals accused me of having a "theological foreign policy" dictated more by political sympathies than by genuinely theological considerations.

Of all these fiery darts, it was the last that struck me in the most sensitive spot and made my conscience smart. To my American critics I could reply that I was not proposing to undo the work of the American Revolution, but only to enrich and mature our thought by bringing it in contact with another national culture where our present problems happen to have been faced some years ago. To my Scottish critics I could quite peaceably explain that Scottish theology was too distinct from English to be treated in the same book, and too close to American theology

to need much interpretation. But when my Continental critics told me that I was helping to widen the unfortunate gulf between Continental and Anglo-Saxon Christendom, by appealing to a natural sympathy of the English-speaking countries for each other, and a natural antipathy they have for the Continental style of thought, I felt bound to offer an apology and if possible to make atonement.

As I told Dr. Visser't Hooft of the *Student World*, nothing was further from my intention than to encourage "theological nationalism,"[1] or to break off relations with Continental thought. My conviction that Americans have unduly neglected English theology, and would find that it "speaks to their condition" more directly than contemporary German theology, still holds good; but I feel bound now to make clear that the potential contribution of Continental theology to American theology is also very great, and its very remoteness from our present condition ought to stimulate our determination to comprehend its significance.

The Oxford and Edinburgh conferences have further convinced me that a piece of interpretation is needed at the frontier between Continental and Anglo-Saxon thought, as well as at the frontier between our American thought and that of the mother country. If we are Christians, nothing Christian can be alien to us. Whenever—as at present in Continental Europe—any segment of Christian thought

---

[1] See my letter to him in the *Student World*, 2nd Quarter, 1937, p. 197, in reply to his review in the 1st Quarter, p. 97.

threatens to become unduly strange and foreign to us, a voyage of rediscovery is in order. This book aims to be a guidebook for those who wish to undertake that voyage.

Obviously, the field to be explored is much vaster than that which I undertook to survey in my other book; and to explore it by the same method, the method of selective sampling rather than exhaustive portrayal, will leave vast areas untouched. Perhaps it is folly to attempt even a bird's-eye view of Continental theology in so brief a compass as four chapters. Conscious of many inevitable omissions, I have nevertheless decided that the method of sampling is the best way to help the theological explorer get his bearings in a strange environment; while to help him sense the vastness and variety of the whole field, I have arranged for him in the last chapter a sort of whirlwind tour of the Continent, with Karl Barth as guide. I have hopes that in spite of the technicality of much of the material we shall have to consider, the average pastor and intelligent layman will find enough human interest and enough sense of motion in this travelogue to carry them over the rough places.

The substance of this book was first tested out with a representative audience of Christian pastors and laymen in January, 1938, when I had the honor of inaugurating the Lewis French Stearns Lectureship at Bangor Theological Seminary, Bangor, Maine. I have to thank President Harry Trust, his faculty, and my auditors for many personal kindnesses on that occasion—not least, for hanging on through some

pretty long and thorny exposition. Since then I have profited by the criticism of Professor Aubrey of Chicago Divinity School, who read the whole manuscript; Professors Spinka and Pauck of Chicago Theological Seminary, who read Chapters I and III, respectively; Drs. Pittenger, Hardy, and Stewart of General Theological Seminary, who read the first two chapters; and Rev. A. A. Ebersole, who read the last. While remaining aware of many inadequacies in my final draft, I send it forth in the hope that it may promote greater interchange of thought between the divided segments of Christendom, and so serve the cause of the "world Christian community" in a time of severe testing. To the many Continentals whom I interviewed during the summer of 1937 I offer my hearty gratitude for their patience and helpfulness, especially to Mr. Paul Anderson of the Russian Y.M.C.A. in Paris, who arranged all my Paris interviews and shared with me his perspective on the whole Continental situation. To Dr. W. P. Merrill, my thanks for permission to use the parody of his hymn which appears in the Introduction; to the editors of the *Journal of Religion*, *The Women's Press* and *The American Scholar*, for permission to use material previously published in their pages; to the following publishing-houses, for permission to quote from their publications: G. P. Putnam's Sons; Sheed and Ward; Charles Scribner's Sons; The Macmillan Company.

HONOLULU, June 16, 1938.

INTRODUCTION

THE English Channel is a very narrow, if somewhat turbulent, strip of water. In these days of fast bombing planes it no longer suffices to isolate the British from the perils and anxieties of Continental Europe. Perhaps after another generation of forcible immersion in the tangled affairs of the Continent, the British may acquire a more excitable temperament, and begin to gesticulate like the French. But up till now, they continue to think and talk as imperturbably as if they still were absolutely secure in their "tight little isle." To come to England after a month on the Continent is literally to enter another world, a world of welcome humdrum and blessed boredom, perfectly symbolized by the conservative, unemphatic pages of the London *Times*—a sudden and almost shocking let-down after the dramatic intensity and nervous instability of life on the other side of the Channel.

The ocean that separates us Americans from the British Isles is wide—so wide that the English Channel is barely noticeable from our perspective, and we tend to classify the British along with other "Europeans." Yet when we encounter Europeans at international conferences, such as the great ecumenical gatherings at Oxford and Edinburgh in the summer of 1937, the most noticeable gulf of misunderstanding is not between Europeans and Americans, but between "Continentals" and "Anglo-Saxons." We have

not the temperament nor the traditions of the British, and when we confront them alone, we are sharply conscious of our differences; but when we confront the Continentals, we suddenly realize that the British are blood brothers to us, and these others are strangers. The Channel, after all, is broader than the Atlantic.

One conclusion to be drawn from this marked kinship between Britain and America, as contrasted with Continental Europe, is that in theology as in politics we should follow British rather than Continental (e.g., German) leadership. That is to say, very simply, that ideas originating in Britain are likelier to fit our situation than German ideas. I have already drawn this conclusion in my recent study, *Contemporary English Theology,* and see no reason to reverse it. But Christian thought, unlike political thought, cannot accept any international cleavage, any limited bloc or alliance, any Washington-London axis, as right or normal. If a gulf of misunderstanding exists between Continentals and Anglo-Saxons, that is no reason for ignoring all that transpires on the other side of the gulf; it is a reason for studying the causes of the misunderstanding, and seeking to transcend them. No follower of Christ can be content to allow any mere geographical boundary like the English Channel to cut him off from fellowship with his brethren in the faith, however differently their minds may work.

Experience has shown that some of the richest insights into religious truth come when two groups of Christians with contrasting backgrounds wrestle with

one another over some fundamental issue, candidly but respectfully, listening for the word that God may be seeking to convey to them through their theological adversaries. The greatest moments at the Oxford and Edinburgh conferences came when such groups of honestly differing Christians found some genuine solution of their differences; something *more* than a mere diplomatic formula of agreement, which would permit them to present a united front to the external world; a higher truth than either group could grasp or enunciate by itself, struck out in the heat of conflict as they grappled with one another in the sight of God. I am sure that Continental theology has something to contribute to Anglo-American theology, just *because* it cuts across our accustomed ways of thinking, *because* it refuses to be drawn over into our system of thought or comprehended in terms of our categories, while yet it springs from a Christian faith, a Christian loyalty which, when we see it tested under hardship or persecution, makes us take off our hats and confess that these are our brethren, of whom we hope to be worthy.

At one point, particularly, I am convinced that the sympathetic study of Continental theology will tend to deepen, correct and steady our faith: at the point where we face the mystery of the future, the mystery of human destiny. We in the Anglo-Saxon world, securely relying upon our vast natural resources, our highly developed science and technology, our relatively sheltered military situation, and our still fairly stable social institutions, have been thinking and talking

far too glibly about the Kingdom of God as of something that we might hope to "bring in" by our own human efforts. Half unconsciously, we have been confusing the ancient Christian hope of the coming of God's Kingdom with the modern doctrine of progress; and we have been identifying our own programs of social reform with the secret designs of the Almighty.

Already at the Stockholm conference in 1925, our Continental friends were warning us about this "activistic" heresy of ours; but in that relatively hopeful era of Stresemann and Briand, it seemed to us as though to doubt our ability to "bring in the Kingdom" meant cowardly quietism in the face of a great opportunity, sluggish inactivity at a moment when the realization of world peace and brotherhood was almost within our grasp. While we were singing,

> Rise up, O men of God,
>   His Kingdom tarries long,
> *Bring in* the day of brotherhood,
>   And end the night of wrong,

it seemed as though our Continental critics were telling us,

> Sit down, O men of God,
>   His Kingdom He will bring,
> Whenever it may please His will;
>   You cannot do a thing![1]

[1] From a parody of Dr. Merrill's well-known hymn sent to him by a Scottish student, who thought the Continentals would have to sing it this way. Quoted by permission.

Between the Stockholm and Oxford conferences, two changes have taken place which have helped clear up the dispute between Continental "quietism" and Anglo-Saxon "activism," so that it proved less irreconcilable in 1937 than in 1925.[2] On the one hand, we Anglo-Saxons have been so chastened by recent discouraging developments in the world situation that we are now pretty generally prepared to draw a sharp distinction between the Kingdom of God and anything we can hope to achieve by united Christian endeavor in the near future. On the other hand, the Continentals have lost their appearance of ethical indifference. They have made it clear in these critical years that their attitude in the face of grave social disorder, wide-spread paganism, and actual persecution is not one of defeatism or inactivity, but one of courage, hope and active service of God and man— service which necessarily refuses to define its objectives very far in advance, since the whole surface of European life is cracking and sinking under foot like a thawing ice floe, but which receives its orders day by day from God, who alone knows what will be required of his servants by tomorrow!

Whether or not we have to look forward in this country to a veritable crisis of civilization and of Christianity, we can at least now freely admit that

[2] The editor of *Christendom* (Vol. II, No. 4, Autumn 1937, p. 585) says that the controversy on this issue which was expected at Oxford "did not come off." As a member of the section on "The Universal Church and the World of Nations," I must report that there *was* a good deal of real tension on this issue in our section at least, but that it proved possible to overcome this tension by clarifying the above two points.

our Continental fellow Christians are facing one; that
their sense of grappling with historic forces too strong
for man to cope with by his own unaided powers
does not spring from a panic-stricken, alarmist frame
of mind, but from a sober recognition of stern actuali-
ties. It is a fact, and not a nightmare, that in several
European countries today the Christian church finds
itself reduced once more to the status of a weak and
struggling minority. It is a fact that the loyalty of the
people, and especially of the youth, is being captured
by great mass movements inimical to the Gospel of
Christ, and that wider and wider areas of life are
being forcibly preëmpted by the totalitarian State.
Surely something is to be learned from a Christianity
which has passed through that crisis and been purged
in those fires, even if we ourselves are mercifully to
be spared the like experience.

But in my opinion, the bearing of Continental
thought and life upon our own is less remote than
that. Modern civilization, in the last few centuries,
has become too interconnected and interdependent
for any part of the world to escape infection when any
part becomes diseased. The disease which in Continental Europe has now reached a critical stage is
not a European disease, but a disease to which our
industrial civilization as a whole is susceptible, and
which it almost inevitably catches at a certain stage
in its development. That stage is not yet reached in
America, and there are many local conditions which
make it likely that the disease will appear among us
in a different and less fatal form; but I am persuaded

that we cannot wholly avoid it. A line of crisis is moving across our world like the shadow of an eclipse; we need not wait for it passively or fatalistically, but we must pass through it. To borrow a simile of Karl Barth's, those upon whom this crisis has already fallen are like soldiers in the front line, already attacked; and the "hasty and urgent report" which they send back to us who are farther from the front is "a quite self-evident signal of the necessity to arise, take up arms, form into line, and march to the front."[3] For Barth, the "report" in question is from the men of the Bible to the church of today. For me, I confess, the reports which come across the Atlantic from the contemporary Continental battle front have begun to blend with the Scriptural Word of God, and take on a sort of apostolic authority. Like the men of the Bible, these our contemporaries live under apocalyptic skies, where the fiery fate of this present world and the dawn of a new world can already be descried; and what they tell us of their struggles and hopes moves our hearts like a premonition of our own duty and destiny.

"So you think we must all go Barthian, after all?" No, not that. I have met Karl Barth personally for the first time during the past year, and conceived for him a deep sense of respect and gratitude; but I am as far as ever from being a Barthian. What I wish to commend to the studious and favorable attention of the Anglo-Saxon world is not just Barth's "Theology of Crisis," but the great, multiform movement

[3] Karl Barth, *God in Action*, pp. 5, 6.

of Christian thought which has emerged simultaneously within the various Continental churches—Orthodox, Catholic and Protestant—and which in all its mutually inconsistent forms bears the general character of *a* theology of crisis. Barth was the stormy petrel of this whole movement; his shrill, raucous storm warnings first caught our ear, and we therefore tend to associate all that followed with his name; but in the strict sense of the word, there is very little "Barthianism" in Europe today. Those who followed his lead at the start, when he set out to do battle against the errors and dangers of the time—men like Brunner and Tillich, among many others—have very generally refused to follow him since he has turned to positive theological construction.

Each in his own style and according to his inherited traditions, *many* remarkable theological architects are at work in Continental Europe today. Some draw their inspiration from Orthodoxy, some from Catholicism, some from the Reformation. There is (fortunately for us) no one system that they agree upon, which we could import and domesticate, as we used to do with liberal German theology. Least of all is Barth's system to be taken as a convenient compendium of Continental theology. Barth, by the boldness and uncompromising severity of his mind, stands out among his contemporaries like a tall, bare measuring rod. One can see how diversely they are related to one another by observing how diversely they are related to him. But although they do thus differ among themselves, Continental theologians have in common one thing

that is usually lacking among us: a sense of what they often call a "fourth dimension," barely suspected in our neat, orderly, three-dimensional world; a fourth dimension full of terror as well as glory, demons as well as angels, and only to be known through suffering; yet so fascinating and compelling to those who have known it that they would never again be content in our plumbers' paradise, nor exchange their apocalyptic torment for an eternity of our bourgeois bliss. It is mainly in the hope of giving Anglo-American readers a glimpse of this "fourth dimension" that the following pages are written.

CONTEMPORARY CONTINENTAL THEOLOGY

CHAPTER I

THE REDISCOVERY OF ORTHODOX THEOLOGY

1. THE ORTHODOX RENAISSANCE

ONE of the notable events of our time is the dissolution of the ancient barrier between the Orthodox churches of Eastern Europe and the Catholic and Protestant churches of Western Europe. For centuries the life of Eastern and Western Christendom has flowed along separate channels, as distinct as though some great mountain range divided them, although the distance from Rome or Geneva to Athens or Moscow was, after all, not very great. Since the middle of the nineteenth century, however, and especially since the World War, the Eastern and Western areas in Europe have begun to interpenetrate on a wide front, and the ancient barriers are undermined from end to end.

The process began with the eastward infiltration of Western industrialism and culture, establishing pathways of communication, creating a new spiritual ferment in the East. Then came the gradual development of the ecumenical movement, which, from modest informal conferences between Eastern and Western churchmen, led at length to the full participation of the Orthodox churches in the "Life and Work" and "Faith and Order" movements, and the establishment of specially close relations between them and the

Anglican and Swedish Lutheran churches. Finally, with the Russian Revolution, came the long persecution of the largest and most powerful of all the Orthodox churches, and the dispersion of multitudes of Russian Orthodox exiles throughout Western Europe—a dispersion which the future historian may reckon, for its far-reaching cultural consequences, along with the Jewish dispersion of A.D. 70, or the scattering of Byzantine scholars after the fall of Constantinople in 1453. For the first time since their separation in the early Middle Ages, Oriental and Occidental Christianity are now clearly aware of one another, and engaged in conversation.

It must be admitted that the average Western churchman, when he first encounters the Orthodox, is not predisposed to sit at their feet and learn from them. He finds their flowing hair and beards picturesque, their costumes and their liturgy often magnificent; but having read Harnack's *What Is Christianity?* he views them with profound suspicion. Harsh phrases from the great Protestant historian stick in his mind:

It [the Eastern Orthodox Church] takes the form, not of a Christian product in Greek dress, but of a Greek product in Christian dress. . . . a continuation of the history of the Greek religion under the alien influence of Christianity. . . . In this sense, then, the Greek Church is a *natural* religion; no prophet, no reformer, no genius, has arisen in its history since the third century to disturb the ordinary process by which a religion becomes naturalized into common history. . . . The Church has since

been at rest, and no further essential, nay, not even any unessential, change has taken place in the condition which it then reached.[1]

Perhaps the first step toward the disarming of our Western churchman's prejudices is taken when he meets some really able Eastern Orthodox historian like Father Florovsky of Paris, who is himself a standing disproof of the notion that Orthodox priests are ignorant, unkempt and bigoted. From such a scholar he may learn that the history of the Eastern Church is not such a complete blank as Harnack might lead one to suppose; that theological activity never died out in the East, and saintly leaders like St. Seraphim and John of Kronstadt never ceased to appear, though no "reformation in head and members," like that of the West, ever occurred; that the subservience of the Church to the State, even in Russia, never reached the so-called "Czaristic" stage until the time of Peter the Great, and was always resented and resisted by a majority of the clergy—as became evident during the Kerensky régime after the fall of the Czar.

What is likely to impress the Westerner even more, however, is the evidence that Orthodoxy today, after centuries of comparative self-satisfaction and immobility, is becoming self-critical and dynamic. One such evidence is to be found in the "Zoë" (New Life) movement in Greece, which aims to revitalize the clergy by training them in the all-but-lost art of preaching, and to encourage private Bible study among the laity.

[1] Harnack, *What Is Christianity?* Lecture XII. By permission of G. P. Putnam's Sons, publishers.

Another evidence is to be found in the holding at
Athens in 1936, for the first time in two hundred and
fifty years, of a Conference of Orthodox Theologians.
This conference was designed "to begin the process
of restating the Faith of the Orthodox Church in
the light of modern problems, of clarifying the right
relations of the Orthodox Church with other Com-
munions and of settling its international controversies."[2] It was largely motivated, according to Professor Zankov of Sofia, by "the penetration of the
Western spirit into the young national life of the
Orthodox countries, with positive and negative effects
(secularism, materialism, capitalism),"[3] as well as by
the "tragic" state of the Russian Orthodox Church.
It was attended by some Western theologians, as well
as by a very representative group of the Orthodox
hierarchy. In Professor Zankov's opinion, it "marks
the end of an essentially passive period of Orthodox
Church history," and "the beginning of closer collaboration between the Orthodox Churches and the
Churches of the rest of the world."[4] A second Orthodox conference is to be held at Bucharest in 1939,
to discuss "The Sources of the Faith" and (a new
note in Orthodoxy!) "The Social Task of the Church."

Of all the Orthodox churches the one that has
suffered most, and in which the symptoms of spiritual
rebirth are most unmistakable, is the Russian Orthodox Church. According to the report of Anglican in-

[2] *Second Survey on the Affairs of the Orthodox Church*, p. 9.
Church of England Council on Foreign Relations.
[3] *Ibid.*
[4] *Ibid.*, p. 10.

vestigators, "In the Soviet Union as abroad, the intrinsic qualities of Spirit and Truth have become more clearly revealed in Church life. . . . Where the Church is free, this strength is dynamic in works of love for the whole of society, and in search of Truth; where externally restrained, in rich adventures into the realm of the Spirit. The Russian Church since the Revolution is a Church of rejuvenated spiritual power."[5] Especially in Western Europe, under the jurisdiction of the Metropolitan Eulogius—one of the jurisdictions into which the Russian Church abroad is divided—there is a very notable development of creative thought and social action among the Orthodox exiles, heading up in the Russian Orthodox Theological Institute at Paris, where "there is liberty of theological research and expression unknown under the old Holy Synod," and from which there now goes out a steady stream of "parish priests of high intellectual and spiritual order, going as missionaries to build up new parishes, wherever sixty or a hundred Russian refugee families are to be found."[6]

As it is our constant desire, in this study, to keep close to those aspects of contemporary theology which bear most unmistakably the marks of the fiery trials through which Europe has been passing, and which face the problems of the day with freshness and originality, we cannot do better, in our review of Orthodox theology, than to concentrate our attention upon the Russian Church, and specifically upon the Paris

[5] *Ibid.,* p. 48.
[6] *Ibid.,* p. 47.

group, whose two principal leaders are a gifted priest, Father Bulgakov, and a gifted layman, Nicholas Berdyaev. We shall be concerned principally with their *ideas*, of course; but before plunging into an analysis of this aspect of their work, it is well to remind ourselves that the work of rejuvenation in which they are engaged has its practical as well as its theoretical aspect. The names of Berdyaev and Bulgakov both appear among the principal sponsors of the "Action Orthodoxe," a society aiming at the development of the ethical, social side of the Orthodox faith, hitherto so much neglected. Specifically, it cultivates (1) missionary work through lectures and literature; (2) practical charities "to working men, to sick, to unemployed, to lonely men and women, etc.—to every miserable and exasperated human soul asking for aid and comprehension"; (3) "brotherly communion" between its members. In the annual report of this organization for 1935-36, I find the following words, which speak for its vitality and sincerity and describe the whole mission of Orthodoxy in exile better than any words of mine could do:

The idea of the formation of this association was inspired by anxiety for the fate of the world and humanity felt by every Christian conscience. Christendom at present is in a very unfavorable situation. It is obvious that the tendency is to turn away from religious belief and life. The secularization of thought and of all forms of life in the years gone by now gives its fruits: nations which were Christian in the past are today not only de-

christianized, but even fight openly against Christendom and religion in general. . . .

Some nations which once were Christian either return to heathendom or live in complete indifference and atheism. Christendom has lost its leading part in social life, the Christian style of life has disappeared. Christendom remains alive only in small groups of worshippers, like small islands forlorn in the vastness of the ocean. . . .

The Russians who went through the catastrophic experience of the Revolution must feel with special acuteness the failure of Christendom. But only few do really recognize it. Russian Christians usually decline any responsibility and consider the revolutionaries as only responsible. In reality the Russian catastrophe is as much our fault as theirs. We, as Christians and as members of the Church, must realize that in the years gone by we were Christians only by name. We must recognize that we seldom stood up to defend our unprivileged brothers, that we often helped the strong against the weak, that the Church has lost its prophetic spirit, has forgotten its duty of evangelization and Christianization of human souls. . . .

What is, under these conditions, the meaning of the Emigration? From the practical standpoint Emigration is a non-sense . . . its only mission is a religious one. Considering the hard fate of the Emigrants we are led to the conclusion that our exile must have some kind of deeper meaning, that this trial has been sent us by God. It is obvious that for the hundreds of thousands of people spread all over the world by the Revolution, the first and most important aim must be to try to understand the meaning of their destiny, to try to understand their

calling. It seems to us that this calling is to conserve and to realize "Christ's truth and justice" for which Russian people were always longing. We have the possibility to undertake this task because, though living in very difficult outward conditions, we enjoy the advantages of freedom. . . .

The Emigration has also a second mission—to get into touch with Western Christianity.

Orthodoxy and particularly Russian Orthodoxy always lived isolated from Western Christianity. Our exile has given us the opportunity to approach the Christians of Western Europe and to communicate with a certain part of them.

We would like to say in conclusion that when in our own country Christian faith, conscience and thought will be freed again, the Emigration will definitely lose its meaning and justification. The Emigrants then will either have to return to Russia or to cease to exist as Emigrants.

It is evident that, so far at least as this Paris group is concerned, contemporary Orthodoxy is not blind to the sins of the Eastern Church, nor to the necessity of a far-reaching renewal of her life and thought—especially on the ethical side. We need to be constantly aware of this fact as we examine the work of the two intellectual leaders of this group.

2. A LAY THEOLOGIAN: NICHOLAS BERDYAEV

It is appropriate that we should begin with Berdyaev, the layman, rather than with Bulgakov, the priest, since in the whole movement of thought which

they represent, laymen have been the pioneers.[7] As far back as the third quarter of the nineteenth century, when the official theology of the Russian Church began to be affected by Western ideas, a group of lay theologians (the so-called Slavophils) arose to combat this Westernizing tendency—not out of bigotry or sectional pride, but because they believed the Eastern tradition in Christian thought, if philosophically developed, was capable of making a distinct, unique contribution to the European mind, at a time when the Western churches were becoming corrupted by the exaggerated naturalism and humanism of the Age of Science. Some of these lay religious thinkers, such as Khomyakov and Solovyev, actually wrote systematic works of a theological or philosophical nature; but equally important as a source of inspiration to this whole movement, was another layman who expressed his views through the medium of creative literature: the great novelist, Dostoievsky.

There is a veritable cult of Dostoievsky in Europe today. Critics place him upon the pinnacle of Russian literary supremacy where formerly they placed Tolstoy. Religious thinkers of the most various tendencies, from Karl Barth, the intransigeant Protestant, to Karl Pfleger, the Roman Catholic, see in him one of the greatest spiritual reformers of the nineteenth century, despised and rejected by his contemporaries and now understood for the first time. But no one

[7] On this and many other interesting features of the Orthodox Renaissance, see Dr. W. A. Visser't Hooft's *Anglo-Catholicism and Orthodoxy*, Chapter II.

has given him a more passionate personal devotion than has Berdyaev, whose book, *Dostoievsky,* is at once the best appreciation of the great novelist's underlying meaning that has yet appeared, and the indispensable introduction to its author's own philosophy.

Western Europe today [says Berdyaev] caught by a tide of disaster, is very conscious of Dostoievsky, and she is more able than she was to understand him. Fate has jerked her out of that state of middle-class self-satisfaction in which, up to the time of the World War, she obviously hoped to stop for ever. . . . In the midst of their calamities people in the West . . . under irresistible impulse and by sure instinct, turned to the great Russian and universal genius who had first explored the inward abysses of men and foretold a catastrophe for the world.
So great is the worth of Dostoievsky that to have produced him is by itself sufficient justification for the existence of the Russian people in the world; and he will bear witness for his countrymen at the last judgment of the nations.[8]

According to Berdyaev, the whole of Dostoievsky's literary production, from *Sketches from the Underworld* (1864) to *The Brothers Karamazov* (1881, the year of his death) was one long protest against the three-dimensional superficiality of the prevailing humanistic view of man, in the name of a four-dimensional "tragic realism." He distrusted modern

[8] Berdyaev, *Dostoievsky,* translated by Donald Bywater. Cheap edition 1936, pp. 226-27. By permission of Sheed and Ward, publishers.

humanistic civilization, both in its bourgeois, idealistic form and in its revolutionary, socialistic form. He had been a revolutionary in his youth and served four terrible years in Siberia for his principles; but he became more and more convinced as time went on that the Socialist Utopia was quite as dreadful to contemplate as the mechanical civilization it aimed to replace. *Both* left no place for human freedom or moral responsibility in their vast "ant heap"; and the material happiness they promised was only to be bought at the price of the soul. As against all systems of determinism and compulsion, Dostoievsky maintained the imperishable reality and worth of the free human spirit, even when its freedom was manifested in crime, insanity and self-destruction. The characters of his novels are so many experiments in human freedom, mostly tragic, but contrasting grandly in their very tragedy with the neat, orderly existence which bourgeois morality and Socialist scheming both envisage. The Man from the Underworld, miserable and tormented as he is, a veritable poisoned rat of a man, speaks for all Dostoievsky's characters when he cries out to the respectable world:

So far as I am concerned, I have but carried to its conclusion what you have not dared to carry half way. And you mistake this cowardice for prudence and thus console and deceive yourselves. It is clear that when all is said I am *more alive* than you, my good friends.[9]

But irrational freedom, blind defiance of all con-

[9] *Sketches from the Underworld,* quoted in Pfleger, *Wrestlers with Christ,* pp. 199-200.

vention and compulsion, is not Dostoievsky's last word. When man exalts himself in his freedom, tries to become a superman or "man-god," he becomes a slave to his own divided, uncontrollable self, and his plans turn out the opposite of what he intends. Even when he loves, he alternates between a possessive, selfish passion, and a too tender pity that destroys the loved one through trying to spare her all suffering. On the strictly human plane, there is *no* solution of life's riddle; and so most of the novels, which are realistic studies of the working of human nature under exceptional pressure of circumstances, end in an impasse. But in the later novels, especially in *The Idiot* and *The Brothers Karamazov*, Dostoievsky allows the reader an oblique perception of the faith which had grown upon him through his own incessant spiritual struggles, and which was especially kindled in him by his contacts with the apocalyptic dreamer Fedorov: the faith that, through free surrender to Christ, the God-man, the human urge to freedom might find fulfillment, and human love be raised to such an angelic plane that birth and death would cease, and generations past and present join in the great feast of the Kingdom of God.

In the first drafts of the later novels, the author's apocalyptic faith is openly expressed; in the finished novels it is only indirectly expressed—best of all in the "Legend of the Grand Inquisitor," which is put paradoxically into the mouth of the atheist Ivan Karamazov. Berdyaev sees in this famous passage the quintessence of Dostoievsky: his faith that tragic free-

dom is better than compulsory happiness, and leads at last, through purgatorial suffering, to the feet of Christ. The Christ in this legend answers never a word when the Grand Inquisitor (representing the Antichrist principle both in the Church and in Socialism) reproaches him for appealing to men's free faith when freedom means torture, not happiness; but his silence speaks volumes, and the Inquisitor betrays himself by his reproaches. In this silent figure, with its tacit promise, is the solution of the whole riddle:

If there is a divine meaning (that the "euclidian mind" cannot see), if there is a redeemer, if earthly life is itself an atonement, if the definitive harmony of the world is in the Kingdom of God and not in a worldly kingdom, then this world can be accepted and its history with all its numberless sufferings can be justified.[10]

Berdyaev does not follow his admired master in all details. He finds in Dostoievsky a characteristically Russian tendency to vibrate between the extremes of nihilistic skepticism and apocalyptic faith—an all-or-nothing attitude inimical to all consideration of the pressing contemporary problems of culture and ethics. Neither does he share Dostoievsky's faith in an earthly millennium, to come not through Western science and intelligence, but "out of the East," through the faith of Russian peasants. That dream, indeed, has been badly shattered; the people of Russia have cheer-

[10] Berdyaev, *Dostoievsky*, p. 157. Note the recurring reference to the "euclidian" or "three-dimensional" mind. Sometimes the figure is varied by calling the ordinary or euclidian world a mere two-dimensional "flatland," without any dimension of depth.

fully given in to the Communistic Grand Inquisitor! But Berdyaev sees in "his true teaching about man, his freedom and his destiny,"[11] the permanent part of Dostoievsky's work; and in his own writings he endeavors to develop and apply this teaching. *The Destiny of Man* is not only the title of Berdyaev's most recently translated and most comprehensive work;[12] it is the theme which runs through all his numerous writings like a leitmotif. The doctrine of *man's freedom and destiny* is to him the central and determinative Christian doctrine. This will become evident if we consider the argument of a much earlier book, *The Meaning of History,* originally a series of lectures delivered by Berdyaev at the Moscow Liberal Academy of Spiritual Culture in the years 1919-20, shortly before his exile from Russia. In this earlier book, the author looks backward over man's history toward its eternal *source,* in order to grasp the significance of the present crisis of modern humanistic culture; whereas in *The Destiny of Man* he looks *forward* through the ethical duties and dangers of our era toward mankind's eternal end and *goal.*

It is not surprising that Berdyaev found it impossible to stay in Soviet Russia after giving his lectures on *The Meaning of History;* for his views are in flat opposition to Marxian doctrine. In Marxian Communism he sees, not the fulfillment of the whole dialectic of history, but only the last gasp of an expiring culture era which began with the Renaissance, and

[11] *Ibid.,* p. 212.
[12] Berdyaev, *The Destiny of Man.* (New York, Scribners, 1937.)

the first clear intimation of the doom which is to overtake modern man in the twentieth century: the "disintegration of the human image" in a vast engulfing tide of impersonal collectivism and mechanical technique.

In his diagnosis of our present transition from an age of true "culture" to an age of mere "civilization," concerned purely with power and technique, Berdyaev reminds us of Oswald Spengler—to whom, indeed, he makes explicit reference.[13] Like Spengler, he is convinced that civilizations pass through life-cycles; that, for example, they all pass through an age of "Enlightenment" like our own eighteenth century, in which they lose their organic connection with their historic sources, and become ripe for destruction. Unlike Spengler, however, he teaches that civilization does not fatally revert to barbarism once this process of degeneration has begun; instead, it may pass through "religious transfiguration" and be reborn as a new culture at the very moment when its death is imminent. History, in other words, is not purely the product of rigid necessity; it is "made up of the complex interaction of the three principles of necessity, freedom and transfiguring Grace";[14] and the deepest of these is Grace.

The ultimate ground of the dialectic of history is not, then, to be found upon the human or temporal plane, but upon the divine or eternal plane. History begins with a mysterious "prologue in heaven," of

[13] *The Meaning of History*, p. 207.
[14] *The Meaning of History*, p. 61. (New York, Scribners, 1936.)

which religion speaks in mythological symbols, vague but profoundly true. We can read these symbols because they correspond to something deep within us; the history they interpret is *our own* history. There is an inner tie between God, the world and ourselves, which is found in Christ, the God-man. The motion of human history toward God and eternity is a response to an eternal motion of God toward man; in Christ, the two motions merge, and the divine love for man finds its perfect response in "freely given" human love for God.

It is only an abstract theology that thinks of the divine nature as fixed and immutable; mythological and mystical thinking dares to ascribe creative activity, love, suffering, historical drama to the inner life of the Godhead; and it is only such a view of God that can give metaphysical grounding to history. The "genesis of God in man and of man in God"[15] is the burden of both celestial and terrestrial history. The earthly appearance of the Christ, and his tragic victory over the contingencies of human destiny, is but the manifestation of a struggle going on in eternity, where God forever broods with passionate longing over the face of that dark Abyss in his own nature of which Jacob Boehme and other mystics have spoken.

Man first appears in history in what we can only describe as a "fallen" state. Sunk in unconscious unity with the forces of nature and of the human herd, he does not know that he is a free spirit, with an eternal destiny. In the pagan world, the cycle of nature with

[15] *Ibid.*, p. 56.

its endless round of summer and winter, growth and decay, had him in its iron grip; and all the divine or demonic beings his imagination conjured up could not deliver him from it, since they themselves were manifestations of the same cyclic process. In Judaism, man for the first time became conscious of history, and found God in history rather than in nature—or to be more exact, *above* history and at the end of history. The Jewish dream of a Messianic kingdom of perfect justice, to be established at the end of history, has continued down to our day to give a dynamic character to Western civilization, wherever it has been felt. Karl Marx is its last exponent.

Berdyaev was himself once a revisionist Marxian, and suffered for his Socialist beliefs under the Czaristic régime; but he is now convinced that both Judaism and Marxism contain a "false Messianism," which demands an abstract, universal justice on earth only to be realized by compulsion—and so, in practice, not realizable at all.[16] The true Messiah, when he came, delivered man not only from the pagan dominion of the cycle of nature, but also from the dominion of social compulsion, and from all-devouring time itself, by revealing the eternal worth and destiny of the individual soul. Judaism continues to reject any Messiah who does not immediately inaugurate the reign of perfect social justice for which it still hopes; and there are Christians who wonder if Jesus could have been

[16] *Ibid.*, Chapter on "The Jews." Berdyaev began to doubt the Marxian theory of history, he says, when as a young man he tried to apply it to the history of the Jews—and found it inadequate.

the Messiah, since "horrors and torments" still persist on earth; but such are not true Christians. The real Messiah must come "as the bearer of a meek and not a triumphant truth on earth,"[17] since his Kingdom can contain only willing subjects. Those who look for complete social justice on earth will always reject and crucify the true Messiah, and welcome the Antichrist.

But if Christianity did not inaugurate or promise a social millennium, it did introduce a powerful new tension into the whole historic process. First and foremost, it prepared the way for modern science and technology by delivering man from his superstitious fear of the powers of nature, and slaying the nature-gods and demons ("Great Pan") with which his fear-struck imagination had peopled his environment. In mediaeval Christianity, the alienation of man from nature went so far as to lead to contempt for the world, ascetic mortification of the flesh, and the attempt of the Church to make all earthly powers directly subservient to her authority. Mediaeval Christianity failed, as all subsequent forms of Christianity will in some respect fail; but its monastic and chivalric ideals disciplined man's powers, and created a great reservoir of spiritual energy, which the modern humanistic era has only just begun to exhaust, after almost five centuries of extravagant and feverish activity.

The modern humanistic revolt against mediaeval Christianity was justifiable and necessary. Man's

[17] *Ibid.,* p. 104.

pent-up powers needed to be released and tried out; a great experiment in freedom needed to be made. The "ebullience" of this epoch-making revolt was at first tremendous. "It brought with it," says Berdyaev, "the liberation of man's creative forces, spiritual decentralization, and the differentiation of all the spheres of social and cultural life. Science, art, political and economic life, society and culture now become autonomous."[18] Against all forms of religious and political authoritarianism, Berdyaev remains an apostle of the Renaissance, an advocate of *free creativity*. But he points out that modern humanism very early developed an inner contradiction which condemned it to final failure. It attempted, on the one hand, to bring man back into organic connection with nature, from which mediaeval asceticism had separated him; and it attempted, on the other hand, to exalt man above nature through scientific analysis and mechanical invention. The success of science and technology gradually destroyed man's sense of his organic connection with nature, and at the same time undermined his sense of his own exalted worth and dignity. So, having attempted to rise above nature to the status of a superman, he finally fell below it, and (whether in bourgeois or in Socialist society) became a mere cog in a machine. *"Man's self-affirmation leads to his perdition; the free play of human forces unconnected with any higher aim brings about the exhaustion of man's creative powers."*[19]

[18] *Ibid.*, p. 142.
[19] *Ibid.*, p. 142.

The collapse of humanistic culture in our day is the definitive disproof of the religion of progress, which for so many moderns has taken the place of Christianity—a rationalized, secularized version of the ancient Jewish hope of a Messianic Age. In all its forms, ancient or modern, this hope provides no solution of the problem of human destiny. It assumes a false and illusory view of time, according to which the past and future have no inner, organic connection, and only at the *end* of the time-process is any meaning introduced. But thus to postpone meaning to the end of history is to postpone it forever. A truer view of the time-process finds eternity penetrating it at every moment, binding the present to the past and future in memory and hope; and time, conversely, penetrating eternity "as a moment in the everlasting mystery of the Spirit."[20] The crises and struggles of history are not merely cyclic, as the ancients thought. History never exactly repeats itself. Nothing like the present age of technology has ever happened before. But the meaning of history is not to be sought wholly on the historic plane, as though a final crashing chord might some day give a perfect ending to the whole symphony. It is rather to be sought outside the temporal framework, in a living eternal Spirit which both transcends and indwells time, and keeps history in motion by the everlasting tension between the temporal and the eternal.

Besides *The Meaning of History* and *The Destiny of Man*, Berdyaev has published a number of works

[20] *Ibid.*, p. 206.

of a more popular nature. In two of these, *The End of Our Age* and *The Fate of Man in the Modern World*, he offered an interpretation of current events (e.g., the rise of Fascism and Nazism) in the light of his general philosophy of history; and it was the extraordinary prophetic insight of these social and political studies that first caught the attention of the English-speaking world. American readers would be well advised to begin with these two books, and thus convince themselves that Berdyaev is a shrewd social observer with his feet on the ground; whereas if they should begin with *Freedom and the Spirit*, they would probably dismiss him as an Oriental dreamer with his head in the clouds. In *Freedom and the Spirit*, Berdyaev frankly declares himself to be a Christian Gnostic or Theosophist, in search of an esoteric wisdom unknown to common or "democratic" Christianity; and he takes the reader on speculative flights that (to the average pragmatic-minded American, at least) are conducive to giddiness, nausea and splitting headaches. Yet if one admits that Christian thought has always been in danger of succumbing to the Grand Inquisitor's leveling system of uniformity—and can any Protestant fail to perceive that danger, at least in Catholic theology?—must one not then sympathize with Berdyaev's attempt to clarify the unsolved problems of conventional Christian thought by pushing his exploration of these problems up to a transcendental height to which the average churchman, content with his well-worn clichés, has neither the impulse nor the courage to rise?

My Christian faith [says Berdyaev, in a passage which reveals the whole temper of the man] is not a faith based on habit or tradition. It was won through an experience of the inner life of a most painful character. I knew no compulsion in my religious life, and I had no experience of an authoritarianism either in faith or in the sphere of religious devotion. Can one oppose to this fact dogmatic formulas or abstract theologies? I answer No, for in my case they will never be really convincing.

Freedom has brought me to Christ and I know of no other path leading to Him. . . .

I must discover for myself what God has hidden from me. God expects from me a free creative act. My freedom and my creative activity are my obedience to the secret will of God, Who expects from man something much more than what is usually meant when we speak of His will. . . . May it not mean, if we so put it, a sweat of blood and agony for God when he sees in how slavish a spirit men interpret His will and how utterly formal is the manner of their obedience to it? The divine will must be carried out to the very end, yet has not God willed that man should also be a free creator? And does He not also love a Nietzsche who fights against Him?[21]

These words from *Freedom and the Spirit* set the tone for all Berdyaev's most recent work. The book to which they are prefixed consists of a series of exceedingly suggestive essays, illustrating a type of religious speculation quite as free as that of the ancient Gnostics and modern Theosophists, but more responsibly Christian, and quite in line with a per-

[21] *Freedom and the Spirit,* pp. x, xviii. (New York, Scribners, 1935. Quoted by permission.)

sistent tradition in Eastern Orthodox and Western mystical thought, from Clement and Origen of Alexandria to Jacob Boehme and Vladimir Solovyev.[22] In *The Destiny of Man*, Berdyaev's masterpiece, the scattered insights which gleam through these essays are gathered up into one comprehensive vision: *first*, of man's metaphysical origin and nature; *second*, of his present duty; *third*, of his final destiny.

It will be recalled that history, for Berdyaev, is a product of three factors: human freedom, natural necessity and divine Grace. Now, the usual teaching of rational or "positive" theology is that the first and second factors are ultimately derived from the third; i.e., God made nature and man, giving to man the power to use nature's resources and his own faculties well or ill, as he chose. This theology, thinks Berdyaev, is a prolific source of atheism, for freedom is admitted to lead to sin and, for at least a great proportion of mankind, to eternal punishment; and yet God, foreseeing these terrible consequences, bestowed this fatal gift upon his ignorant and unsuspecting creature! In contrast to this teaching of "positive" theology is the teaching of "negative" or mystical theology (Boehme, Eckhart), according to which God the Creator himself is eternally born out of a dark Abyss

[22] It should of course be understood that this tradition has never had official church sanction, and has always been under some degree of suspicion, even when it took pains to distinguish itself from heretical Gnosticism and non-Christian Theosophy. Berdyaev endeavors to distinguish his position carefully from such spurious brands of speculation; but many of his warmest admirers, like Father Florovsky, refuse to follow him in this aspect of his thought.

of deity, the so-called *Ungrund,* or divine Nothingness; and man and universe are then created by God out of the same ultimate, indeterminate metaphysical stuff from which he himself proceeds. Since indeterminacy or non-being ($\mu\dot{\eta}$ $\check{o}\nu$) are of the very essence of this primal stuff, freedom is uncreated, coeternal with God, and man may be described as the child of two parents: God, the formative agent in the process, and "meonic freedom," the passive stuff which simply "consented" to God's creative act. The element of uncreated freedom in man's nature is the source of his instinctive urges and creative powers; it is also the source of his ability to rebel against God and resolve himself back into the chaos of non-being.

The story of man's Fall belongs to the dim borderland between time and eternity, and can be narrated only in mythological symbols. "Paradise" stands for the original unconscious unity of God, man and nature after the Creation—a blissful state, and yet an imperfect one, since God was then "merely a sustaining power"[23] and his rich tri-unity was not yet revealed to his creatures. It was, in one sense, an advance to pass from this pre-conscious state to one of conscious "division, reflection, valuation, freedom of choice";[24] and yet in the act of becoming conscious of his creative powers, and the diversity of choices open to him, man came under the sway of the chaotic element in his nature; indeed, it may have been the

[23] *The Destiny of Man,* p. 48.
[24] *Ibid.,* p. 51.

pain and loss of this revolt that *made* him conscious
in the first place. Man having thus fallen away from
his original unity with God, the world fell away from
its original unity with man; the gates of the first paradise were closed to him forever, and the only way
back to bliss was onward through conscious struggle
and suffering, toward a new and higher level of existence, super-conscious and not merely pre-conscious.
As man treads this long and tragic road, he is not
alone; for when man falls away, God prepares a "second act" in the divine drama of destiny: as God the
Son, he descends into the dark abyss of meonic freedom to struggle unarmed (except by love and sacri-
fice) with his evil creation, to redeem it "by enlighten-
ing it from within without forcing."[25] Apart from
such divine and gracious aid, man could not fulfil his
destiny, for freedom misused congeals into necessity—
outward necessity in nature, inward necessity in sinful
propensity—and man presently finds himself in a
state of hopeless contradiction and bondage. There
is no deliverance for man through sheer, dogged assertion of free will, but only through an infused divine energy which lifts him above the act of choice,
and even above all concern for his personal salvation,
to a level of creative freedom where his choosing is
done for him, by the Spirit that controls him.

Berdyaev's ethical teaching, which is found in the
long middle section of his book, is dominated by the
theory of *levels* to which we have just alluded. Most

[25] *Ibid.*, p. 35.

ethical teaching seems to him to move on the level
of *law*, which lies just above the level of *instinct*, at
the point where conscious self-control is first attempted. The ethics of law have a certain validity in
that they condemn sin and hold it in check, especially
in the social sphere; but their very existence is a
testimony to man's fallen state, and they can do
nothing to raise him above it. To be *good* in the
legalistic or moralistic sense is not to be on the way
to salvation. The publicans and sinners go into the
Kingdom of God before the Pharisees, the Christian
ascetics and the followers of Kant and Tolstoy. Moral
virtue in all these forms rides rough-shod over unique,
personal values. It is tyrannical, dull and smug, and
there is divine right on the side of the Nietzsches who
rebel against it. Yet there is danger that in attempting
to rise above moralism we may fall below it; and especially in *social* ethics, plain justice, guaranteed by
law, cannot be set aside in favor of a Gospel love that
only hypocrites would claim to be able to practice
in that sphere.

Above the level of law is the level of *redemption* or
grace. Strictly speaking, the ethics of redemption set
forth in the Gospels are beyond good and evil, as
God himself is. They are not ruled by any abstract
norms or impersonal ends, like Kantian ethics; "you
must not act so that the principle of your action could
become a universal law; you must always act individually, and every one must act differently."[26] The

[26] *Ibid.,* p. 137.

level of redemption is the level of pity, of love, of forgiveness, free from all compulsion, all sense of effort, all harshness of judgment. "To be strict with oneself and kind to others—this is the truly Christian attitude."[27] It is not a weak and slavish attitude, as Nietzsche supposes; it overcomes the weak sense of resentment and replaces it with "the noble sense of guilt."[28] From this attitude of divine, unworldly humility and compassion to a practical social ethic is of course no easy step. "There never has been and there can be no Christian state, Christian economics, Christian family, Christian learning, Christian social life." And yet the Gospel vision of the Kingdom of God has affected all these departments of life, "inwardly and imperceptibly," by "healing and regenerating the texture of the human soul."[29] All sorts of concrete issues must be creatively met by the Christian; the Gospel does not settle them for him; it only gives him a new perspective upon them, and a new spirit.

But Berdyaev is not yet done. Above the ethics of redemption he places the ethics of *creativeness*, and he remarks that there is a tragic conflict between these two highest levels of life, the better and the best. The ethics of redemption are still occupied with man's deliverance from moral evil; and the danger is that he may become fixated upon the problem of his own salvation. His redemption is incomplete until he

[27] *Ibid.*, p. 144.
[28] *Ibid.*, p. 148.
[29] *Ibid.*, pp. 160-61.

learns to forget himself in creative activity, whether
in the arts or in the sphere of personal relationships—
for there is such a thing as creative living—and thus
learns to know the divine joy of bringing positive
value into being. Creative genius is a strange thing.
It has its own type of ethical imperative which may
conflict with the imperative of personal saintliness.
"If Pushkin went in for asceticism and sought the salvation of his soul, he would probably have ceased to
be a great poet."[30] There is no simple solution of this
tragic conflict. Creativeness, when distorted by sin,
is a great evil, but the Kingdom of God needs crea-
tors, and human activity never reaches the highest
level until it takes on a quality of creativity, an element of *beauty*, of *inspiration*, of *joy* that rises victorious above the possessive lust of life, the Freudian
libido in us all, capturing and using our instinctive
energies in the service of absolute and eternal values,
in which all can share. Creativeness is man's free response to his divine vocation. It rises toward eternity
in the act of contemplation, then stoops again into
time, like God's own grace, to give substance to the
creative vision, and share it with humanity. In creativity, the image of God is restored in man, and Paradise regained.

We are not directly concerned, from our theological point of view, with the specific conclusions which
Berdyaev draws from his ethics of freedom, compassion and creativeness. Suffice it to say that he com-

[30] *Ibid.*, p. 168.

bats ethical smugness and conventional goodness at every turn,[31] and shows deep sympathy with tormented mortals in their tragic choices. Divorce and war he is ready to tolerate as tragic necessities; while capital punishment, because of its cool deliberation and moral self-complacency, arouses him to furious denunciation. What concerns us more directly is the application of this same attitude to the ultimate problems of eschatology, in the last main section of the book: "act so as to conquer death and affirm everywhere, in everything and in relation to all, eternal and immortal life."[32]

The conquest of death is not to be achieved by the modern method of immersion in the biological and social life-stream; for nations and civilizations—yes, and the cosmos itself—must die, like individuals. Along the plane of time there is no deliverance from death, or from that "bad infinity," separated from God's eternity, which is the essence of hell. At best, we experience moments when eternal meaning manifests itself in time, eras when the creative response of men to God's redeeming grace brings temporary victory over evil. But it is our final destiny to return to eternity enriched with the spoils of time, bringing with us a universe redeemed and "deified" by our creative efforts.

A double issue of the cosmic process, in hell and heaven, is no more tolerable to Berdyaev than to

[31] The motto of the book, taken from Gogol's diary, is: "It is sad not to see any good in goodness."
[32] *Ibid.*, p. 322.

Origen. Hell is essentially human and temporal; it is man's protection against "being forced to be good and compulsorily installed in heaven";[33] it is the punishment man inflicts upon himself when he refuses the divine grace, and as such it may stretch out to an infinity in subjective time; but an *eternal* hell is a contradiction in terms, a wicked invention of "good" people who have not understood the goodness of God. Either the sinner obstinately returns to the nothingness out of which he came, and then ceases to suffer; or, if he remains in being at all, he is open to the ceaseless solicitation of God, who seeks him out in Christ and the Church. Hell as well as death has been vanquished by Christ, and his followers can never be at peace in heaven unless they participate in his wrestling with the powers of darkness. No rational or "positive" theology can adequately deal with this great paradox; but mystical theology sees in symbolic terms a solution of the world-riddle: "The cross and the crucifixion enter into the bliss of paradise. . . . To conquer evil the Good must crucify itself. . . . The 'good' do not relegate the 'wicked' to hell and enjoy their own triumph but descend with Christ into hell in order to free them."[34] The cosmic drama thus ends with a victory of eternity over time (prefigured by many creative moments in history) which takes up into the richness of eternal life the whole meaning of historic existence.

[33] *Ibid.*, p. 339.
[34] *Ibid.*, p. 371.

3. "FROM MARXISM TO SOPHIOLOGY": FATHER BULGAKOV

We have dwelt long upon Berdyaev's lay theology, because it has a freshness and a boldness that are congenial to the modern emancipated mind. Because of these qualities it is probably the best contemporary avenue to the understanding of the spirit of Eastern Christendom. But Berdyaev would be the last man to claim complete originality for his system of thought. He appears more original than he is because he is the first rediscovered portion of a lost intellectual continent. This will become apparent, I think, if we consider more briefly another portion of that lost continent—this time, the theology of a priest, Father Bulgakov—and note how well it fits in with Berdyaev's.

Father Bulgakov is best known for his advocacy of two highly interesting and (to us) strange theological concepts: the divine *Sophia* as the organizing principle of theology; and *sobornost* as the determinative mark of the Church. These concepts are not equally acceptable in all parts of the Orthodox world, and the former has been condemned as heretical by some members of the Orthodox hierarchy; but both are familiar concepts in Russian Orthodox thought, traceable respectively to Vladimir Solovyev, "the first Russian sophiologist," and Khomyakov, the Slavophil theologian, who found in *sobornost* "the soul of Orthodoxy."[35]

Of the two, the concept of Sophia is the more diffi-

---

[35] Bulgakov, *The Wisdom of God*, p. 23; *The Orthodox Church*, p. 74.

cult and abstruse, and we shall therefore attack it first. As an aid in our approach to what looks like an almost impossibly remote idea, let us consider Father Bulgakov's own story[36] of how he found in it the key that delivered him from the prison of Marxian materialism and unlocked for him the door to the Christian Church.

He was in his youth a Marxian Socialist, and as professor of economics in Moscow had occasion to study the works of Marx and Engels with exceptional thoroughness. They were to him, as he feels they are to contemporary communists, not only economic and political but religious documents; and he describes himself at this time as "a devoted and pious layman of the Marxist religion"; yes, more,—a sort of "theologian of Marxism," seeking to deduce from its principles a comprehensive view of the world and man. He found to his dismay that where the Marxist theology was clearly formulated, it resolved itself into a series of contradictions: *Mind* is "but a superstructure of economics"; therefore it is "able not only to know, but to transform the Universe"! *Man* is "but a species of monkey," whose ideals are only the reflex of the social order under which he lives; therefore he is called upon to create an "earthly paradise," a "kingdom of freedom" in which compulsion is no longer necessary, and the State withers away! *Personality* "does not really exist, because classes or social groups alone have reality"; therefore we are called

[36] "From Marxism to Sophiology," in *The Review of Religion*, I, pp. 361-68.

to "heroic duties and revolutionary actions," under personal leaders canonized like saints and implicitly obeyed.

Bulgakov found he must either give up his social idealism, or seek a better metaphysical grounding for it. He chose the latter. In search of a metaphysic that would really be consistent with social idealism, he turned from Marx to the "really great thinkers": the Greek philosophers, the Christian fathers, the German idealists, and last of all, Dostoievsky and Solovyev. Following Solovyev especially, he came to see the solution of the problem of man's place in the world in the Christian teaching that man is made in the image of God. This implies that although man is a finite, dependent creature, receiving his existence, like all other creatures, from an energy derived from above, he has an "inner connection," a "correspondence or likeness" with the divine energy that forms him. "This energy," says Bulgakov, "is named in the Holy Scriptures the Divine Wisdom, the Holy Sophia, sometimes the Divine Glory . . . and this Wisdom is, I should say, a divine part of the created world, its very foundation."

In the world at large, the divine Sophia dwells as an "eternal seed of the divine life," an "inner goal," "reason" or "entelechy," which is "immersed in a process of becoming" and gradually manifesting itself. Man is the microcosm, the "created god" through whom and in whom the divine Sophia indwells and unifies the world. "In that sense," says Bulgakov, "the world is godlike in man, the Wisdom of God

illuminated this world through man, who is the highest goal of creation." To be sure, man has misused his godlike freedom and creativity, and fallen into a state of "feebleness and incapacity"; but sin cannot destroy the "Wisdom of God, the divine seeds of creation" in man. Through Christ and his Church, God the Creator became united with humanity, "the Prototype identified Himself with His image in man"; and thus, in spite of all remaining contradictions and oppositions, humanity has been restored to its true divine nature and its creative task. "History," says Bulgakov, "is not a mechanical process of senseless agents, but it has a definite spiritual content, which is to be realized in this material world in its conditions. The dead areas of immense distances in the world have to be spiritualized and become vital through the efforts of mankind. Man is logos, the wisdom of the world, he is its master and artist, because he is godlike." In this conception of man's nature and place—obviously identical with the view that inspires Berdyaev's vision of man's creative destiny—Father Bulgakov finds that metaphysical grounding for social action which he missed in Marxism.

In his recent book, *The Wisdom of God,* Bulgakov works out the idea of the divine Sophia in the most elaborate detail. He points out that the churches dedicated to Santa Sophia in Constantinople, Kiev, Moscow and many lesser Eastern cities are not named in honor of any earthly saint, but of that divine Wisdom by which God dwells in the world, and the world in

God. There are many different meanings of this great unitive concept, corresponding to the stages in the eternal process by which God imparts himself to his creatures. First of all it means the *nature (ousia)* of God, which is "the depth, the root, of Deity,"[37] mysteriously hidden in God the Father, but revealed by the Son and the Spirit. Next, it means *the content of God's self-revelation*, the words of the Word, "the ideal *all*, the all-embracing 'organism' of ideas, and the ideal unity of them all,"[38]—in short, the world as it is in God's mind, before creation. Now, if it is possible for the divine nature to be united with human nature in Christ, that implies that there is deep, basic unity between Creator and creature, God and man, in spite of the real and unbridgeable distinction between them. There is an eternal humanity in God, and an eternal divinity in man. The humanity in God is *divine* Sophia, as already defined. The divinity in man is *creaturely* Sophia, which through man potentially extends to the whole world. Since man is bisexual, the creaturely Sophia or "emergent God-man"[39] cannot be revealed completely in the male humanity of Jesus Christ, but is revealed in complementary fashion in Our Blessed Lady, the first human being to be completely transfigured or apotheosized, and in the Church, the "Bride of Christ," through which the whole social order and the whole cosmic order are destined to be creatively transformed.

[37] Baillie and Martin, *Revelation*, p. 178.
[38] Bulgakov, *The Wisdom of God*, p. 76.
[39] Baillie and Martin, *op. cit.*, p. 179.

There are endless subtleties in this analysis, on which we cannot dwell; but enough has been said to indicate that for Bulgakov (unlike Karl Barth) the doctrine of the immanence of God is as precious as that of his mysterious transcendence; and the Incarnation is regarded as the central point in a process of divine self-impartation which began with the creation, continues in the Church, and points forward to an age when God, man and world will be actually *one*.

The doctrine of Sophia is closely related to Bulgakov's other favorite doctrine, the *sobornost* of the Church. The word is practically untranslatable. It is the Russian word for "catholicity," but it also implies "conciliarity," "ecumenicity," "harmony," "unanimity" and many other shades of meaning derived from the specific genius of the Eastern Church. Khomyakov, who first popularized the term, used it to imply that the true Church "is opposed both to authoritarianism and to individualism. It is a unanimity, a synthesis of authority . . . liberty in love which unites believers."[40] Bulgakov points out that the Orthodox Church, although more dogmatic than any liberal Protestant church, "contents itself with the indispensable minimum of obligatory dogmas," whereas the Roman Catholic Church "tends to canonical formulation of an entire dogmatic inventory of the Church."[41] The Nicene Creed is found to be a sufficient norm to furnish an "immoveable base" for the development of new "theologoumena," which

[40] Bulgakov, *The Orthodox Church*, p. 74.
[41] *Ibid.*, p. 119.

continually amplify and adapt the Church's teaching, and must win their way in the Church by discussion and free consent. In all such matters the consent of the laity is as essential as that of the hierarchy, for the *sobornost* of the Church most emphatically includes the laity. It also includes the dead and the unborn, for the Church's life is nourished by a holy tradition to which every generation contributes its thought and life, and which reaches out toward universal comprehensiveness. This tradition is a check upon mere individualism, but no check upon original and creative activity. The unity that this tradition creates is a free and manifold unity, in which all views "conciliate" one another, as the spirit of Christian love demands.

The relation of *sobornost* to the doctrine of Sophia is found in the fact that the unity and catholicity of the Church are ascribed to the influence of the divine life that indwells her. Like Christ himself, the Church is a union, without confusion, of *divine* and *creaturely* Sophia. As *divine* Wisdom, the Church is "uncreated," "eternal," "grounded in God"; as *created* Wisdom, she enters into the world-process to strive with the forces of evil and chaos, one mighty body of Divine-humanity in which the saints on earth are intimately united with the saints above, the angels and the Blessed Virgin. "The world has already, in principle, become godly in becoming Churchly";[42]

[42] *The Wisdom of God,* p. 203. The association of the quality of *sobornost* with the indwelling presence of the Divine Wisdom in the Church, and the resultant intimate connection between saints above and saints below, suggests another meaning of this baffling and

but the work of the Church will not be accomplished until all human society has been permeated by that free unity-in-diversity which is the essence of *sobornost*, and all nature has been made the willing servant of the highest human needs. "We may say that all the inner life of the Church is *soborny*, all its outward life is social."[43] True sociality in every sphere is a growth of *mutuality*, of organic unity between man, world and God. It is part of the mission of the Church to develop true sociality in the family, the State and the economic order, redeeming these natural social groupings from their natural perversions; for "sociality is the sophianic development of mankind through history,"[44] the communication to the world of the hidden and intimate *sobornost* of the Church. This is the theological basis of Father Bulgakov's "Christian humanism," or "social Christianity," the outlines of which he sketched in his Hale Memorial Sermon at Seabury-Western Theological Seminary (Evanston, 1934), on "Social Teaching in Modern Russian Orthodox Theology."

---

wonderfully rich expression: *the communion of saints.* Perhaps the best commentary on *sobornost*, if one is to get the full height and depth of its meaning, will be found in the chapter on "The Communion of Saints" in the report of the Edinburgh Conference, where the influence of Orthodox thought is very marked. This communion includes not only "the mutual sharing of both spiritual and temporal blessings on the part of all living Christians," and "unbroken communion between the living and departed in Christ," but also, for the Orthodox, "fellowship . . . with the holy angels, and, in a very special sense, with the Blessed Virgin Mary." *Christendom*, Autumn number, 1937, p. 667.

[43] *Ibid.*, p. 212. *Soborny* is the adjective, "freely unanimous"; *sobornost* is the noun, "free unanimity."

[44] *Ibid.*, p. 213.

It should be understood that Bulgakov is no believer in the infallibility of the organized Church. There is real unity between the Church invisible and the Church visible; but the true divine Church must be carefully distinguished from the empirical churches in which she is embodied. Christ and his saints are in perpetual combat with Antichrist, not only outside the organized church but inside as well. Reinhold Niebuhr misunderstands Father Bulgakov's attitude at the Oxford Conference, when he accuses him of always identifying Christ with the Church, and Antichrist with the Communist revolution.[45] In an article entitled "Judas Iscariot," published in 1935 in *Orient und Okzident*, Bulgakov interprets the Communist revolution as a divine punishment for the sins of the Orthodox Church, which through alliance with the Czaristic régime had, like Judas, betrayed her Lord—a close approximation to calling the Church Antichrist! At the same time, he sees in it a deliverance of the Church from the confining fetters of the State, and a preparation for a new era in which she will cease to rely upon power and prestige and make her way by suffering and persuasion, like Christ himself.

I think it will be noticed that in Berdyaev and Bulgakov we have a type of theology which, with all its appreciation of Orthodox tradition and all its severity toward modern secularism, humanism and Protestantism, is nevertheless distinctly *liberal* in tone.

[45] In his article on "The Catholic Heresy" in the *Christian Century*, Dec. 8, 1937, p. 1525.

Far from disparaging all use of human reason in theology, these Eastern thinkers venture upon flights of speculation which the Western mind can hardly follow without losing its bearings. Far from despairing of man, they are serenely confident of his divine dignity, infinite capacity and immortal destiny. Far from despairing of the Church, these exiles who have seen the collapse of organized Christianity in their native land and felt the force of savage persecution, are ready to see in the Church the human expression of the divine Wisdom, the divinely ordained organ for the redemption of human society. In view of their courageous reaction to a truly terrifying situation, it cannot be said that contemporary Continental theology is universally pervaded by a defeatist or obscurantist temper. Whatever may be true of German Protestantism, Eastern Orthodoxy today is not anti-liberal. It is, in fact, almost idealistic, for all its bitter disillusionments: and it presents to disillusioned American idealists the possibility of deepening and correcting their faith without denying it. I am not suggesting that many of us are likely to join the Eastern Orthodox Church—though a number of young intellectuals in Europe have already done just that—but I am sure that we can all profit much from the contemporary rediscovery of its life and thought, especially as expressed in such appealing figures as Berdyaev and Bulgakov.

CHAPTER II

THE REVIVAL OF CATHOLIC THEOLOGY

1. THE CATHOLIC "RETURN FROM EXILE"

THE Eastern Orthodox Church today is having her baptism of fire, and going through her long-delayed Renaissance and Reformation. The Roman Catholic Church is in a very different but not less interesting condition. The whole development of modern Western civilization since the Protestant and Humanist revolts has been one long trail of her patience. Like the mother of two unruly children, she has continually warned the modern "heretical" church and modern "secularized" society against the error of their ways, entreating them in the name of all that was holy to come back under her experienced direction; but they have steadily disregarded her warnings, derided her for being "behind the times," and (when her importunities became too annoying) deprived her of civil rights or sent her into exile.

From her long period of exile and disfavor she is now returning, clothed with new authority. The times have changed, and she now appears to be ahead of them instead of behind them; or rather, she seems to have been wise in standing her ground, and a chastened generation is beginning to exhibit a new willingness to listen to her counsel. Christopher Dawson[1] describes the situation very fairly and clearly when he says,

[1] Dawson, an English Roman Catholic literary man, has en-

In the eighteenth and nineteenth centuries, it is true, the whole trend of Western civilization was hostile to Catholicism. The absolutism and realism of Catholic philosophy was incomprehensible to an age which followed Rousseau and Kant, or Bentham and Herbert Spencer. When Pius IX denied that it was the duty of the Church to come to terms with Liberalism and Progress and Modern Civilization, his pronouncement was greeted with a chorus of execration from every country in Europe. It seemed as though the Papacy was pronouncing its own sentence of death, for the triumph of material progress seemed inevitable and no one could conceive the possibility of its failure.

Today all this is changed—Liberalism and Progress and Modern Civilization appear in a very different light from that of seventy years ago.[2]

This "return of Catholicism from exile,"[3] as Peter Wust calls it, appeared to be immanent once before, over a hundred years ago, but the earlier Catholic revival became compromised through association with non-Catholic trends, and was disowned by the Church. I refer to the remarkable movement of Catholic thought which began in the early nineteenth century with the Romantic reaction against rationalism, took

deavored to call this situation to the attention of his fellow Catholics by editing a series of *Essays in Order*, to which leading Continental Catholics have contributed. It is the best single book to read, to get a comprehensive view of the whole movement described in this chapter. To this and other recent Catholic literature, Prof. Aubrey's chapter on "Neo-Thomism" in his *Present Theological Tendencies* (Harpers, 1936) is the best introduction available in English.

[2] *Essays in Order* (1913), General introduction, pp. xiii, xiv. Quoted by permission of The Macmillan Co., publishers.

[3] *Ibid.*, pp. xix, xx.

on a liberal tinge as the century advanced, and finally perished in the duel between Modernism and scholasticism in the first decade of the twentieth century.

The French Revolution marked the nadir-point of Catholicism in Europe. It attacked the Catholic Church as vigorously as the Russian Revolution has attacked the Orthodox Church. When its fury was spent, the Church which had suffered most from it came back into popularity. Catholic nobles and priests who had endured exile or imprisonment were among the intellectual leaders of the new era. In France, the Vicomte de Bonald and Joseph de Maistre argued that the horrors to which the Revolution led proved the unwisdom of trusting human *reason* instead of time-honored *tradition*, both in the political and in the religious sphere. In Germany, many Catholics found in the Romantic exaltation of *intuition* and *faith* the specific antidote for the virus of rationalism with which the fathers of the Revolution, Voltaire and Diderot were said to have poisoned the European blood stream. In the poetry and art and literature of the period—think only of Walter Scott and Victor Hugo—a nostalgia for the Middle Ages overcame the eighteenth century's scorn for all that was not "modern" or "classic."

Oddly enough, this revival of mediaevalism both helped and hindered the Catholic revival. So long as it could appeal to a somewhat idealized and sentimentalized portrait of the Middle Ages, Catholic Traditionalism or Romanticism could represent itself as the legitimate heir of mediaeval Christianity.

But when Leo XIII in his famous encyclical turned the Catholic clergy back to the study of mediaeval philosophy in the person of its ablest exponent, St. Thomas Aquinas, a grave discrepancy appeared between the authentic mediaevalism of St. Thomas and the imaginary mediaevalism of the modern Catholic reactionaries. St. Thomas was a pronounced intellectualist, while these self-styled "mediaevalists" were anti-intellectualists, and their teachings smacked more of Kant and Schelling than of Aquinas or Albertus Magnus. For a while, during the last third of the nineteenth century, they continued to claim mediaeval sanction for their position, appealing to the strong Platonic-Augustinian tradition which runs through mediaeval thought and connects it with modern Romanticism; but in the opening years of the twentieth century they abandoned all such precedents, admitted that they were "Modernists," and denounced mediaeval scholasticism in sweeping terms as the ally of that same rationalism which is the bane of the modern world. They were severely and effectively disciplined by Pope Pius X in 1907 and 1908, and the first phase of the Catholic revival thus ended in fiasco.[4]

---

[4] For a fuller account of the development of Catholic thought in the nineteenth and early twentieth centuries, see my book on *The Philosophy of the Abbé Bautain*, especially pp. 3-55, 284-98 (New York University Press, 1926.) On the Catholic Modernistic movement, consult articles in the *Catholic Encyclopaedia* and Hastings' *Encyclopaedia of Religion and Ethics*, and two contrasting treatments in French, *Histoire du Modernisme catholique*, by Houtin (a Modernist) and *Le Modernisme dans l'Eglise*, by Jean Rivière (a Catholic theologian).

To many Protestant observers, the end of the Modernist movement looked like the end of all genuine *thought* in the Catholic Church. It seemed as though the taking of the anti-Modernist oath condemned the Catholic clergy to complete intellectual sterility, and complete helplessness to grapple with contemporary problems. What such observers failed to realize was the range of latitude for free "opinion" which is always left open between the rigid boundaries laid down by Catholic "dogma." Of all Christian churches, the Catholic is the most dogmatic; but even in this church, dogma does not draw a chalkline which everyone must walk, looking anxiously at his feet and ignoring his surroundings. Rather, it defines limits beyond which he must not stray to the right or the left, but within which he may chart his own course. Any one familiar with the warm theological disputes between the Jesuits and the Dominicans must realize that on many important matters Catholics are free to differ among themselves, and make full use of the privilege.

The victory of scholasticism over Modernism did not mean the end of theological debate in the Catholic Church, then; it only meant that one of the parties to the debate had stepped out of bounds, and been disqualified. To treat scholasticism in general and Thomism in particular as a sort of disease to be stamped out—and it is hardly an exaggeration to say that this was the attitude of the Abbé Laberthonnière, one of the ablest of the Modernists—is now quite out of bounds for any loyal Catholic; but loyal Catholics may and do differ as to the relative merits

of the various schools of scholasticism, and as to how far the teachings of St. Thomas need to be adapted to fit the new knowledge and new exigencies of the modern age. St. Thomas, after all, had one of the broadest and most hospitable minds that have ever turned their attention to religious thought; and within the comprehensive bounds of his great *Summa* a half-dozen assorted systems of thought could be placed end to end without bridging the span. It is not necessarily cramping to be a Thomist; it may even be a liberating experience to become one, as many Continental thinkers have lately discovered.

There is today, according to Christopher Dawson, a widespread "intellectual revival" of Catholicism on the Continent. For the last twenty-five years, he reports, young intellectuals and literary men have been turning toward Rome, much as they did during the Catholic revival of the early nineteenth century. "Half a century ago," he remarked, "it was taken as a matter of course in France and Germany that the intellectual should be an unbeliever, and that the practicing Catholic should be an exile from the living thought of the age. Today this is no longer the case, and it is among the intellectuals and the men of letters that the influence of Catholicism is most marked."[5] Among the French literary men who have figured in this movement, he names Péguy, Claudel, François Mauriac and half a dozen other prominent authors—not all of them professed Catholics, but all tending sympathetically toward the Roman Church, as G. K.

[5] *Op. cit.*, p. xx. By permission of the Macmillan Co., publishers.

Chesterton did for so many years before his formal conversion.[6] Among the leading philosophers and theologians of the movement he names Sertillanges, Maritain, Gilson, Rousselot and Maréchal for the French-speaking world; and Przywara, Wust, Carl Schmitt, Theodor Haecker and von Hildebrand for the German-speaking world. As in the Orthodox revival, laymen and priests are working side by side in this Continent-wide movement.

No individual Catholic thinker, or school of thought, is entitled to speak for the whole Church, and a really thorough study of contemporary Catholic thought would be obliged for this reason to depend largely upon great anonymous, collective works like the *Dictionnaire de Théologie Catholique*, the *Lexicon für Theologie und Glaube*, and the theological reviews published by the various faculties and orders; but for our special purpose, it will be more illuminating to confine our attention to two representative figures: Jacques Maritain of Paris, lay apostle of Thomism, and Erich Przywara of Munich, Jesuit theologian, preacher and poet. In the former, we have the best expression of the Catholic critique of modern culture; in the latter, we find a new constructive alternative to modern philosophy—an alternative worked out in close and understanding

---

[6] Two names that should be added to Dawson's list are those of Léon Bloy and Bernanos (author of the recently translated *Diary of a Country Priest*). A marked tendency to asceticism is one of the interesting features of this literary Catholic movement; another is, a marked interest in the diabolic and the supernatural.

relationship to all the principal currents of contemporary thought.

2. A CATHOLIC CRITIC: JACQUES MARITAIN

Literary criticism is a type of writing which has been brought to peculiar perfection in France. Especially since Sainte-Beuve's *Causeries du lundi*, which were appearing in certain Paris newspapers just about a century ago, the art of criticism has been elevated to a rank comparable with that of the poet, the novelist and the dramatist; and the task of the critic has expanded until it has come to be as much (or more) concerned with *ideas* and *cultural trends* as with artistic *style* or *expression*. Criticism has, in short, become an important species of philosophy, unsystematic in form but inculcating a unified point of view by persistently bringing it to bear upon all sorts of topics. Thus it was that Taine persistently inculcated the purely "positivistic" or scientific point of view which explains everything in terms of heredity, environment and historical situation (*race, milieu, moment*), while Brunetière, on the contrary, proclaimed the "bankruptcy of science" and called his countrymen back to classicism and Catholicism. In our own country, this philosophical type of criticism has been lately carried on by Irving Babbitt, Paul Elmer More, and the other "literary humanists"; in England, by Hilaire Belloc and G. K. Chesterton. In contemporary France, it has no greater exponent than Jacques Maritain, who from his chair in the *Institut Catholique* in Paris views the whole modern age with

a critical eye, diagnoses its diseases, and prescribes "Integral Thomism" as the infallible antidote for all its ills.

For the reassurance of those many people who mistrust the Catholic point of view in politics, and see in it the clerical equivalent of Fascism, Nazism and other forms of reactionary dictatorship, let it be said at once that Jacques Maritain is a liberal in his political sympathies. He has no desire to see the mediaeval supremacy of Church over State restored; he only hopes for a day when "an entirely moral and spiritual activity of the Church shall preside over the temporal order of a multitude of politically and culturally heterogeneous nations, whose religious differences are still not likely soon to disappear."[7] He deplores the social inertia and reaction which beset the Catholics, and is only glad to note that they are not quite so recalcitrant to their humanitarian mission as are the Eastern Orthodox, who "go down the road from Jerusalem to Jericho with their eyes raised to Heaven," weeping for wounded humanity but not daring to "lay the unctions of justice on its ailing body."[8] He wishes that sixty years ago some Catholic had "written a book on Capital as decisive as that of Marx, but based on true principles!"[9] He has lately incurred considerable opprobrium among his fellow Catholics by refusing to see in General Franco the perfect Christian knight-errant that the

[7] *Essays in Order,* pp. 28, 29.
[8] *Ibid.,* p. 30.
[9] *Ibid.,* pp. 30, 31.

Spanish landed proprietors—yes, and the Vatican itself—seem to take him to be. He feels that it is such
compromising alliances as this which have brought
Christianity "to the pass she is in today," and he declares that "Christianity must be restored by Christian means, or it will never be restored at all."[10]

If it be asked how a loyal Catholic can thus take
sides against the interests of his own church, the
answer is very clear. Maritain refuses to identify the
interests of Catholics with the interests of the Church,
or the Kingdom of God. The Invincible Armada was
sent out by his Most Catholic Majesty, Philip II of
Spain, with holy intent and with prayers upon the
lips of the faithful; but in Maritain's candid opinion,
God was against it. Far more truly Catholic and
Christian was St. Louis, who, though a warrior and
a king, fought mainly with "weapons of light," and
even in defeat was therefore victorious.

Catholics [says Maritain] are not Catholicism. The errors, apathies, shortcomings and slumbers of Catholics
do not involve Catholicism. . . . Consider the Pope and
the episcopate teaching the faith and morals, consider
the saints in Heaven and on earth, avert your eyes from
us poor sinners. Or, rather, consider how the Church
heals our wounds and leads us hobbling to eternal
life. . . .
Catholicism is not a religious party; it is religion, the
only true religion, and it rejoices, without envy, in every
good, even though it be achieved outside its boundaries.

[10] Quoted from an article in *La Nouvelle Revue Française* by Roy
Temple House, in his article on "Spain's 'Holy War,'" *Christian
Century*, Oct. 6, 1937, pp. 1228-29.

. . . The expansion of the Kingdom of God has no common standard with any temporal conquest or any temporal victory. If the dragoons of Louis XIV harass and martyrize the Huguenots, nothing is thereby gained for the Kingdom of God. If, in a country oppressed by schismatics [Abyssinia?] the Catholics gain the upper hand and plunder the schismatics as the schismatics plundered the Catholics, nothing is gained for the Kingdom of God.[11]

Maritain's ability to distinguish between Catholicism and Catholics springs in part, no doubt, from the fact that he was not born a Catholic, but became one from conviction. Of Protestant antecedents, he became in his university days a rabid anti-clerical, and "published a children's paper designed to inspire French children with a loathing for the clergy and the army."[12] Bergson's philosophy, which he began to study together with a young Russian Jewess who is now his wife, purged his mind of "pseudo-science," and made him more favorably disposed toward religion; but he found in Bergsonian intuition no reliable antidote to the "scepticism which was the logical consequence of all modern philosophies."[13] It was at this juncture that the two young religious seekers paid a memorable visit to an eccentric literary genius, Léon Bloy, who lived a life of exalted spiritual aspiration amid squalid surroundings in Montmartre. Let Maritain relate the episode in his own words:

[11] *Essays in Order,* pp. 39, 40, 42, 43. By permission of The Macmillan Co., publishers.
[12] Pfleger, K., *Wrestlers with Christ,* p. 95.
[13] *Ibid.,* pp. 36, 37.

On the twenty-fifth of June, 1905, two young people of twenty climbed the endless steps leading up to the Church of the Sacred Heart. They bore with them that profound suffering which is the one important product of modern civilization and a kind of active despair which—they knew not why—was heightened by an interior confidence, a confidence that the truth for which they hungered and without which life seemed scarce worth having would one day be revealed. . . . They visited a strange beggar who, scorning all philosophies, shouted the Divine Truth from the house-tops, and who, though an orthdox Catholic, judged his age and all who put their trust in this world with a greater freedom than all the revolutionaries in the world. . . . To cross his threshold was to expose ourselves to an invisible force which transposed all our values. We understood, or at least felt that there is only one genuine sorrow, not to be a Saint. Everything besides became unsubstantial.[14]

Maritain's pilgrimage of faith did not end when he met Léon Bloy. Bloy convinced his heart; St. Thomas, somewhat later, convinced his head. In the preface which he wrote for Bloy's posthumously published *Letters to Veronica*, Maritain says, "Bloy—we may think—sought the Absolute for whom he lived a little too much in the personal intimations of his heart and the intuitions of artistic genius, so that he took too slight account of the universal deliverances of the intellect and reason; and often made his sentiments . . . the basis of unqualified assertions."[15] But he continues to regard this eccentric

---

[14] *Ibid.*, p. 37. By permission of Sheed and Ward, publishers.
[15] *Ibid.*, pp. 60, 61.

"Pilgrim of the Absolute" as his father in the faith, the human agent of his conversion. We may say of Bloy what we said of Dostoievsky: that he is one of the clear precursors of that "four-dimensional," mysterious, tragic view of life which has affected *all* the principal leaders of Continental thought today, and which sets them apart as a group from the prevailing temper of the Anglo-Saxon world. What Dostoievsky did for Berdyaev and many others, Léon Bloy did for Maritain: he cracked the shell of the accepted nineteenth century world-view, letting in the outer darkness and celestial glory that were concealed from his self-satisfied pre-war contemporaries. As Karl Pfleger puts it,

This was part of Bloy's despair that these people were so satisfied and so comfortable in their mediocrity, so contented with *this* world; and the desperate was alone with his despair. They were healthy and cheerful; they babbled about progress and enlightenment and the blessings of democracy, all these folk with the souls of flunkeys and eunuchs, and not once did an inkling of the fact that the old chaos prevailed enter their senile brains. The chaos of a sinful and accursed world where nothing is in its right place, no one knows his real name or his true features, or whether he be worthy of eternal love or eternal hate.[16]

The disease of the modern world which Léon Bloy

[16] *Ibid.*, pp. 51, 52. By permission of Sheed and Ward, publishers. In our Anglo-Saxon world, prophetic voices like T. E. Hulme's have cried out the same message; but they are still echoing in an unresponsive void. On Hulme's *Speculations, see* Chapter II in my *Contemporary English Theology*.

felt so keenly, and which drove him to such frantic excesses of denunciation and ascetic revulsion, Jacques Maritain has now coolly diagnosed in intellectual terms; and he is thus enabled to take up a more friendly and constructive attitude toward modernity. He insists that he is not "anti-modern," except in so far as he combats modern hatred of the past and modern self-complacency; in a deeper sense, he is really "ultra-modern," for he desires to preserve and assimilate the truths in modern culture which are in danger of being lost unless they can be integrated from some higher perspective than the modern mind can reach by itself. He protests that he loathes Neo-Gothic architecture, and has no longing for a romantic and impossible restoration of the Middle Ages, but rather "to see restored in a new world, and informing a new matter, the spiritual principles and eternal laws of which the civilization of the Middle Ages, in its best periods, offers us only a particular historic realization."[17] Ultimately he hopes to see the scientific achievements of the last four centuries gathered up in a new Thomistic philosophy of nature, and the artistic contributions of modernity assessed and interpreted in a Thomistic philosophy of art. In view of the magnitude of this task, he exclaims, "As far as I am concerned, I consider I have done nothing as yet."[18] But surely, to have taken up the critic's task, and to have reached a

[17] *The Angelic Doctor,* Preface.
[18] *Ibid.*

high perspective from which the ills of our time can be judged, is to have done something.

The disease of modernity began, according to Maritain, in the realm of the mind. When modern philosophy abandoned its dependence on theology, it started a process of dissociation which could not be checked short of the very verge of dissolution. Revolt early broke out within the camp of philosophy itself, when what we now call "physical science" declared its independence of metaphysics; and in the system of Descartes "the human mind began to profess independence of God and being."[19] This led inevitably to a series of revolutions which ultimately divorced all the major cultural factors (art, politics, economics, etc.) from each other and from that living center in which they had once been united. "Indocile to the object, to God, to being, the mind becomes also and to the same extent indocile to all human authority, a rebel against all tradition and spiritual continuity."[20] The three great symptoms of this state of dissociation, in its last stages, are (1) *agnosticism*, or the complete separation of the knowing mind from the object of knowledge; (2) *naturalism*, or the complete separation of the world from its divine Source and Ground, and (3) *individualism*, or the complete separation of the rebellious human will from any object of trust and obedience. Thomism is the specific antidote for these three alarming symptoms, and for the disease that underlies them.

[19] *Ibid.*, p. 109.
[20] *Ibid.*, p. 111.

(1) Placing our ideas in continuity with things through the intuition of the senses and resolving all our learning into the self-evidence of being and first principles . . . the philosophy of St. Thomas is [able] to save the mind from the enchantments of agnosticism and to counter the devil of idealism . . . with a realism which is not naïve but soundly critical. . . .

(2) Assuring, through a sound conception of the universal, the value of nature and its laws, and pointing out that nature still remains in the sight of God immensely ductile and immensely perfectible—penetrable throughout to the divine influence—it reduces to absurdity the naturalist postulate and the metaphysical hypocrisy which, concealed behind the curtain of the positive sciences, attempts to endow the creature with the aseity of divinity. . . .

(3) Placing the human mind on the lowest rung of the ladder of spirits, abruptly dismissing all its pretensions to play at being a pure spirit, making proper allowance for the autonomy which becomes us as spirits and the dependence which becomes us as creatures . . . it destroys by the root . . . an individualism which in reality sacrifices human personality to an illusory and devouring image of man.

[Thus, in short, Thomism] brings the mind back to its nature . . . tells it that it is made for being.[21]

In applying this general solution to the various problems of the modern era, Maritain gives special attention to two closely related questions which we have already seen to be the central concerns of Berdyaev's system: the question of *freedom*, and the

[21] *Ibid.*, pp. 126, 127. By permission of Sheed and Ward, publishers.

question of the *destiny of man*. It may be helpful, as we consider Maritain's views on these subjects, to compare them with Berdyaev's.

It will be remembered that Berdyaev traces the origin of freedom of choice to that uncreated, "meonic" freedom from which both God the Creator and man his supreme creature are derived. In *Freedom in the Modern World*, Maritain offers a more rationalistic account of the origin of freedom. The world of freedom, he says, is not to be *opposed* to the world of nature, as in Kant's philosophy; neither is it to be *confused* with it, as in the philosophy of Spinoza and Hegel; it is to be seen as *grounded* in the world of nature, but *distinct* from it. "The whole root of freedom," as St. Thomas says, "lies in reason." Freedom arises in nature precisely where reason arises. Inanimate and irrational beings have no freedom; in this part of nature, God rules without an adversary. Freedom of choice arises in man, a rational yet corporeal creature, because on the one hand he is capable of envisaging the universal Good, and tending toward it, while on the other hand his sensitive faculties present to him all manner of concrete "goods," which *attract* but do not permanently *hold* his will. The Infinite God is his chief end, and alone can satisfy him; but he is capable of being temporarily attracted by many specific ends that conflict with his chief end; and even when his speculative reason *grasps* the true good, his practical reason may fail to perform the act that *chooses* it. In this world of freedom, then,

God appears as legislator and as end of that special order which constitutes the moral order, and from this point of view He has adversaries, for He permits created spirits to resist His will, which is ideally manifest to them as the supreme rule or norm of Freedom. . . . God has the power but does not will to prevent the creature (when it is so inclined) from interposing its refusal. For the hands of God are tied by the inscrutable designs of His love as were those of the Son of Man upon the Cross.[22]

If Berdyaev and Maritain differ on the *origin* of freedom, they substantially agree about the practical solution of the problem it presents. Freedom of choice is not true freedom. True freedom consists in choosing the Good. When a man chooses the Good, he participates in that "freedom of autonomy" which God possesses in its perfection. God is so fixed upon the Good that he cannot choose otherwise; and the saints, who participate in God's holiness, participate also in his fixity of character and will. Yet, although the pilgrimage of virtue thus leads toward the abandonment of choice, the saints are the least slavish of men. What they do, they do of themselves, with an inner and not an outer compulsion; and in this sense they are truly free. Their freedom is a type of God's freedom, where the tension between nature and freedom, the "is" and the "ought," is completely resolved. If there is any significant difference between the Catholic philosopher and the Orthodox Gnostic, it lies in the fact that the goal of freedom, for Mari-

[22] Maritain, *Freedom in the Modern World*, p. 27. By permission of Chas. Scribner's Sons, publishers.

tain, is found in obedience to the rational Good; while for Berdyaev it is found in a creative experience that lies "beyond Good and Evil."

Maritain's views on the destiny of man are most clearly expressed in his *Humanisme intégral*, a book that reminds one frequently of Berdyaev's historical writings, and must surely have been influenced by them. Like Berdyaev, Maritain feels that Christianity necessarily involves a very exalted view of man. The tragedy of modern humanism springs not from its having been "humanistic," but from its having been *man-centered*. Anthropocentrism is fatal both to the idea of *man* itself and to the ideas of *culture* and *God* that are linked with it. The idea of *man*, beginning with a proud assertion of human rationality (Descartes), goodness (Rousseau), and moral self-sufficiency (Kant), has passed through successive deflations at the hands of Darwin and Freud, and is now completely disintegrated. Humanistic *culture*, beginning with a noble heritage from the Christian Middle Ages, passed into a second phase in the eighteenth century, when it began consciously to turn against its own historic sources, and into a third phase with the Russian Revolution, when it replaced all ideal ends by purely material ones. In the first of these three phases, *God* is still believed in as a real power, but becomes the *guarantor of man's success* (Bacon, Descartes) in dominating nature; in the second phase, when man begins to trust in his ability to dominate nature single-handed, by his own science and technology, God becomes *a mere idea* (Kant), or, with

Hegel, the "ideal limit of the development of the world of humanity"; in the third phase, with the disappearance of the divine image in man, the *death of God* is announced, and there are only two alternatives left: *pure atheism,* and a return to *pure Christianity.*[23]

The attempt to revive pure Christianity in our day has two principal forms, according to Maritain: the "reactionary" attempt to turn humanism upside down by the "annihilation of man before God" (Karl Barth), and the "integral" or "progressive" attitude of Neo-Thomism, which aims to preserve the dignity of man and rescue the valuable elements in humanistic culture by incorporating them in a new Christian civilization.[24] Maritain is not too hopeful about the possibility of a new Christian civilization in the near future. He rejects with equal decisiveness the view that this world is simply the kingdom of Satan, and the view that the Kingdom of God is ever fully to be realized in it. "The true Christian doctrine of the world and of the earthly city is that they are *at once* the kingdom of man, of God, and of the devil."[25] History is marching both toward the harvest of wheat and the harvest of tares. Just now, the age of humanism is marching toward its own "liquidation"; and it is very improbable (though not impossible) that it will escape judgment by a deathbed repentance. The end of this age, however, does not

---

[23] Maritain, *Humanisme intégral,* pp. 36-42.
[24] *Ibid.,* pp. 79-81.
[25] *Ibid.,* p. 119.

mean the end of the world. History is not yet ripe to be swallowed up in eternity. Both the development of the human race's secular possibilities and the unfolding of the social implications of Christianity are still at a very "primitive," nay, "prehistoric" stage; and we must therefore believe that the Providence of God has yet to guide us through many acts in the human drama. What Christians ought most clearly to do, during this present period of "liquidation," is to form a "network of centers of Christian life," dotting our decaying civilization like cells of a new type of social organization. Each of these centers should, of course, try to penetrate its environment, by political and social action, as far as possible; but if direct political influence ("rich means," as Maritain calls it) shall fail, the spiritual influence of such centers of Christian life, working by the "poor" but powerful means of moral contagion, cannot fail to be used of God for the building of the new age. When the old order at last collapses, these Christian *foyers* or cells will become the nuclei of the new order; and they may even prevent the transition from being unnecessarily violent and destructive. In all this, one feels that Maritain, if he has not the apocalyptic vision of Berdyaev, has a clearer and wiser grasp of the issues and probabilities of the immediate future than his Russian contemporary. The Roman Catholics, through direct implication in the political development of Western Europe, have acquired a feeling for the historical process which the more mystical and unworldly Or-

thodox cannot yet match, with all their new-found interest in social questions.

A recent visitor to South America, Mlle Suzanne de Dietrich, reports that young Catholics in that part of the world, when asked who are their spiritual leaders, almost invariably respond, "Maritain and Gilson."[26] A few years ago, Spanish or Italian Catholic thinkers, such as Unamuno or Dom Sturzo, might have been mentioned in the same breath with Maritain; now, apparently, so far as the "Latin" section of the Catholic world is concerned, it is only his fellow-Parisian Gilson who stands by his side. Before leaving the Latin Catholic world for the Teutonic Catholic world, which has its cultural capitals in Munich and Vienna instead of Rome and Paris, it may be well to pause for a moment to note the likeness and difference between the two French Catholic thinkers whose names are today being coupled together so frequently.

Etienne Gilson is not primarily a critic of culture, like Maritain; he is probably the greatest living authority on the history of mediaeval philosophy. He has lectured on this subject for many years, at the Sorbonne, at Harvard, and at Toronto—for he speaks excellent English, and is thoroughly cosmopolitan in his outlook upon the modern world. As might be expected, he sees St. Thomas in a somewhat different

[26] I am indebted to a conversation with Mlle de Dietrich, not only for this point about South America, but for the suggestion that certain "four-dimensional minds" (Dostoievsky, Bloy, Kierkegaard) furnish the key to the whole pervading temper of Continental theology.

light from Maritain, for he has an extraordinary grasp of all the various cross-currents of mediaeval and patristic thought, and a great respect for many Christian thinkers whose philosophy is not easily pressed into the Thomistic mold. He sees St. Thomas rather as the most outstanding and representative figure in a vast and many-sided movement of thought, the "*common* doctor" who sums up and sets in order what many others have said in other ways; whereas Maritain, who came straight to St. Thomas out of infidelity, paying comparatively little attention to any other teachers, naturally sees in him the *unique* doctor, in whom *alone* we find the cure for our modern ills.

It is important to remember that Gilson's attitude toward St. Thomas has just as much standing in the Catholic Church as Maritain's. In fact, one is interested to note how often Maritain's "integral Thomism" is criticized by born-and-bred Catholics as colored by the excessive zeal of a fresh convert; while the broader and more adaptable Thomism of men like Sertillanges, Maréchal and Gilson is preferred to this narrower variety.[27] What most of these men would join in defending is what Gilson, in his Gifford Lectures on *The Spirit of Mediaeval Philosophy*, has called simply "Christian philosophy"—

[27] There are no interpreters of St. Thomas more respected than the Jesuits of Louvain—Father Maréchal, Father Noel and others— and their interpretation is in accord with Gilson's, rather than with Maritain's. Still farther to the left are some interpreters of St. Thomas apparently influenced by the philosophy of Maurice Blondel, whose famous book, *L'Action*, figured prominently in the Modernist controversy.

a point of view of which St. Thomas is the most eminent but not the only genuine exponent. Christian philosophy is attacked in modern times from two opposite angles: by the Protestants, who complain that it is not truly Christian, and by the rationalists, who complain that it is not truly philosophical. Gilson maintains, on the contrary, that the Christian religion has been from the start "a religious source of philosophical development,"[28] and while the great example of Christian philosophy is given by the Latin Middle Ages, the formation of some such philosophy "was inevitable . . . is so today, and will so remain as long as there are Christians."[29] At its best, such a philosophy asserts nothing incapable of rational proof, and is therefore *real philosophy*; while its adherents continue to live, in ultimate matters, by faith and grace rather than by reason and nature, and are therefore *really Christian*. Against the Protestant doctrine of *sola gratia*, based on a complete pessimism about the world and man, Gilson defends the Catholic conception of grace and faith as the perfection, not the destruction, of nature and reason; and he cries out, both as a Christian and as a philosopher, against the notion "of a grace that saves a man without changing him, of a justice that redeems corrupted nature without restoring it, of a Christ who pardons the sinner for self-inflicted wounds but does not heal them."[30] But if it be

[28] Gilson, *The Spirit of Mediaeval Philosophy*, p. 405.
[29] *Ibid.*, p. 419.
[30] *Ibid.*, p. 421.

granted against Luther and Barth that the world
and man still bear vestiges of the work of a wise and
good Creator, then a Christian philosophy of the
Catholic type has all the charter it needs: *"maintaining on the one hand a philosophy of nature while
at the same time building up a theology of supernature, and integrating the first with the second in
a coherent system."*[31] This, essentially, is the principle according to which Erich Przywara of Munich
is working out his Christian philosophy at the present day.

3. A CATHOLIC SYSTEM-BUILDER: ERICH PRZYWARA, S.J.

When we pass from Paris to Munich, we cross a
linguistic and cultural frontier which is very important, from the point of view of religious thought as
well as from the point of view of politics. Even so
international a church as the Church of Rome is
much more divided by such frontiers than either her
admirers or her enemies commonly suppose. I was
told, when I set out to explore the Catholic mind

[31] *Ibid.*, p. 423. In his recent brilliant and witty discussion of *The
Unity of Philosophical Experience*, pp. 49-62 (Scribner's, 1937) Gilson criticises a mediaeval thinker whom he otherwise greatly admires, St. Bonaventura, for having committed the fallacy of
"theologism"; i.e., having absorbed philosophy in theology and
nature in grace, to the ultimate detriment of the religious interests
he sought to conserve. St. Thomas, he evidently feels, avoided that
fallacy as no other Christian thinker has done, and is therefore our
supreme though not our only guide. "While so many men were
trying to base philosophy on theological foundations, a very simple
and modest man was putting everything in its place. His name was
Thomas Aquinas, and he was saying things so obviously true that,
from his time down to our own day, very few people have been
sufficiently self-forgetful to accept them."

on the Continent in the summer of 1937, that I would find Catholics in the French-speaking world less aware than Protestants of what their brethren in the German-speaking world were doing.[32] I found this at least to be true, that the name of Erich Przywara—surely an odd enough name to stick in any one's memory—was little known among French Catholic theologians. One of the many French Catholics whom I asked about Przywara's influence upon contemporary Catholic thought, said that he had heard of the man, but he was a mere popularizer, of no real profundity; whereas, as we shall presently see, Przywara is so solid a thinker that he is almost impenetrable! But cross the linguistic frontier, and it becomes evident at once that in the German-speaking world Przywara occupies a position of eminence.

I need cite no other proof of this than the fact that Karl Barth, the staunchest defender of the Protestant faith, and Alfred Rosenberg, author of *The Myth of the Twentieth Century*—next to Hitler's *Mein Kampf*, the most influential piece of Nazi literature—both attack Przywara as though he were the one opponent worthy of their steel in the Catholic camp. The idea of the "Analogy of Being" (*Analogia Entis*) which Przywara has elaborately expounded and justified in his principal work, is to

[32] My explanation of this is that an international church is forced to prove, in every country where she goes, that her members can be good citizens of that country in spite of their foreign ties, and she ends by being excessively nationalistic; whereas the Protestant Church, troubled by her nationalistic divisions, has done much to overcome them through ecumenical movements.

Karl Barth "the invention of Anti-Christ" and the one great reason for not being a Catholic. The idea is equally hateful to Rosenberg, but for an opposite reason. Barth hates it because it suggests that there is a bridge of connection between the transcendent God and his human creatures, a bridge which human reason can traverse, from this side. Rosenberg hates it because it suggests that human nature and human reason point beyond themselves, and beyond this world (to which Rosenberg's religion of blood and soil is confined). Barth complains because Przywara emphasizes the immanence of God; Rosenberg, because he emphasizes the transcendence of God.[33] When Rosenberg discusses Przywara's teaching, one would think he was discussing Barth; when Barth discusses it, one would think he was discussing Rosenberg. That alone is enough to indicate the key position which Przywara holds in contemporary religious thought in Germany.

Before setting down his philosophy in definitive form in his book on the *Analogy of Being*, Przywara had struggled for many years with the problem of the relation between God and the world. The problem first arose for him in a purely metaphysical form, in the course of a study which he made (in 1912-13) of St. Thomas's distinction between *essence* and *existence* (*essentia* and *esse*, or *Sosein* and *Dasein* in German). The relation of enduring metaphysical

---

[33] See the Author's Foreword to Barth's *Church Dogmatics: the Doctrine of the Word of God*, p. x, and Rosenberg's *Mythus des XX Jahrhunderts*, 87th-90th edition, 1935, p. 245.

Reality (*being* or *essence*) to transient existent things
or entities turned out, when closely analyzed, to be
a relation of both *in* and *above*. Reality is *in* things,
but it is also *beyond and above* them. In an analo-
gous way, God's relation to the world and to man
involves a paradox: He is both *in* us and *above* us.
Pursuing the meaning of this paradox, Przywara read
the same mystical theologians to whom Berdyaev so
often appeals—Dionysius the Areopagite, Meister
Eckhart and others—and like him, for a time, began
to emphasize *negative* or *mystical* at the expense of
positive or *rational* theology. Goethe's philosophy of
polarity, Newman's "dynamic antithetics," and the
philosophy of the German Catholic Romanticists
(Baader and Görres) also influenced him profoundly;
and among his contemporaries, Max Scheler and
Husserl of the "phenomenological" school. All this,
though he does not say so explicitly, would seem to
have threatened to make him an anti-intellectualist
and anti-scholastic, like Laberthonnière and other
Catholic Modernists. It was probably his careful
study of Kierkegaard and Heidegger and his "fruit-
ful personal encounter"[34] with Karl Barth that made
him react, against their extreme anti-intellectualism,
toward a new appreciation of scholastic rationalism,
and a new balance between the "negative" and "positive" sides of Catholic theology.

Przywara's first important *constructive* book—he
has published many historical, critical and poetical

[34] Erich Przywara, *Analogia Entis: Metaphysik I: Prinzip*. Kösel
and Pustet, München, 1932. Foreword.

works which for our purpose are less significant—
was his *Gottgeheimnis der Welt* (1924). The formula
he used in this book for the relation between God
and world was "Dynamic polarity." The word "dynamic" implies that there is "tension" (*Spannung*)
between God and his creation; while the word "polarity" implies that God makes the mystery of his
nature partly known in an inexhaustible series of
polar opposites such as object-subject, being-becom-
ing, etc. These polar opposites are not to be resolved
into identity, as Hegel and other idealists have tried
to do, but held in dynamic antithesis to each other,
so that they point above and beyond themselves to
a transcendent Reality.

In another important book, *The Philosophy of
Religion Presupposed in Catholic Theology* (*Religionsphilosophie Katholischer Theologie*, 1926),[35]
Przywara distinguished the Catholic world-view from
three main types of world-view which have been
struggling with one another since religious thought
began: *pure immanence,* which identifies God with
the world and with man, as in pantheism; *pure
transcendence,* which utterly separates God from the
world and man, as in deism; and *transcendentality,*
which pushes upward from earth to heaven, from
man to God, by successive bursts of transcendental

[35] English translation, *Polarity,* by Bouquet. The German original
is a long essay in the Catholic *Handbuch der Philosophie.* Bouquet
published a summary of it in *Theology,* December, 1934. In many
respects this is a more religiously persuasive and appealing book than
the one we have chosen for review; but it does not show Przywara
quite so clearly in the character of a *system-builder.*

insight, until it sees all things in God, *sub specie aeternitatis*. Catholic thought, says Przywara, stands aloof from all three of these world-views, even the third, though it can appreciate the measure of truth in them all; for in all of them it detects a false assumption that brings them to grief in the end, and lands them in some form of logical self-contradiction: the assumption, namely, that human beings are capable, or will some time be capable, *in this world,* of coming to a perfectly harmonious solution of their practical and intellectual problems. Against this assumption Catholic theology sets the teaching of the Fourth Lateran Council (1215) that the world, as God's creation, has no possibility of attaining final rest or harmony within itself, but only in God, who is both like and unlike his creation, both *in* it (as a principle of aspiration) and eternally *beyond* it (as its infinitely exalted Source, Meaning and Goal). This is essentially the doctrine of the Analogy of Being (*Analogia Entis*) as developed in Przywara's most recent and authoritative statement of his position.

The notion of an Analogy of Being, which permits rational thought to rise from nature and man to God, without ever fully penetrating the mystery of the Godhead, is of course a very ancient and venerable idea in the history of Catholic thought. There are many passages bearing upon this idea in St. Augustine and other early Fathers, but it received most careful treatment in the works of Dionysius, Albertus Magnus, St. Thomas Aquinas and, much

later, the celebrated Jesuit theologian Suarez (1548-1617), who has a section in his *Metaphysical Disputations* entitled "On the Analogy of Being to God and the Creature" (*De analogia entis ad Deum et creaturam*). The word "analogy" in general implies "similarity mixed with difference." As applied to God, it connotes that when human and earthly similes are used in speaking of the divine nature, such language is neither "univocal" (meaning just what it ordinarily means—which would land us in Anthropomorphism) nor "equivocal" (meaning something wholly other than what it ordinarily means —which would land us in complete Agnosticism), but there is a sufficient bond of likeness between God and his creation to make such language really significant and truthful. In the philosophy of St. Thomas Aquinas, a metaphysical basis is laid for the use of analogical reasoning in relation to God, in that the created world is described as a chain or hierarchy of beings of every sort and degree, exhibiting separately and imperfectly those qualities which are found simultaneously and perfectly in their infinite Creator. There is thus between God and his creatures an analogy of *being* in the strict sense— not as though the transient *existence* of creatures was the same *sort* of being that the eternal God possesses, but still *being* of a sort, sufficiently like the being of God to be a significant image or reflection of it at some restricted points. The proper way of arguing from the creation to God is therefore to begin with the *via causalitatis*, treating the creatures as effects

of divine causation, and ascribing to the Cause whatever qualities are necessary to make the effect intelligible. This is a positive, purely rational method of argumentation; but it must be immediately supplemented by the *via negationis*, which "negates" in the divine Cause everything finite or imperfect in the effect, and the *via eminentiae*, which ascribes all positive perfections to him in such a "supereminent" degree that the difference between effect and cause becomes a difference in kind—or rather, as St. Thomas says, God is *extra omne genus*; there is no conceivable kind or genus that can contain him. The analogy of *being* between creature and God is therefore not a simple analogy of "attribution" or proportion, as if it were between commensurables, but an analogy of "proportionality" between incommensurables: God's being is to man's as man's is to nothing.

The originality of Father Przywara's handling of this ancient theme lies in the way he has adapted it to the characteristic dialectical method of modern German philosophy. Although of Slavic extraction, as his name indicates, he has evidently made German culture completely his own, and learned what used to be called the "secret of Hegel": how to evolve a whole system of philosophy out of the magic words "Being is" or some other equally abstract and contentless proposition. That is not to say, of course, that either Hegel's method or Przywara's is devoid of empirical illustration—history is brought in afterward, by both, to check and confirm their metaphysics—but page after page of our Jesuit philos-

opher's argument moves in that atmosphere of the *allgemein* and the *überhaupt* which only Germans seem to be able to breathe for long periods of time without fainting for lack of oxygen. Even after our experience with Berdyaev's speculative flights, we shall have difficulty in following Przywara; for the Russian mind rises toward the eternal heights on wings of apocalyptic imagery, while of the German mind it might be said, as was said of the mind of a certain German-trained American philosopher, that it represented the "deep-down-divingest, under-water-stayingest, mud-up-bringingest" type of mentality with which God had endowed any of his creatures!

The argument of Father Przywara's book falls into three main divisions—each full of a wealth of subtle detail which we must omit. In the first division, the concept of metaphysics is analyzed, several possible attitudes toward its problems are discriminated, and the hopeless difficulties to which some of these attitudes lead are shown to point to a theistic ("creaturely"), and in fact specifically Catholic, type of metaphysics. In the second division, the Catholic method of analogy is first differentiated from simple rational logic and from various types of modern dialectics, and is then applied to that favorite problem of German idealistic philosophy, the meaning of the principle of contradiction—with results as fertile and amazing as any that Fichte achieved in his *Wissenschaftslehre*, or Hegel in his *Logik*, but vastly different! In the last division, the historical development of the principle of the "analogy of being" is

traced from Plato and Aristotle through St. Augustine and St. Thomas to its final formulation in the decrees of the Vatican Council of 1870, and the historical doctrine is found to correspond with the requirements of abstract reason, as worked out in the "objective problematics" of the first two divisions. Let us trace these three stages of the argument in their bare outlines.

1. *Catholic metaphysics the only logically possible type.* The fundamental problems of metaphysics are *metaöntics* (the problem of the ultimate ground and meaning of objective being) and *metanoëtics* (the problem of the ultimate ground and meaning of subjective consciousness). Whether we take these problems in their most abstract form (objective *reality*, subjective *truth*) or complicate them by bringing in the *good* and the *beautiful*, in either case we discover that the objective and subjective sides of the investigation are as inseparable as the two ends of a stick. It is impossible to investigate *being* without making assumptions about *knowledge*, or to investigate *knowledge* without making assumptions about *being*. The most natural order is to proceed from *knowledge* to *being*, then to the *relation between them*, and so back to the starting point for another circuit. This simple, highly abstract circumstance is enough to eliminate from the very start all purely subjective and purely objective types of metaphysics (such as subjective idealism and certain types of "phenomenology") in favor of a metaphysic which rises from the thinking subject to an objective ground of both

being and thought, and then descends to view its starting point from above. This already is the fundamental pattern of a "creaturely" or theistic metaphysic. (Sec. 1 & 2)

Whether we start from the subjective or the objective pole of experience, we find that metaphysical investigation leads us to distinguish between the *Ground, Goal or Meaning* of existence and that which is *grounded, determined, clad with meaning* by this more ultimate reality, whatever it is. Hence arises a conflict between another contrasting pair of possible types of metaphysics: the *apriori,* which proceeds from Ground to grounded, and the *aposteriori,* which proceeds from grounded to Ground. As before, we discover that each of these two opposite types is simply impossible in its pure form. We cannot proceed either with *apriori* or *aposteriori* reflection without tacitly assuming something derived from the other type of procedure. The only practicable method is to begin with our immediate experience of transient thoughts, acts or things, rise to their metaphysical Ground, and then grasp the relationship between grounded and Ground, criticizing the ungrounded assumptions with which we inevitably began, from the higher perspective thus gained. (Sec. 3)

The principle thus abstractly stated is of decisive significance for determining the proper relations between theology and philosophy. The method of theology is more *apriori* (from God down), that of philosophy more *aposteriori* (from the world up); but

if we try to operate exclusively from either one of these two poles of thought, we fall into error. The ultimate religious outcome of a purely philosophical, or *aposteriori*, world-view is *evolutionary pantheism*, which equates God with the world process. The outcome of a purely theological, or *apriori*, approach is what Przywara calls *devolutionary theopantism*—the view of Zwingli and Calvin, and of Barth, their modern descendant—which makes God the sole cause and robs the world and man of all independent reality.[36] The only perfectly adequate solution of this antinomy is to be found in the Catholic principle that faith and grace (theology) are not the destruction of reason and nature (philosophy), but their support and their fulfillment, because the Creator (the ultimate metaphysical Ground of the world) is both infinitely above his creation and imperfectly imaged in it. This is the principle of the "analogy of being," which requires a constant tension of two contrasting attitudes in the mind of the Catholic metaphysician: complete philosophical *open-mindedness* in the study and interpretation of *nature*, and complete *submissiveness* to God's revelation of his hidden *supernature*, in Christ and the Church. Theology is in-and-above philosophy, as God is in-and-above the world; philosophy, although free and independent, points beyond itself to theology, as the world points beyond itself to its transcendent Source

---

[36] Gilson calls this "theologism," as we saw, and finds it in some Catholic and Moslem thinkers, as well as in Protestants.

and Goal. (Sec. 4, closing with elaborate diagram of the formula for a Catholic "creaturely metaphysic".)

2. *The analogy of being, the only solution of the problem of the principle of contradiction.* Having disposed of his chief opponents (let us say, Rosenberg and Barth) on general principles, Przywara now proceeds to show up their weakness on a specific issue, the *principle of contradiction*—the principle out of which the German idealists spun so many airy consequences in the heyday of the Romantic era. Przywara does not deny that it is capable of yielding important metaphysical truths if properly handled, but he denies that it has been properly handled either in the "logical dialectics" of Hegel and the speculative idealists, or in the "dialectical logic" of Kierkegaard, Heidegger and Barth. These two schools of dialectics err in opposite fashion. The school of Hegel, aspiring to a completely intelligible vision of reality that can belong to God alone, finds the highest logical rationality in the flattest logical contradiction (identity of opposites). The school of Barth, conscious of the vast gulf between man and God, finds the highest wisdom possible for man in the humble acceptance of a series of *unresolved* contradictions. But this is only another form of the same abyss of skepticism into which Hegel led. The principle of contradiction is in both cases made to mean the same thing as the principle of identity, which should be its opposite! Either Hegel and Barth are both wrong, or the human mind is stark, raving mad, and all science is impossible. (I am attributing to

Father Przywara more oratorical emphasis than is actually to be found in his cool, dry analysis; but this is, to me, the rather exciting upshot of the verbal distinctions which he draws in section 5, and the first three subdivisions of section 6.)

How then is the problem of the principle of contradiction to be handled? Przywara points out that it had its origin in the ancient debate between Heraclitus and Parmenides, over the question of *change*. Heraclitus, with his insistence that all is in perpetual flux and perpetual self-contradiction, and Parmenides, with his insistence that all apparent changes and differences are unreal, both threaten to rob language and thought of any intelligible meaning, and confuse truth and falsity in the most bewildering manner. Aristotle erected the principle of self-contradiction as a canon of criticism against both; and it is equally effective against all their later intellectual descendants. It decrees that if it is true that A is B, then it cannot possibly be true that (at the same time and in the same respect) A is *not* B. Reason can operate in a world of change, flux and mystery because, holding fast to this principle, it can find enough enduring qualities, enough B's that remain true of their respective A's, to trace lines of stable identity through a world of change and difference. Between the potential and actual state of a living being, Aristotle found what he called a "middle term" or "analogy," which is its "entelechy," its enduring goal or formative principle. Catholic philosophy proceeds in a similar way when it passes

from the world of change and flux to the Creator who is its enduring Ground. It finds a middle term, which is *being*; and although it grants and even insists that God's being is different in kind from our finite being, there is enough in common to make an endless chain of being between God, man and nature, along which thought can forever truly aspire toward that which is finally too mysterious for it to grasp. Catholic *theology*, of course, supplements and fulfills Catholic philosophy through faith in Christ, the great Middle Term between God, man and world, through whom and in whom their final unity is to be achieved. Between God and his creation we must always say, *"Tanta similitudo, major dissimilitudo,"*—"their likeness is never so great as their difference"—and hence there must always be a "dynamic tension" (*schwebende Spannung*) between love of the God revealed, and restless aspiration toward the God unrevealed; but in this attitude alone is there any prospect of maintaining a clear head and a sense of logical order in the midst of a world of contradictions. (Sec. 6)

3. *St. Thomas the classic exponent of the analogy of being.* The notion of an analogy of some sort between God and the world goes back to Plato's original attempt to solve the problem of contradiction set by Heraclitus and Parmenides. In the last third of his book, Father Przywara traces the historical development of this idea of analogy, and shows that only in the form given it by St. Thomas Aquinas does it fully solve the problem it set out to deal with.

In *Plato*, the analogy takes the form of a likeness between the eternal ideas and their earthly copies— a likeness which permits the soul to retrace its path back to the eternal world by following this analogy with passionate desire (*Eros*). Yet there is so great a gulf between the copy and the original that the world of transient objects is robbed of all genuine meaning and rationality, and an "immortal struggle" (*Machē athanatos*) between the two worlds is the final issue of the whole system.

In *Aristotle*, the whole endeavor is to draw the Platonic ideas down into the flux of this world, and find in them a stable analogy or middle term by which the harmonious unity of the world can be completely grasped. As Przywara puts it, in Plato the prefix "ana-" in "analogy" means "up" (*anō*), and points "upward" to a transcendent realm; whereas in Aristotle it means "upon" (*ana*), and refers to an indwelling principle of order or form, whose influence acts "upon" everything, so that a law of correspondence links the whole world together. But Aristotle's attempt to see the world as a complete, harmonious whole failed; he admits that his world is in the last analysis a "torso" (*Kolobon*) which points beyond itself to a transcendent deity as its Final Cause.

In *St. Augustine*, the "Christian Plato," the idea of analogy is further enriched. As in Plato, the way to eternal truth points steeply "upward" (*anō*), and this world is a realm of darkness and disorder; but there is a new connection between the world above

and the world below: God's gracious love (*Agape*), coming down from above, in Christ, is a more powerful bond between time and eternity than man's feeble aspiration (*Eros*) rising up from below could ever be. So if this world is a realm of night, its gloom is the darkness before dawn, at the end of a long "night of waiting"; the "most nocturnal mystery of the creation" is at the same time "a revelation of the 'superluminous darkness' of the Godhead." As in the teaching of Kierkegaard and Barth (the modern disciples of Augustine), man is thought to be closest to God when he despairs of himself and allows his natural reason to go out in darkness, swallowed up in the mysterious *chiaroscuro* of self-distrustful faith, that hopes only in God.

In *St. Thomas Aquinas*, "the Christian Aristotle," the problem that neither Plato, nor Aristotle, nor Augustine could resolve is finally settled, at least in principle. By his clear distinction of the two orders, nature and grace, St. Thomas rescued the natural universe from the threat of meaninglessness which always hung over it in Platonism and Augustinianism, and gave to the supernatural world a richness of meaning and religious mystery which it completely lacked in Aristotelianism. Reason is set at peace with itself, and set free to explore the relatively independent world of nature, which has its own perfection. Religious aspiration is delivered from all chafing fretfulness, and launched upon its way to the mysterious and transcendent God, with a running rational start. If

the world of Plato is one of "eternal combat," if Aristotle's world is a "torso" and Augustine's a realm of "night," St. Thomas's is one of clear "boundaries," within which each realm is at peace, while at the same time it leads on to another realm which brings it near to its final fulfillment in God. Man is at the boundary between nature and spirit, the completion of one realm and the beginning of the next. He is the great "analogy of being," for his natural being is the key to all natural perfection, while his supernatural being, restored in Christ, is the key to the realm of grace above. There is a *proportio excedens*, an "unequal proportion," between his nature and God's. Man is at the same time really like God, and infinitely unlike God. In the likeness (*proportio*) we have the truth in Aristotle, the *aná* in analogy, perfectly allowed for; in the unlikeness (*excedens*) we have the truth in Plato and Augustine, the upward-looking *anō*, which mysticism and "negative theology" have always stressed. (Sec. 7, 8.) The reader will note the close similarity between this Roman Catholic doctrine and the Russian Orthodox doctrine of Divine-humanity, or Sophia.

Although St. Thomas, according to Father Przywara, has solved the whole problem of metaphysics in principle, it remains for every generation of Catholic philosophers to restate his solution in terms of contemporary science, contemporary philosophy and contemporary social problems. In a second volume of the *Analogia Entis*, not yet out, Przywara intends to discuss the nature of mind, the nature of

being and the nature of the world, in terms of contemporary knowledge. Perhaps it is now fairly clear along what lines he may be expected to proceed in his work of construction.

It may be asked why, in a book on "theology," we have given so much attention to *philosophy* as we have in this chapter. The answer is twofold. In the first place, one of the most acute issues in contemporary theology is that concerning the proper relationship between theology and philosophy; and the most distinctive thing about Roman Catholic theology is that it makes room for philosophy, and sets it in close relation to theology within its total world-view, while clearly distinguishing the one from the other. Personally, I think that this is the *right* solution of the whole problem, and we must all come to it in the end. In the second place, however, I must confess my opinion that Catholic *philosophy* is much more interesting and rewarding to study, as a possible source of light and guidance, than Catholic *theology*. The Catholic Church is right, I believe, in her distinction between matters of faith, which must be dogmatically handled, and matters of reason, in which dogmatism is out of place; but she has erred in turning many doctrines into dogmas which ought never to have been classified as matters of faith—for example, the dogma of the Immaculate Conception.

I agree with Father Bulgakov in his view that it is better to keep the dogmatic element in theology very simple and flexible, as in the Orthodox Church, rather than to define it legally and elaborately, as in

the Roman Church. If Rome has saved for us all many precious theological truths, behind her heavy chain mail of dogmatism, she has also saved many odds and ends of tradition which might better not have been preserved, at least in the form of *required beliefs*. So, although I consider Roman Catholic *philosophy* superior to Eastern Orthodox philosophy —and indeed to most contemporary philosophy—in sobriety and balance, I find Eastern Orthodox *theology* much more helpful than Roman Catholic.[37] I may be mistaken in this judgment, and obliged to change it in time, as I become more conscious of the inner connection between Catholic theology and Catholic philosophy. But whatever one may think about Roman Catholicism, this tribute must be paid to it by anyone who meets with it in the most casual way: *it knows where it stands, and why, and so holds steady in a world that is being shaken to its foundations*. It may be well that, before plunging into the maelstrom of contemporary Protestant thought—where so many are rapidly changing their stand, or maintaining their position by sheer pugnacity—we have dwelt for a time in the serene light of the Catholic world and acquired (perhaps) a certain sense of perspective.

[37] By all odds the most readable and disarming presentation of Catholic *theology*, for non-Catholics, is *The Spirit of Catholicism* by Professor Karl Adam of the University of Tübingen—a friendly old university town, where Catholics and Protestants have long worked together in peace in the same institution, and where they are now collaborating to combat the New Paganism. But in the nature of the case, what is most original in a book like Adam's is not its substance, which is determined by Church dogmas, but its method of presentation and its spirit, which I think wholly admirable.

CHAPTER III

THE CRISIS IN GERMAN PROTESTANT THEOLOGY

1. THE COLLAPSE OF GERMAN LIBERAL PROTESTANTISM

WE HAVE spoken of the "rediscovery" or "renaissance" of Orthodoxy, and the Catholic "revival" or "return from exile." How shall we denominate the state of Protestantism in Continental Europe today? Only one word seems adequate to describe the situation. European Protestantism is now in a state of *crisis*—hanging between death and recovery—and the crisis is most acute in the very lands where the Protestant Reformation first began: Germany and German Switzerland. To these lands, now at the center of a great wreckage-strewn maelstrom, the present chapter is devoted, while we reserve for the next chapter those Protestant lands which are only on the *edge* of the maelstrom.

The most striking feature of the situation in the German Protestant world today is the almost complete collapse of liberal Protestantism. Throughout the nineteenth century, Protestant theological faculties in the German and Swiss universities enjoyed a degree of academic liberty (both from ecclesiastical and from political censorship) and a reputation for thorough scholarship and bold speculation which made them the world's greatest centers for theological study. Liberal Protestants in the English-speaking

world are still barely abreast of the achievements of German theology in this "liberal" period. The names of Schleiermacher (1768-1834), Ritschl (1822-89), and Troeltsch (1865-1923) are still names to conjure with among us; indeed, it is not rash to prophesy that their works will be studied hundreds of years hence, as repositories of some of the richest intellectual treasures that Christian scholarship has ever gathered together in one place; yet they have all simultaneously fallen into profound disrepute, within a very few years, throughout the German-speaking world. How explain such a phenomenon?

In the first place it must be understood that the liberal theological faculties to which foreign students flocked in such numbers before the World War were always a little aloof from the life of the German churches. The object which liberal theology set for itself was to meet the intellectual challenge presented to Christianity by modern science and philosophy. It did so with much success, on a high academic plane; but it failed to bring its modernized Evangel convincingly home to the average preacher, still less to the average layman. The working class and the intellectual class became more and more alienated from Christianity, despite all the arguments of the liberal theologians; while "as far as there was still religious life in the Protestant Churches it was either indifferent towards all kinds of academic theology, or it was in manifest opposition to it."[1] The prevailing the-

---

[1] Otto Piper, *Recent Developments in German Protestantism*, p. 35. It may be added that academic theology itself, especially in the field

ological trend in the average German Evangelical or Swiss Reformed church was not, perhaps, so conservative as that of the Lutheran and Reformed Churches in America; but it was much closer to it than we might infer from a reading of Schleiermacher, Ritschl and Troeltsch.

In the second place, we must note the fact that all schools of liberal theology, despite their many differences, had a common intellectual basis in idealistic philosophy; and idealism, as we know, has lost prestige throughout the Western World since the World War. The school of Schleiermacher differed from the school of Hegel, as *romantic* idealism, with its trust in poetic intuition, differs from logical or *speculative* idealism, with its faith in dialectical reasoning; but both schools interpreted nature and history as the organic embodiment and progressive unfolding of the all-embracing divine Idea. The school of Ritschl differed from pure Kantian idealism in the stress which it laid upon the historic revelation of God in Jesus Christ; but it interpreted the life of Jesus as the fulfillment of a Kantian moral postulate—"victory over the world"—

---

of Biblical criticism and Luther research, has tended to promote the swing toward conservatism by revealing the incorrigible supernaturalism of the Christian religion in two of its most vital eras: the New Testament period, and the Reformation. Among those who have done most to destroy the usual "liberal" conception of Jesus, Paul and Luther we may mention M. Kähler, K. L. Schmidt, Bultmann, M. Dibelius and Karl Holl. Their work, carried on by the most approved modern methods, has undermined modernistic illusions, very much as Albert Schweitzer's work has undermined them for many British and American thinkers. Cf. the effect of such a book as Cadbury's recent book, *The Peril of Modernizing Jesus.*

and the pledge of man's eventual triumph in his idealistic endeavor to build the Kingdom of God on earth.
If the idealism of Schleiermacher and Hegel was
metaphysical, and that of Kant and Ritschl was ethical, Troeltsch's was *skeptical*; it was idealism already
stricken with paralysis, already aware of the Gorgon's
head which was about to freeze its remaining vitality.
That Gorgon's head was the World War.

Troeltsch passed through the War, and never re-
covered his idealistic faith after it; for what he had
said (too hastily) of the Christian religion certainly
proved to be true of the idealistic philosophy: it was
relative to a particular culture, and even to a particular *state* of that culture. As I have pointed out else-
where, idealism's fundamental postulates seem most
plausible in an age of general prosperity and expand-
ing opportunity, such as that to which the World War
put an end. In the pre-war era, "every triumph of science and invention seemed to demonstrate the rationality of the universe and the power of mind over matter. . . . Man spake and it was done; he commanded
and things stood fast. But now it appears that this
delusion of power was from the same cause as
Chanticleer's delusion that his crowing made the sun
to rise. The world has appeared to be responsive to
our ideals because it was moving automatically, for
the time being, in the direction that we wanted; now
it has suddenly gone into reverse, and all our cackling
expostulations cannot stop it."[2]

[2] From an article in the *Womans Press* for June, 1936, pp. 264-5,
301-2, on "One of Religion's Great Divides: idealism, realism, and
the Christian cause."

Worse than any formal logical disproof of the idealistic philosophy, was the sense that grew upon men, during the World War, that they were in the hands of a tragic destiny which their reason could not comprehend nor their best efforts master; that life was an essentially dangerous and incalculable enterprise which even the boldest spirit could not face alone, and which was entirely meaningless except as one joined some group of fellow wanderers and confronted fate together, like comrades in the trenches. Nowhere was this sense of the power of fate and the irrationality of life so strongly felt as in Germany, both during the War itself and during the terrible "fourteen years of shame and dishonor" (*vierzehn Jahre von Schmach und Schande*)[3] which followed the War. The inevitable result of this experience was the disruption of the idealistic tradition in philosophy, and its replacement by various philosophies in which the incomprehensibility and stubbornness of objective Reality, the power of evil, the weakness of human reason and desire, and the necessity of heroic decision were emphasized. The two representative German philosophers of post-war Germany are Karl Jaspers and Martin Heidegger. Both are in reaction against pre-war philosophy, whether of the idealistic or the positivistic school; and both admit their debt to two insurgent nineteenth century thinkers: Nietzsche and Kierkegaard.[4] The thing that they find most distinctive in

[3] *See* Anders Nygren, *The Church Controversy in Germany*, Chap. I.

[4] On Jaspers and Heidegger, and their relation to Nietzsche and Kierkegaard, *see* Werner Brock, *Contemporary German Philosophy*.

these insurgents, which sets them off from the main current of nineteenth century thought, is that same tragic sense of life, that same consciousness of an extra dimension of reality, inaccessible to the cool intellect but accessible to some warmer and more vital faculty, which we have noted in Dostoievsky and Léon Bloy.

Kierkegaard's name for this faculty, "existential thinking," has become classic. It means that form of thinking which, in contrast to "abstract speculation," occurs only at those crucial moments in a man's life when, in the face of "choice of profession," "conflict in love," "catastrophic change in social conditions" or "the imminence of one's own death," he "gathers his whole strength to make a decision" which reshapes his whole nature and makes him a new man.[5] As illustrations of this, Kierkegaard lays before us, in his *Either . . . Or,* a series of life alternatives, each intelligible and justifiable in its own terms, but separated from each other by tragic gulfs never to be bridged by logic, only to be overleaped by a solemn, responsible decision that involves the whole man facing the whole mystery of life. Kierkegaard's disclosure of the "ultimate potentialities of the human soul" has been compared with that which one finds in Dostoievsky's novels; and his appreciation of the meaning of Christianity has been compared with Augustine's and

---

A still more radical follower of this insurgent trend is Klages, the apostle of the dark wisdom which pounds in the blood, and reveals itself in our vitalistic urges.

[5] Brock, *op. cit.,* p. 83.

Luther's.[6] Certainly the translation of his works from Danish into German, begun shortly before the War, must be described as one of the determinative influences upon contemporary German philosophy and theology.

Reinforcing the influence of "existential philosophy," we must note the influence of two recent religious thinkers, Rudolf Otto and Martin Buber, each of whom in his own way conveys the sense of a forgotten dimension in reality.

For Otto, this dimension is that of which all genuine religion, even the most primitive, is conscious: *the Holy*. The ethical and rational elements in the idea of God mark off the higher from the more primitive religions, but if the element of the holy, the "numinous," the *"mysterium tremendum,"* is absent, we are not dealing with the God of religion at all; and this, he implies, is the trouble with many highly rational theologies. The God of religion, says Otto, is "wholly other" (*ganz anders, totaliter aliter*) than any rational concept or natural manifestation with which he may chance to be associated; he is radically transcendent and supernatural, as every mystic testifies. This expression, the "Wholly Other," has become a catchword with Karl Barth and many other contemporary German thinkers.

Another favorite catchword is "the 'I-Thou' relationship," used to describe the relationship between man and God. This is derived from the Jewish mystic, Martin Buber, who in his striking little book, *I and*

[6] Brock, *op. cit.*, p. 75-77.

Thou, draws a sharp contrast between the meta-physical depth of the world of personal relationships ("I-Thou") and the comparative shallowness of the world of impersonal, objective relationships ("I"—"He"—"It") with which science deals. A god who is a mere *object* of thought, a mere "He" or "It," is not God at all; only to the man, who, standing in Kierke-gaard's "existential moment," says "Thou" to God, and finds himself held personally responsible in God's sight—only to such an one does the dimension of deity ever truly open up. We shall find this idea espe-cially prominent in Karl Heim's theology.

But we must not linger too long upon the decline of idealistic philosophy and the rise of new philo-sophical tendencies, for a third historical cause of the collapse of German liberal theology confronts us: the failure of democratic government in Germany, and the rise of the totalitarian state. Already during the last years of the Weimar Republic, "liberalism" in all its forms was rapidly losing favor, for Germany was sick and helpless from too many parties and too much free discussion. With the advent of the Third Reich, the term "liberal" became a criminal accusation to level at any one. A "liberal" was a man who claimed the right to perpetuate the individualistic, democratic trend of which his country had nearly died; who hung back, uncooperatively, when his country needed every man's "*Ja!*" in order to confront a hostile world with one united front.

As we all know, the effort to bring the German Evangelical Church into complete *Gleichschaltung*

with an otherwise unified Germany has dramatically failed; but none of the parties in the German church conflict can be called "liberal" in any proper sense. The occasion of the conflict was, of course, the announcement of the National Socialists that their government was not religiously indifferent, like the Social Democrats, but took its stand against Bolshevism on a basis of "positive Christianity," desiring nothing more than to see all Germans members of a church that would be at once truly German, truly national and truly Christian. There was even some talk at first of including Catholics and Protestants in one church; but that proving quite out of the question, the Chancellor appointed his friend Mueller—in the face of much ecclesiastical opposition—as *Reichsbischoff* for a united German church that was to include all but the Catholics, and was of course to exclude all "non-Aryans" from its ministry if not from its membership.

The very possibility of such an astounding proposal sprang from the fact that, during the past two generations and especially during the period of church disestablishment under the Republic, a vast proportion of the population of Germany had become alienated from the church, and naïvely ignorant of the nature of historic Christianity. Most of the people, especially by contrast with atheistic Communists, regarded themselves as "religious," and by contrast with the Jews, regarded themselves as "Christians"; but their religion had more to do with loyalty to home and country, and enthusiasm for the new-found sol-

idarity of the German *Volk* than with loyalty to Christ and faith in his Gospel. In the course of the protracted conflict which began almost as soon as Reichsbischoff Mueller took charge of the situation, three main parties have emerged, each standing upon the platform of "positive Christianity" and claiming to be its true exponent, but none able to unite all non-Catholic non-Aryan Germans in one inclusive church:

(1) *The German Christians* (Mueller's own party) believed it possible to unite the Nazi cult of blood, race and soil with the historic Christian Gospel, in one harmonious religious system. This program broke down when some of the more zealous German Christians, in the famous Sport-Palace meeting in Berlin, called for the dropping of the Old Testament, and other radical anti-Semitic reforms intolerable to orthodox Christians.

(2) *The Confessional Church* (the party of Karl Barth, Niemoeller,[7] and a large proportion of all the German Evangelical clergy) took its stand squarely on the historic confessions of the Protestant church, and like the Reformers found in Scripture, and "Scripture alone," the final basis of its faith and order. It did not set itself against the Nazi régime in any *political* sense,

[7] By grouping Barth and Niemoeller together, and calling Barth *the* theologian of the Confessional Church, I do not mean to imply that Niemoeller and other Confessionalist leaders are "Barthians" in theology. There are comparatively few full-fledged Barthians in the Confessional Church; most of the leaders are conservative Lutherans, who take their stand quite simply upon the Augsburg Confession. But Barth has provided the most aggressive leadership and most consistent theological defense of the movement.

but opposed every attempt to give a *religious* interpretation of the German revolution, or to offer *religious* veneration to the State and its Leader. It mobilized enough of the clergy to break the power of the
German Christian movement; but when the government attempted to make the Confessional Church the
nucleus of a united church, disunity broke out worse
than ever, among the Confessionalists as well as their
opponents. One great weakness of the Confessional
movement was that it used such technical theological
language that comparatively few laymen understood
what it was all about.

(3) *The German Faith Movement* (the party of
Wilhelm Hauer and a few other extremists) has never
been more than a small minority group, but its significance is nevertheless great, on account of the harmony between its views and those of many influential
Nazi leaders, such as Rosenberg (the head of the
ministry of culture) and Baldur von Schirach (the
head of the Nazi youth movement). By an ingenious
play on words, the adherents of this movement describe historic Christianity as "negative" Christianity,
crippled by the Jewish sense of sin and inferiority;
and to this they oppose the "positive," or Aryan, form
of Christianity, which is a religion of heroism and
honor, rejoicing in the world and finding God in
the common life. The calendar of saints of this new
cult begins with Meister Eckhart and the Hindu
mystics to whom he was so closely akin, includes
Goethe and Schiller, and winds up with Friedrich
Nietzsche. It will evidently not succeed any better

than its rivals in organizing German Protestants into one church; but it is exercising a powerful influence upon the education of the youth, and is felt by many to be the tacit creed of the whole Nazi movement, wherever it becomes conscious of itself as religious. In one sense, this is the most "liberal" of all parties in the conflict in its receptivity to untraditional religious ideas; and some former liberal Protestants are to be found in it, as well as in the German Christian movement; but liberalism has certainly suffered a "sea change" here, which makes it barely recognizable.

It is against the background of this church conflict that all theological teaching in the German-speaking world must now be understood. What Barth writes in Basel, and Brunner in Zurich, is as relevant to this situation as anything written in Bonn or Goettingen—as the German Government recognizes when it forbids the latest works of these Swiss theologians to circulate in the Third Reich. Since Barth was (prior to his expulsion) the most extreme exponent of the Confessional position in the German conflict, the best method of surveying contemporary German theology will be to begin with Barth as the theologian of extreme Confessionalism; pass from him (after a criticism of his position) to the opposite extreme, represented by Rosenberg and Hauer and (in a more Christian form) by Emanuel Hirsch; and then consider the theology of more moderate men, like Heim and Althaus, in whom the final upshot of this terrific controversy is perhaps foreshadowed.

2. EXTREME CONFESSIONALISM: KARL BARTH AND HIS CRITICS

Karl Barth is not (like Bishop Manning) a constitutional conservative. With quizzical eyes peering out from behind thick lenses, and a satirical, lopsided grin, he looks more like a Bolshevik than like an ecclesiastic, and his appearance is not deceptive. Before the World War he was what used to be called an "advanced" thinker: a Christian Socialist, a sharp critic of the modern bourgeois church, and a theological liberal of the Ritschlian School, trained under Wilhelm Herrmann at Marburg. He is still a Socialist in politics, and his suspicion of the decadence of the modern church has grown to prophetic certainty, but he does not identify the Socialist Utopia with the Kingdom of God; and in theology he has pushed beyond liberalism, through radical skepticism, to a militant, revolutionary orthodoxy reminiscent of Luther and Calvin.

It was during the War, as minister of a little Reformed church in northwest Switzerland, that Barth passed through the radical crisis which made him orthodox. Trying to preach his liberal social gospel in wartime, while big guns over the horizon in Alsace punctuated his exhortations with ironical comments, he was thrown, he tells us, into a profound "embarrassment." Here were people pathetically expectant, longing to be assured of the reality of God in a world suddenly gone mad. Here was a Book, the burden of whose every page was the reality of God. And here

stood he, supposed to preach the Word of God to these people but unable to believe in his own sermons!

One thing he found he could no longer do with honest conviction—explain God by identifying him with any contemporary social movement or tendency, or with anything temporal or human. Hegel might do that, Utopian Socialists might do that, but Kierkegaard and current events had conspired to remove the scales from Barth's eyes. Taught by the great Danish critic, whose works had such a vogue in the German-speaking world during the War, he learned to doubt whether the antitheses of human society were really leading on toward a glorious divine synthesis which would comprehend all tragic differences in some equable and rational "Both . . . and." Human life, as he observed it and as he found it magnificently analyzed in Dostoievsky's novels, seemed to be an insoluble paradox, a question without an answer. Both the Christian Church and the Socialist party seemed to be rushing to perdition, rather than marching toward the Millennium. A God one could trust and reverence must be wholly above and beyond all this. There must be, as Kierkegaard said, an "infinite qualitative difference" between the temporal and the eternal.

Such pessimism as this was no doubt irreligious, according to liberal Christian notions, but as Barth despairingly searched the Scriptures it struck him that a certain pessimism about human affairs was characteristic of their teachings; and when he turned

to the Biblical commentaries of Luther and Calvin he was pleased to discover that these men of faith viewed the secular scene pretty much as he did. Perhaps, after all, it was not wrong to be "embarrassed" when one attempted to make God intelligible in terms of contemporary social movements; perhaps a God who could be discovered on the human plane would not be God; perhaps "embarrassment," inability to talk without involvement in verbal contradictions and rational paradoxes, was something one was *bound* to experience in the presence of the true and living God who is "wholly other" (*totaliter aliter*) than all our ideas of him. Perhaps theology itself is but "the description of this embarrassment." This was Barth's first great theological insight, and it has remained fundamental for him.[8]

The book which brought Barth to the attention of the world was his *Commentary on the Epistle to the Romans,* which has passed through many editions and radical revisions since it first appeared in 1918. It is a strange book, full of the most astonishing paradoxes —deliberately so, since Barth is convinced that wherever God impinges upon human life he reveals himself in some apparent contradiction; death that is life, despair that is hope, an insoluble enigma which is its own triumphant answer. It is not a conventionally pious book, for in the name of God, Barth heaps his scorn upon religion and the church—above all upon that liberal Christianity which fails to see that "one

[8] See Barth, *The Word of God and the Word of Man,* translated by Douglas Horton, pp. 100, 101.

can *not* speak of God simply by speaking of man in a loud voice."[9] But for all this, it is a religiously stirring book, for Barth has now found in the Bible what he regards as the absolute Word of God, lifted high above all the perishable counsels of men. This does not mean that he has turned his back upon the critical, scientific study of the Bible, or failed to recognize the human and fallible elements in the teachings of the prophets and apostles. He has no animus against the "higher criticism"; but for him the real task of Biblical interpretation begins where the critic's task ends, where the interpreter stops to listen for the Word which the God who produced the Bible has to speak to our own time. Barth's *Romans*, coming after a generation of cool, objective Biblical scholarship, gave the theological world a sudden shock, for it dared to translate Paul's epistle to the Romans into a special-delivery letter from God to the twentieth century.[10]

The publication of Barth's earlier works created a stir throughout the German-speaking world, and led to a formation of a theological movement or school known as the "theology of crisis" or "dialectical theology."

The term "crisis" here refers not only to the crisis of modern civilization and modern theology, but to the perpetual crisis in which man is always involved

[9] *Ibid.*, p. 198.

[10] The above five paragraphs are reprinted (by permission of the editors) from my article on "The New Orthodoxy" in *The American Scholar*, Vol. VII, pp. 3-11.

when he tries to solve his problem by his own powers. Over every man, every institution, every culture, every so-called Christian church that takes this anthropocentric and self-reliant attitude, God's judgment (Greek, *Krisis*) lowers like a thundercloud, and sooner or later it descends *senkrecht von oben*, straight down like a thunderbolt, to proclaim that all things human are bounded by the "death-line."

The term "dialectical" describes the tortuous, indirect way that human thought must take if it is to deal at all with a God whose eternal Reality is related to our temporal reality like another dimension or plane cutting across the earthly plane at right angles. A truly reverent theology, which knows that God is in heaven and man on earth, must never pass directly from human thought and experience to God, as Schleiermacher and Hegel sought to do. It must reverse the Hegelian dialectic, as Kierkegaard suggested: look for no syntheses on the earthly plane, but balance every thesis with an antithesis, every Yes with a No, and then, standing helplessly in the contradiction, appeal to God for a revelation, an act of grace. There is no way from man to God, there is only a way from God to man, the way of revelation and grace; and even here, God's solving Word envelops itself in paradoxes and mysterious antinomies when it impinges upon the human plane. A dialectical theology must be a persistently critical theology, which recognizes that no straightforward *argument* for God and Christianity is possible, but only a constant polemic against human perversions of the revealed

Word of God. So long as we stand "between the
ages," between the age of Christ's Revelation and
that eternal end-of-history which forever hangs over
us as promise and as judgment,[11] we walk by faith and
not by sight, as ignorant, sinful men mysteriously
upheld by divine light and strength. This conception—consciously aimed against the Thomistic conception of the Analogy of Being, and consciously
modeled on St. Augustine's conception of human life
as a watch-night between twilight and dawn—gave its
name to the organ of the movement, *Zwischen den
Zeiten* (*"Between the Ages"*), in which Barth found
many collaborators, preëminently Edward Thurney-
sen, Emil Brunner, and Friedrich Gogarten.

It seemed to many like the downfall of a prophet
when Barth accepted a call to the University of Goettingen in Germany and devoted himself there (as
later at Münster and Bonn) to the working out of a
dogmatic theology. Had he not said that his teaching
was not a theology, but only a pinch of spice to be
taken with any theology one might happen to have?
With characteristic humor, Barth replied that he had
never set out to be a prophet; he had only been
climbing the steeple to get his bearings; and he was
more surprised than any one else when, in the dark,
he accidentally grasped the bellrope and the great bell
of prophecy began to boom! If such ringing of the
alarm was necessary at first, it was equally necessary
to work out in patient, pedestrian style the principles
by which the right preaching of the Gospel and the

[11] *See* Barth, *The Resurrection of the Dead*, p. 106.

right administration of the sacraments in the Church were to be discriminated from their perversions, and safeguarded against future errors.

The two successive editions of the first volume of Barth's *Dogmatics* (*Christliche Dogmatik im Entwurf,* 1927, and *Kirchliche Dogmatik,* 1932)[12] mark two stages in the clarification of his controlling principles. In the first volume, he was still directly under the influence of the "existential" movement in philosophy and the "dialectical" movement in theology, and allowed the structure of his system to be molded by the leading concepts of these schools of thought. In the second edition, he endeavors to expunge from his work all traces of *every* human philosophy and every partisan school of theology, and make it (as its new title indicates) strictly a *Church* theology, taking its material from "Church proclamation," and its norm from Scripture. The preacher's problem, which first drove Barth to theology, has in this volume led him to what may be called the most consistent *preacher's theology* that has ever been formulated, every element in which is derived from the living process of communicating the Word from God to man.

The Word of revelation, from this point of view, has three principal forms: the *spoken* word of the preacher; the *written* word of Scripture from which the preacher's word is derived and by which it is con-

[12] A second volume of the *Kirchliche Dogmatik,* over 1,000 pages long, has just appeared in German, and will presumably appear very soon in an English translation. It follows the plan of its predecessor with no new radical alterations. At last, Barth sees his road clear, and will probably follow it swiftly to the end.

trolled; and finally, the *revealed* Word of God to which the spoken and written word are only human testimonies. Concretely, this revealed Word is Jesus Christ, the Word made flesh, in whom the majesty of God took on the form of a servant, and so remained veiled in the very act of revelation. The Virgin Birth and the Resurrection point forward and back to this central, concealed revelation. So, on a grander scale, do the prophets of the Old Testament and the apostles of the New. So does the witness of Christian preaching throughout the ages. So, in the last resort, does each Christian life to which the Word is announced. But Scripture, preaching, Christian life, all point up and away from themselves to a God who is forever and always beyond our apprehension of him: the triune God of Christian revelation.

The root of the idea of the Trinity is to be found in the idea of the *deus absconditus* who becomes for us the *deus revelatus* in Christ. As Father, as Son, as Spirit, God is always the *Lord*, the majestic Other who has authority over his creatures. In this unity the being of God consists. As Father, God is the *Creator*, the mysterious and absolute Source of all being, all authority, all light and grace. As Son, God is the *Reconciler*, who is Lord in spite of our enmity toward him, and asserts his Lordship by throwing out a bridge of reconciliation toward us. As Spirit, God is the *Redeemer*, the Lord who sets us free, not by imparting his being to us—he never does that—but by giving us faith to "acknowledge" him and depend on him from moment to moment. This triune God

reveals himself to us in the Bible and in Christian preaching, using human language consecrated (like the sacramental elements) to divine uses, and sacred only so long as it is divinely used. The man who hears this Word is like Peter in the Biblical narrative: he can walk on the water only so long as he has faith in the revealed God; as soon as he begins to trust himself, or even to trust that light and grace which God has already communicated to him, he sinks.

It is instructive to compare this whole point of view with Father Przywara's, against which it is explicitly aimed. Both Barth and Przywara recognize that everything human and worldly points beyond itself to a transcendent divine Source and Ground, forever veiled from human sight in clouds of mystery. The long, upward-pointing finger of John the Baptist in Grünewald's Crucifixion,[13] which is to Barth the perfect symbol of all human witness to God, even that of Scripture itself—which continually points up and away from itself—this pointing finger would be accepted by Father Przywara as a good symbol of *one side*, and the more *important* side, of the truth as it is found in St. Thomas. It represents the Platonic, Augustinian element in Catholic thought, the *anō* in the method of analogy. But, he would add, there is another side represented by the *aná*, the orderly and rational indwelling of the infinite God in this finite world, whereby it is possible for us to escape from total agnosticism with regard to God, and rise to the knowledge *that* he is, if we cannot penetrate *what* he

[13] *Church Dogmatics*, p. 126.

is. By denying to man the possibility of this minimum natural knowledge of God, Barth not only threatens to turn all religious faith into an irrational leap in the dark; he threatens to destroy that principle of order in the universe on which *all* natural knowledge, including science itself, is based.

Such, I am sure, would be the verdict of Catholic theology upon Karl Barth; and personally, I find the verdict just. If Barth represents the typical Protestant point of view, then I, for one, am compelled to turn toward Catholicism. But I am obliged to recognize that it is precisely this intransigent stand of Barth's on the pure Word of God, this radical rejection of all natural knowledge of God, which has brought him forth once more in the rôle of a prophet since Adolf Hitler came to power in Germany.

To many religious-minded Germans today, the new experience of national solidarity and self-respect which has come to them through the revolution of 1933 has been nothing less than a fresh revelation of God; and they feel toward Hitler, the human instrument of this revelation, the same sort of religious veneration that millions of Hindus feel for Mahatma Gandhi. It seems to them no irreverence to couple this new revelation of God with the supreme revelation of God in Christ, somewhat as the Old Testament has always been related to the New Testament—perhaps, indeed, *in place of* the old Old Testament!

For a Catholic, or for a liberal Protestant, prepared to admit the reality of a natural contemporary knowledge of God, it is a delicate question where to draw

the line between the true and the false in this contemporary German sense of God. Not so for Karl Barth. He stands over against all this in complete prophetic opposition, like Amos at Bethel or Elijah at Mt. Carmel; and in his tremendous pamphlet, *Theological Existence Today,* he calls upon all faithful Christians to take to the catacombs rather than bow the knee to this new Baal. No doubt his Swiss citizenship and his Socialist political principles had something to do with his cool detachment from the intoxication of the new German faith—just as Amos' Judean citizenship had something to do with his cool perception of the sins of Israel—but the root of his opposition lay deeper, in his radical denial of all natural knowledge of God.

Whether the Confessional Church would ever have seen through the idolatrous element in the German Christian Movement, and come out so emphatically against it, without Barth's leadership, is problematical. Those who admire the Confessional Church unreservedly—as most Americans do—will have to pay at least a grudging tribute to Barth's theology. Those who are unreservedly opposed to his theology will have to make an attempt to appreciate the truth in the German Christian Movement. Personally, I believe there *is* truth in it.

This latter alternative (i.e., to move away from strict Confessionalism toward the German Christian position) has been chosen, in varying degrees, by two men who stood very close to Barth in the early and middle periods of his development: Friedrich Go-

garten and Emil Brunner. It may help us to perceive the extremeness of Barth's views, and prepare us to understand the relative validity of the opposite extreme, if we listen to their criticisms of their former leader. In any adequate survey of contemporary German theology, each of these men would deserve a full-length treatment; but in our brief sight-seeing tour they can be treated only in their relationship to Barth, lest our perspective upon the whole German situation be destroyed.

The great lack which both of these men feel in the Barthian theology is the absence of any adequate grounding for *ethics*, and especially *social ethics*. From Barth's point of view, every possible line of ethical and social action would appear to be equally profane in the sight of God. While the times demand decisions on social issues, and it is every Christian's business to take his stand upon them as in God's sight, theology can offer no advice to him save to read his Bible, pray, and make his own decision. To Friedrich Gogarten, a German Barthian caught in the maelstrom of social conflict that led up to the revolution of 1933, it seemed intolerable that theology should have so little definite help to give; and he fell back upon a traditional Lutheran doctrine which has experienced a great revival of popularity since the War: the doctrine of the *orders*.

According to this doctrine, the basic social institutions (the family, the economic order, the political order, etc.) are divinely ordained in their basic structure; and though they have been corrupted by sin,

they still bear the imprint of the "order of creation," and must be respected as embodying God's will for their members. In relation to the State, it is admitted that man's political conduct is naturally sinful; but herein lies the necessity and authority of the State: unless it existed, and had the power to wield the sword, men would be at each other's throats like wild beasts—a situation which actually existed in Germany in the period of anarchy that followed the War. Sometimes this preservative rôle of the State is expressed by referring it to the "order of conservation," whereby God "keeps" our wicked world in existence till the Judgment Day; while the "order of creation" is more clearly discernible in the family. In any case, it is the Christian's duty to obey the requirements of the social order in which he finds himself as though God's law were embodied in its very structure. To be sure, he is "a free man, subject to no one," delivered from the curse of the law by the Gospel of Christ; yet as Luther said, he is at the same time "a bond slave, subject to every one" by virtue of the new law of love and service which he gladly obeys out of gratitude to Christ; and in all his social relations his service is one of obedience to the constituted authorities, whoever they may be. The Christian's world is thus divided into "two kingdoms": the kingdom of the Gospel, in which he is free (in practice, confined to the sphere of private life and personal contacts) and the kingdom of the Law, in which he is bound to honor and obey all those in authority over him as he honors and obeys his own father and mother.

Gogarten's doctrine of the "orders" is essentially this traditional Lutheran doctrine, except that he lays special stress upon the importance of the State, in view of his Barthian pessimism about human nature. Even in the Christian, human nature is so fundamentally godless, loveless and egotistic that it can be kept in order only by violent political means. Hence there is no such thing as a specifically Christian ethic, and the will of the State—without which the world would fly to pieces—is the basis of all ethics. "Ethics as a whole is necessarily simply a political ethic"[14]; and *Politische Ethik* is accordingly the title he gives to his principal work. Since the Nazi revolution, he has modified his position by distinguishing between the State and the *Volk* or nation, and making the ethics of the State dependent on the will of the nation for their ultimate criterion. Even with this change, it is obvious that Gogarten's position plays into the hands of the totalitarian State, much as Hobbes's *Leviathan* played into the hands of the political absolutists of his day.

In his pamphlet on *Natur und Gnade* ("Nature and Grace"), Emil Brunner tells of "an unforgettable conversation" between himself and Karl Barth over this dangerous new departure in their friend Gogarten's teaching. The two Swiss theologians agreed that Gogarten's conception of the "orders" implied "a whole political and cultural program of a decidedly authoritarian type"; but Brunner maintained against

[14] Ehrenström, N., *Christian Faith and the Modern State*, pp. 72-73. The last four chapters in Ehrenström contain the best material available in English on Gogarten, Hirsch, and the whole doctrine of the "orders."

Barth—who refused to have anything to do with the doctrine of the "orders"—that there were two possible interpretations of the doctrine; an "unbroken" or totalitarian conception, which had purely conservative implications; and a "broken" conception, which "might as well be called revolutionary as conservative."[15] What he meant by a "broken" conception of the orders, Brunner proceeded to show in his great ethical treatise, *Das Gebot und die Ordnungen* (English title, *The Divine Imperative*), easily the most masterly work which has come from his pen. Like Gogarten, he recognizes that institutions like marriage and the State are divinely willed in their fundamental structure—either as part of the "order of creation" or as part of the "order of conservation"; but he recognizes that human sinfulness is capable of corrupting these institutions to the point where rebellion against them and not obedience to them may be our duty. The State is not only a *check* upon human selfishness; it is also an *expression* of human selfishness; and it may be the highest obedience and service that we can render to the divine groundwork of political order, to refuse to obey the command of our government. If, for example, modern warfare develops to the point where it becomes mere collective suicide—and Brunner thinks it is rapidly approaching that point—it may become the highest duty and truest loyalty of the Christian citizen to refuse to fight at this country's command.

Barth having expressed his utter dissatisfaction with

[15] Brunner, *Natur und Gnade,* pp. 36, 37.

this development in Brunner's teaching, Brunner then proceeded to make clear, in the aforesaid pamphlet, *Nature and Grace,* why he could no longer follow Barth all the way. It seemed to him that Barth was drawing, from six fundamental truths—truths which he had done more than any recent theologian to restore to their rightful primacy—a series of unwarranted logical deductions, which plunged him into absurdity: (1) From the truth that man is a sinner, who can only be saved by divine grace, he was deducing that the image of God in man is completely obliterated by the Fall. (2) From the truth that Scriptural revelation is the sole norm of our knowledge of God and the sole source of our salvation, he was deducing that there was no general revelation of God in nature, conscience and history. (3) From the truth that we must acknowledge the grace of the Lord Jesus Christ as the only saving grace, he was deducing that there was no expression of God's grace in the creation and preservation of the world. From the same truth he was deducing (4) that there was no expression of the divine will in the so-called "law of nature" embodied in the basic social institutions; (5) no *Anknüpfungspunkt* (point of contact) or "divine image" in human nature to which divine grace could make its appeal; and (6) no developmental relations between nature and grace, the natural man and the new man in Christ, but only one of "substitution" (*Ersetzung*).

In conclusion, Brunner expressed his amazement at the extent of Barth's opposition to the Catholic

doctrine of *analogy*, and insisted that it has never been good Protestant doctrine to dispute the Catholic teaching that there *is* an analogy between God and his creation—else how can we talk about the "personality" or "fatherhood" of God?—but only *how* the principle of analogy is to be used.[16] To this point of view (which parenthetically, offers me my only chance of remaining a Protestant!) Barth's only reply was such a burst of theological anger[17] as has rarely been exhibited in modern history. This burst of anger has seemed to me and many others a clear indication of the fact that Barth's zeal has led him to an absolutely untenable extreme, which can be defended only by sheer dogmatic vociferation.

3. EXTREME "ARYANISM": ROSENBERG, HAUER, AND HIRSCH

It must be admitted that Barth's zeal and Barth's wrath have not been engendered by any mere trifle. They are directed—over Brunner's shoulder—at one of the most formidable heresies with which the Church of Christ has ever been faced: the anti-Semitic cult of the Aryan race and the German soil—*Blut und Boden*—in which the ideology of the Nazi revolution finds its focus, and in which many Germans are finding a new Gospel or at least a new Old Testament. In our discussion of German Protestant theology, we are primarily concerned with the views of the so-called "German Christians," who have incorporated

[16] *Natur und Gnade*, pp. 7, 8, 39-41.
[17] Barth, *Nein! Antwort an Emil Brunner*.

the Aryan myth into their Christianity. It may be helpful, however, to consider "Aryanism" in its pure, non-Christian form ("German Faith Movement") before considering the views of those who have attempted to Christianize it.

The Bible of the Aryan cult is Rosenberg's *Myth of the Twentieth Century*. Published in 1930, before the Nazis came to power, it is full of that same passionate love of all things German and passionate hate of those forces which keep the German racial soul from awakening, which one finds in Hitler's *Mein Kampf*. An intemperate book in every way, it uses a genuinely wide erudition in the service of a racial theory of history which—to all outside the chosen race—looks as obviously biased as Marx's economic theory of history looks to those outside the chosen proletariat. It seems to be the fate of such intemperate books to focus and express a rising tide of popular feeling, and then become canonized (with all their bias) when the movement to which they give a voice rides into power. When I bought my copy of Rosenberg's *Myth* in 1935, only two years after the revolution, 353,000 copies of it had already been sold; and the end is not yet!

It would be easy—*too* easy—to give a purely contemptuous account of Rosenberg's doctrine. His racial theory, based upon writers like Houston Stuart Chamberlain, Madison Grant and Lothrop Stoddard, has for years been discredited by most schools of anthropology. His animus against the Jews, the Slavs, the yellow race and—as he persists in calling them—the

"niggers," is so emotional and undiscriminating as to bear all the marks of a Freudian complex. His political wisdom is typified by the remark that the only way to solve the Negro problem is for all Nordic countries—including the United States—to ship their Negro citizens back to Africa, and see to it that, if possible, there shall be left within their boundaries "no more Negroes, no more yellow men, no more mulattoes, and no more Jews!"[18] Yet with all its hysteria and virulence, I am convinced that Rosenberg's book, in its positive features, is in some respects prophetic. It gives voice to a passionate revolt which is destined to gain great headway in the twentieth century, and which has justice as well as passion on its side: the revolt of national culture, of "folk consciousness," against the leveling and disintegrating effects of international capitalism and international socialism.

There is imminent danger, of course, that the new nationalism will show itself as a demonic force, asserting itself expansively without regard for the rights of minorities or respect for other nationalities; but this is not necessarily the case. In one of his more temperate moments, Rosenberg suggests that world peace can never be achieved until the expansive drive of imperialistic capitalism and revolutionary socialism are replaced by a new political system based upon a policy of inward national *Sammlung* or concentration, which will divide the world into a series of self-

---

[18] Rosenberg, *Mythus der XX Jahrhundert*, pp. 668, 669 (Book III, Chapter VI, Section 5).

respecting and relatively self-contained, mutually respecting and organically related national cultures
based upon racial homogeneity. One may doubt the
necessity of basing national unity upon racial homogeneity; but I believe the democratic nations should
take more seriously than they do this Fascist program
of world peace. India, China and Turkey, as well as
Germany and Italy have shown that autonomous national culture represents a sacred value that cannot
and ought not be destroyed by the expansion of stand-
ardized machine civilization; and world peace de-
pends upon the full recognition of this fact. As Brunner might put it, the resurrection of the *nation* in our
time is the restoration of an inalienable part of the
divine order of creation, which our technological civilization had nearly destroyed. From this point of
view, nationalism has in it a real "divine imperative"
for all of us, in spite of its demonic potentialities.

It ought not to shock us, then, if Rosenberg takes
his nationalism religiously. As a matter of fact, the
religious chapters in his book—apart from the constant polemic against Judaism and Catholicism—have
much that is beautiful and persuasive about them.
Meister Eckhart is his hero, and if he admires the
great mystic for somewhat perverse reasons, his admiration is nevertheless genuine. He finds in Eckhart
the first clear expression, in German thought, of the
typically Aryan conception of *the identity of man and
God*. In Indian thought, this conception is expressed
in the equation, Atman = Brahman. In Iranian
thought, it appears in the view that man is a compan-

ion at arms with Ahura Mazda, God of light, in his struggle with the forces of darkness. In Greek mythology, Platonic idealism and the ancient Norse religion, a similar attitude of manly freedom and pride in dealing with the gods is manifest.[19] The very antithesis of all this is the Syrian and African attitude of groveling before a divine despot,[20] of which the Jewish attitude toward Yahweh is taken as typical.

The Roman Church managed to impose the worship of Yahweh upon the Nordic peoples only by mixing the Hebraic conception of God with a good deal of Greek philosophy. In Albertus Magnus and St. Thomas, with their strong emphasis on human reason and their appeal to the *analogia entis*, the artificial mixture of Aryanism and Hebraism was almost ready to break down; but it was Meister Eckhart, with his proud assertion that "If I did not exist, neither would God,"[21] who delivered the pure Aryan conception from all entangling alliance with Hebraic submissiveness. Not love, sin and grace, but freedom, honor and will, are his great words. It was an awful betrayal when German Protestantism, born of the German mystical movement and showing much of its spirit of manly freedom, delivered the German people back under the dominion of the Hebrew Bible.[22] German philosophy and literature in their great age—

[19] *Ibid.*, pp. 246, 247 (Book I, Chapter III, Section 5).

[20] Rosenberg points with pride to the fact that when the Emperor Hadrian visited his Syrian and African domains he went enthroned as a god, and demanded abject submission, but when he visited his Teutonic subjects, he came among them on foot, as a simple soldier.

[21] *Ibid.*, p. 225.

[22] *Ibid.*, p. 218.

the age of Goethe and Schiller, Kant, Fichte and Hegel—followed a better path. The religion of manly self-reliance and equality with God which these great writers teach is the same true Aryan religion to which Eckhart first gave voice.[23] In our own day, it is best expressed in the organically related concepts of the Blood and the Soul, the Race and the Ego, the Folk and the Personality. The Soul, the Ego, or the Personality of the modern German realizes itself by asserting its identity with the Blood, the Race, the Folk from which he is sprung, and in whose glorious destiny he finds his joy and pride. "The God we honor would not exist if our Soul and our Blood did not exist: so would the confession of a Meister Eckhart run in our day."[24]

Rosenberg is not personally an adherent of the German Faith Movement. Doubtless for reasons of policy, he at one time found it more convenient to classify himself as a Protestant of the "German Christian" type; though he has now officially left the church. Yet when one passes from Rosenberg to Wilhelm Hauer, the scholarly leader of the German Faith Movement, one is conscious of moving *toward* rather than *away from* an appreciation of historic Christianity. Professor Hauer (of Tübingen) is, in fact, a former Christian missionary to India, whose sympathetic study of the religions of India led him to lose his

[23] *Ibid.*, sec. 7. pp. 259 ff.
[24] *Ibid.*, p. 701. On the fundamental importance of Eckhart for the whole idealistic tradition in German thought, *see* Bréhier, *Histoire de la Philosophie Allemande*. At this point Rosenberg's thesis is certainly well founded.

missionary zeal and return home as a teacher of Oriental thought and culture. His most characteristic work, *The German View of God* (*Deutsche Gottschau*, Stuttgart, 1934), is a much milder, fairer and more tolerant book than Rosenberg's *Myth*, although it follows much the same lines.

In the introduction, the rival characteristics of the Indo-Germanic and Near Eastern culture-areas are traced without rancor and with a wealth of genuine scholarship, and the conclusion is drawn, *not* that Christianity is a hateful intruder on Nordic soil, but that it is not so *artgemäss*, not so well suited to the specific genius of the Indo-Germanic soul, as a religion drawn from purely Aryan sources: the German mystics, the German idealists and the German literary classics. It is admitted that the Aryan race is very mixed, and in no way so sharply distinguishable from other races as to be easily purified by artificial methods; but it is insisted that every great culture area, while respecting the religion of other areas and other peoples, needs, in the words of Frederick the Great, to worship God *nach seiner Façon*, in its own style.[25] The Nordic style is simply not the Christian style. It has no such deep consciousness of sin or guilt as the Old and New Testaments display; instead, the Norse Eddas are pervaded—like Greek tragedy—with a sense that men and gods together are in the grip of a mysterious Fate (*Schicksal*) which they together must

[25] Frederick meant simply to imply that individual religious differences were to be respected by the State—*Hier muss jeder nach seiner Façon selig werden*. But his remark has been applied to racial and national differences.

boldly and proudly bear. The book closes with a plea
for tolerance. The author is ready to grant the genu-
ineness and nobility of the Christian faith which many
of his countrymen still profess—as he once did himself—if they on their part will recognize that for a
considerable group of Germans the only possible remaining faith is one that has its focus not in Palestine
but in their own native soil and cultural history.[26]

To a hostile eye—let us say, to a strict Confessionalist—there appears to be only a shade of difference
between the frank neo-paganism of Wilhelm Hauer
and the Christianity of Emanuel Hirsch, whom we
have chosen to represent the theology of the German
Christian party. Professor Hirsch (of Goettingen) has
very little use for the Old Testament, and considers
that the German people have genuinely met God, the
"Lord of history," and received a fresh revelation of
his Will, in the World War and the Nazi revolution.
Yet he claims to be a devoted evangelical Christian,
and exhibits every mark of the characteristically Lutheran type of piety. It will repay us to consider carefully and sympathetically how his paradoxical position is to be interpreted.

In the first place, it should be understood that

[26] A pamphlet of the German Faith Movement, by B. Loewe, which
I picked up in Germany two years ago, contains the following Credo:
"For us there is only one real sin: unfaithfulness to our blood, and
our native land (*Heimat*) . . . Our faith is in God; our church is
the German native land; our congregation is the German folk; our
priest is—every race-conscious German man; our Bible is the Ger-
manic soul and its imperishable works; our sacraments are work,
combat and loving devotion; our confession reads: *Blood and
honor!*"

Hirsch's abandonment of the Old Testament is not the result of a sudden wave of anti-Semitic feeling, but the outcome of a long spiritual struggle, whose steps are convincingly traced in his little book, *The Old Testament and the Preaching of the Gospel*.[27] In his student days, he wrestled with the problem of the imprecatory Psalms, and found the answer in a conception of the whole Old Testament which, while it recognized the reality and depth of the Hebrew experience of God, regarded the whole religion of the Law and the Covenant as a culturally conditioned and definitely superseded stage in religious development. "It has never been doubtful to me," says Hirsch, "and even today is not doubtful, that the Old Testament figures had dealings with the living God under the mantle of their Yahweh-faith . . . a deeper (and that means also a more terrible) knowledge and experience of what it means to deal with the living God, than other men in non-Christian religions, who also under *their* mantle have had dealings with the living God."[28] In several respects, however, there is a clean break between the Old and New Testaments, which should forbid us to use the Old Testament in Christian preaching without a fundamental recasting of every text: (1) Old Testament religion is "bound to the Temple, and thereby to cult-purity and cult-offerings." (2) It is a pure "folk-religion," in which people and church are *one* as they can never again be since

[27] *Das Alte Testament und die Predigt des Evangeliums,* Tübingen, 1936.
[28] *Op. cit.,* p. 5.

Christ. (This is a side thrust at the German Faith Movement.) (3) It has no knowledge of eternal life, and mistakenly looks to "see the goodness of the Lord in the land of the living." (4) It seeks to win God's forgiveness by fulfillment of law, and so is ignorant of God's free grace, which is his very heart.[29]

The problem of using the Old Testament as a Christian book was again forced upon Hirsch during the World War, when he was horrified to find one of his parishioners pinning her faith in her son's safety at the front upon the text, "a thousand shall fall at thy side, and ten thousand at thy right hand, but it shall not come nigh thee"—a perfectly, good Jewish hope; and abominably bad Christian hope! It became more and more evident to him, from such illuminating episodes, that Luther's retention of the Old Testament was made possible only by an elaborate process of misinterpretation and even mistranslation, whereby the Gospel was read back into the Law. In his homiletic seminar he warned his students against such historical misunderstandings of the Old Testament, and urged them never to use an Old Testament text without distinguishing between its (superseded) historical meaning and the utterly different meaning which the backward-streaming light of the Gospel might reveal in it. The study of Kierkegaard meanwhile convinced him of the interesting fact that, after the spiritual crisis through which he passed in July, 1843, the great Danish thinker had had "absolutely

[29] *Ibid.,* pp. 72-76.

no further inner relation to the Old Testament."[30] Most decisive of all for Hirsch, was a lack which he felt in all "Old Testament Christians," whether of the Barthian type or of the American Social Gospel type: a lack of anything like the Lutheran theory of the "orders" and the "two Kingdoms"—without which, they either fell prey (like the Americans) to the illusory Jewish hope that the Kingdom of God might be perfectly realized on earth, or (like the Barthians) stood aloof from the social strivings of their people because they saw no hope of accomplishing anything by human effort. Against all such Old Testament Christians, Hirsch now protests that Christians should no longer pretend to find the direct Word of God in the Old Testament; while against the undiscriminating anti-Semitism of Julius Streicher and the scurrilous abuse of his paper, the *Stürmer*, Hirsch objects that the Old Testament has permanent *indirect* worth, as the historical *Gegentheil* or foil which makes the New Testament Gospel clear by contrast.

It would not be wholly unfair to say that in Hirsch's theology the Old Testament Law and Prophets are replaced by the new Law and Prophets of the German Third Reich. But again—and this is our second main observation about Hirsch—the statement would have to be carefully qualified. When he says that one and the same God meets us in the Gospel's call and the call of the stormy events of our

[30] *Ibid.*, p. 12.

time,[31] he does not mean to put the two calls on the
same absolute plane. The God of contemporary history is a *verborgener Gott*, a God that hideth himself,
whereas in the Gospel we have the face of God revealed. The God of history imposes on us our present
duty; the God of the Gospel opens up to us our eternal destiny. Nor is the voice of the God of history to
be heard unambiguously in the decrees of the State.
Any good Nazi would have to admit that when the
decrees of the State conflict with the good of the Folk
(as they allegedly did under Stresemann and Bruen-
ing), we should endeavor to transform the State.

Is then the will of the Folk the will of God? No,
for Folk and Race are transient and mortal things,
which must not be deified. Hirsch sees in the myth of
the "eternal Folk" a "lack of absolute religious re-
flexion"; and remarks that what inspired the deep
love Germans felt for their country in war time was
the sense that she was indeed mortal and destructi-
ble.[32] What is truly divine in contemporary history
is the new sense of *horos*, *logos* and *nomos* which the
shattering events of our time have driven home upon
us. By the sense of *horos*, or "boundary," Hirsch
means the sense that the power of human science and
art to create a world civilization according to the
heart's desire is not so illimitable as was supposed.
In the facts of race and nationality there is an im-
passable barrier set up between us and the cosmo-

---

[31] *Deutsches Volkstum und evangelische Glaube,* p. 39. (Hamburg, 1934.)

[32] *Die Gegenwärtige Geistige Lage,* p. 162. (Göttingen, 1934.)

politan Utopia of (let us say) Mr. H. G. Wells. By
the sense of *logos*, he means the new wider "rationality" ("existential thinking," "responsible action in
the face of mysterious destiny") which we have had
to substitute for the old purely scientific mentality of
before the War. By the sense of *nomos* ("law"), he
means the sense of the right of the group to control
the conduct of its members, which has replaced the
old irresponsible individualism of the age of liberalism and democracy.[33] In all these ways, God has been
speaking to us out of the whirlwind, and it is only as
we try to take our stand, with our Folk, in answer to
his contemporary call, that the Word of God in the
Gospel becomes intelligible to us. The Christian
should be *more* devoted to his people than other men,
not less; "for only to the man whom the hidden God
meets and binds to the earthly life with sacred ties,
only to him can faith in God's love in Jesus be a
meaningful reality.[34]

The tragic dilemma of contemporary German Protestantism is nowhere more clearly evident than in
the writings of Emanuel Hirsch. He faces with exceptional honesty and earnestness the danger that the
Christian message may soon come to seem wholly irrelevant and meaningless to the citizens of the Third
Reich. He perceives that a Christianity which continues, with Barth and the extreme Confessionalists,
to talk the language of the Scriptures and the Reformers without making any attempt to interpret it

[33] *Ibid.*, pp. 38-44.
[34] *Der Weg der Theologie*, p. 17. (Stuttgart, 1937.)

in contemporary terms, is going to become a sheer unintelligible anachronism for contemporary German youth; and the doctrine that there is nothing religious, nothing divine, in the shattering political events of our time, is going to be resented as downright blasphemy.[35] But if there is danger that the "canned theology gone stale" of certain Confessionalists will become *irrelevant by anachronism*, there is another kind of irrelevance which dogs the steps of the "German Christians," and which we might call "*irrelevance by tautology.*" The German Christians are likely to be ignored in the long run by the German youth, because in their endeavor to keep up to date they repeat the same identical slogans that all good Nazis repeat, and act as though the only effect of their Christianity were to make them excessively zealous in imitating the behavior of their compatriots. Within a measurable space of time, Aryanism that has been baptized into the name of Christ is going to be staler, more irrelevant, and more out of date than the Latin phraseology of the Augsburg Confession—which has become startlingly alive in some branches of the Confessional Church! With all his careful distinctions, Emanuel Hirsch does not wholly escape from this second type of irrelevance; and his failure leads one to ask whether, in all the land of Luther today, there is any theologian who does not fall into one or the other of the pitfalls which have been indicated. There is one region that remains to be explored: the region between the extreme Confessionalism of a Barth or a

[35] *Ibid.*, pp. 26, 27.

Niemöller, and the moderate Aryanism of a Hirsch. Two very significant figures belong somewhere in this region: Karl Heim (Tübingen) and Paul Althaus, Jr. (Erlangen).

4. TWO MEDIATING THEOLOGIANS: HEIM AND ALTHAUS

To call Karl Heim a "mediating theologian" does not mean that he is simply concerned for a middle way between Barth and Hirsch, and has no distinctive principles of his own. Ever since 1902, when he gave up his post as Secretary of the German Student Christian Movement to become a philosopher and theologian, he has been steering a pretty consistent course through the tortuous channel of German life and thought, alert to every new development, but keeping one supreme objective continually in view: "Confronting Young Men with the Living Christ." These are the words of John R. Mott, and I have deliberately used them to suggest that Karl Heim is still at heart the same man who served as one of Mott's chief assistants in the Student Christian Movement: a Christian evangelist and an Evangelical Christian, springing from that Pietist tradition in German Lutheranism which has always kept in close touch with British Methodism and American evangelism. His philosophical and theological studies have given him a masterful understanding of the modern secular mind, but he has pursued these studies with an evangelistic purpose, in order to speak to the modern man's precise condition, and confront him *where he is* with the necessity of deciding for Christ.

Karl Heim has never allowed his message to grow "irrelevant by anachronism." No new tendency in modern thought has developed in the last thirty-five years but that he has rushed at once to the spot, entered sympathetically into it, and then proceeded to show, by merciless analysis, how with all its merits it has failed to solve the ultimate human problem, to which only Christ has the answer. Before the war, he was most concerned with the problem of scientific naturalism and agnosticism. His first important book, *The World-View of the Future* (*Weltbild der Zukunft,* 1904) was an attack upon the adequacy of the naturalistic portrait of the universe, and a prediction that one of two things would occur: *either* religious faith and certitude would continue to retreat toward the vanishing point which modern liberal theology seemed already to be approaching; *or* a new world-view would appear in which religious certitude would be possible. The question of religious certitude continued to occupy Heim for many years. In 1911 he published a monumental history of the problem of certitude in theology from St. Augustine to Schleiermacher; and in 1916, during the tragedy of the War, brought out an impassioned defense of *The Certainty of Faith* (*Glaubensgewissheit*), in which he attributed to the man of firm religious decision a capacity for a *Durchblick durch das Ganze*, a penetration into the total meaning of things, from which the natural man is excluded. The conclusions of this period in his thought were gathered up in his *Dogmatics*, published immediately after the War; but almost at once he

started out on a fresh line of investigation, suggested by the new physics of Einstein, and the new philosophy of Heidegger and Buber. Almost alone among pre-war theologians, he has been able to keep fully abreast of these developments, and so compete with Karl Barth for the ear of the younger generation. The revolution of 1933 found him in the midst of writing a comprehensive treatise, *Protestant Belief and Modern Thought: Outlines of a Christian View of Life.* The first volume of this *Belief and Thought (Glaube und Denken)* had already appeared, and passed through two editions; but with astonishing energy for a man in his sixties, he rewrote the third edition completely and followed it up with two more volumes, *Jesus the Lord* and *Jesus the World-Fulfiller,* all three volumes definitely directed against the new paganism of Rosenberg and Hauer. Another volume, *Christian Belief in God and Modern Science,* is still to come. It is with this latest phase of Heim's thought that we are exclusively concerned.

We have referred repeatedly, in our analysis of Orthodox and Catholic, as well as Protestant theology, to the sense of a "fourth dimension," divine or demonic, as a persistent characteristic of contemporary Continental thought. In Heim's first volume, *God Transcendent,* this important but elusive concept of *dimensions* is more specifically discussed and carefully analyzed than in any other book I know. It may seem a bit strange that this should be the chief concern of a book directed against the German Faith Movement; and some of the discussion is undoubtedly a

"survival" from the first edition; but the connection
of ideas is real, and is indicated in the author's
preface:

In the dispute concerning the relation between God
and racial distinctions, the old question of the transcendence of God has again become prominent. The
question has emerged, This power enclosing me, this
world of concrete reality, is it the Divine? Or is there,
between the highest which this world can show and God
Himself, always a deep gulf, across which we can throw
no bridge from our side, which must be bridged, if at
all, by God Himself, without our aid? . . . What is the
truth about the transcendence of God, and how is this
transcendence different from any transcendence within
the sphere of this world?[36]

Since Copernicus, it has become impossible to think
of the transcendence of God in a merely spacial sense,
as though God were "up there," separated from the
world by a simple "boundary of content," between
two portions of the same infinite space. But within the
modern or Einstein universe, there is another type of
transcendence with which we have become quite
familiar: that which is constituted when two infinite
manifolds or spaces are divided by a "boundary of
dimension." The simplest illustration of such transcendence is, of course, that between literal physical
dimensions: lines, planes, solids, and the space-time
continuum of Einstein. Each of these dimensions is
capable of filling a whole world of its own "space";

[36] *God Transcendent*, translated by Dickie, 1935, p. xviii. By permission of Charles Scribner's Sons, publishers.

but although they are co-ordinate with one another, these separate "spaces" represent worlds so distinct, so transcendent, that no two-dimensional creature could possibly imagine what it would be like to live in a three-dimensional world. Much more important, however, than this merely physical sort of dimensionality is the metaphysical dimensionality of our total world of experience, which, following Martin Buber, Heim refers to us the "I-Thou-It" world. (1) *My* objective world and *thy* objective world are both infinite; and although related to the same content and comprehended within the same "world-space," they are separated from one another forever by a boundary of dimension—like two snap-shots of Milan Cathedral from different angles. (2) *I* and my *It* (my objective world) are separated from one another by another great boundary of dimension: that between the living present and the dead, static "Already-become." (3) *I* and *Thou*, as living centers of consciousness, mutually transcend each other, and can only communicate (across the boundary of dimension which separates our rival infinitudes) by means of a mysterious something called a "word," which Heim describes as a "concrete content" active in my space and passive in thine, or vice-versa.

Now arises the question whether the transcendence of God is to be compared with any of these intra-mundane forms of transcendence; whether the Divine world is simply a forgotten "dimension" of our familiar world of experience. Heim feels that the philosophy of dimensions *does* immensely facilitate

the religious understanding of life. It breaks down the supremacy of the objective, three-dimensional world of naturalistic philosophy—as both idealism and vitalism failed to do—by showing that the dynamic, decisive world of *I* and *Thou* is an infinite dimension of reality, in which the human sense of freedom and responsibility has free scope, whereas "the dead 'It'-world is but the secondary precipitate of the Reality whose primary form we live as the struggle of will against will."[37] But if the transcendence of God were merely a dimensional transcendence, God would still be but an aspect of this world; and we should still have to choose between two equally unacceptable alternatives when attempting to frame a conception of his nature: *idolatry,* which takes some relative and finite aspect of the world, like Blood or Soil, and exalts it to the absolute; or *pantheism* which makes an absolute of the whole "interminable series"[38] of the world-process.

Only when the impossibility of resting, morally or intellectually, in either of these alternatives has come deeply home to a man—and it is Heim's great objective to force it home upon the naïve adherents of the German Faith Movement—only then does he perceive the significance of the Biblical view of God as the absolutely transcendent Creator and Lord, to whom all hearts are open, all mutually transcendent "spaces" perfectly known, because He stands above and beyond

[37] Heim, *God Transcendent,* p. 185.
[38] *Ibid.,* p. 201.

them all, not dimensionally but in a still higher sense, which no earthly analogy can adequately convey. Heim makes no attempt to prove that such a God exists; for he has demonstrated that such a procedure would be fruitless. A God so transcendent as the God of the Bible can only be known as he reveals himself, as he speaks his Word; and his Word is audible only to the man who speaks to him in the second person, as an "I" to a "Thou," crying out after God "as the hart panteth after the water-brooks."

In the second and third volumes of his trilogy (originally planned as a unit) Heim turns to expound the Christian answer to the world riddle, and his whole tone changes. Some of us who heard his American lectures noticed a similar change of tone, and wondered how the first and last lectures could possibly have been written by the same man. The answer is simple: Heim the philosopher has given way to Heim the evangelist; he has stopped arguing and begun to preach. The upshot of the first volume is that philosophy shows the impossibility of knowing God by philosophy; we can know of God only what he tells us of himself. *Jesus the Lord* and *Jesus the World-fulfiller* give us a theology that is as truly a preacher's theology, a theology of the Word, as is Karl Barth's. The main difference is that Heim's preaching is not so much that of the *prophet*—thundering out the Word irrespective of who hears it—as it is that of the *evangelist*, who begins with a sympathetic analysis of his hearers' state of mind, and

leads them by stages to the point where the Word strikes home.

Only a slight indication can be given of the wealth of concrete imagery and the depth of human sympathy which make Heim's positive teaching so moving and impressive.[39] The message centers in three epithets describing the work of Christ: Jesus as *Lord* and *Leader* (Fuehrer), Jesus as Savior from sin (*Versöhner*), and Jesus as *Deliverer* of the world from the powers of darkness and death (*Weltvollender*).

(1) *Jesus as Fuehrer*. The fact that Heim deliberately applies to Jesus the epithet which in the Third Reich is reserved for Adolf Hitler illustrates the difference between his method of combating the new paganism and Karl Barth's. Barth denies all religious significance to the Third Reich. Heim grants that a genuine religious motive is at work in this great political upheaval, but denies that this motive can find any secure grounding in anything human or temporal. The men of today, he feels, know better than previous generations what it meant for the early Christians to follow Christ, since they have learned to follow the personal direction of men like Lenin, Gandhi, and Mussolini *without knowing whither*

[39] Professor Wilhelm Pauck, who has read the manuscript of this chapter, remarks, "The dark and ominous clouds which hang on the horizon of the systems that you discuss do not come fully into view as in a larger exposition they should." Nowhere is this criticism more justified than with respect to the following too brief analysis of Heim's doctrine of the work of Christ. Heim's writing has what Otto would call a "numinous" quality about it, impossible to convey in a brief outline. To read his last two books in German is like living through the Apocalypse.

they are being led, without being offered any clear program that their minds can grasp.[40] Heim believes that such leaders appear by a kind of divine appointment, in times of desperate crisis; but of them all, one can say what Napoleon said of himself: "As long as I am necessary, no power in the world will be able to brush me aside. But the moment I become unnecessary, an atom will be enough to smash me."[41] To reverence such an earthly leader as the temporary and imperfect organ of God's Providence is a very different thing from giving him absolute religious trust. Only Christ deserves such trust. He is God's answer to the unquenchable human thirst for guidance, a thirst that can never be quenched in this world of polar opposites and unresolvable antinomies.[42] He is God's Word to us, that guides us over the abyss of mystery that engulfs us: not by giving us knowledge of the way, or a plan to follow, but by personally accompanying us, and reaching out a guiding hand to which we must cling closely, every step of the dark way. If it seems incredible that one who appeared in the first century should thus guide the men of the twentieth, that is only because we forget that time is an irrelevance in the meeting between an "I" and a "Thou"; and that this unique "Thou" comes to us from the transcendent world to which all times and spaces are immediately open.

[40] Heim, *The Church of Christ and the Problems of the Day*, pp. 99-120.
[41] *Ibid.*, p. 107.
[42] *Jesus der Herr*, pp. 32 ff.

(2) *Jesus as Savior from sin* (*Versöhner*). Heim combats with the utmost earnestness the teaching of the German Faith Movement that man's helplessness to know the absolute and be his own leader is simply the result of his *fate* as a finite creature. This teaching (constantly repeated by Heim's colleague, Wilhelm Hauer) has truth in it just in so far as it points to a universal tragedy in which the whole creation is involved. But unless we are to violate our most sacred moral intuitions, and let down the bars to temptation, we must recognize that we are *guilty* creatures, and the estrangement of all creation from its divine Source is a *guilty* estrangement. Heim finds the secret of this estrangement and disorder, which is at once our *destiny* and our *fault,* in the New Testament conception of *Satan*: an evil Will, of supercosmic dimensions, which seeks to dethrone God's Will and capture ours, but has no power over us unless we inwardly yield to it and allow it to possess us, as God's Will possesses us when we yield to it in the same inward fashion. It was the mission of Jesus not merely to save individual souls but to break the power of Satan in the world, with all the evils that it entails. It was with this cosmic power that he was silently grappling, like a wrestler mutely laboring for a final decisive grip, when he stood speechless before Caïaphas and Pilate. But the decisive grip was the forgiveness of sins. The problem of guilt is the key to the problem of power, as the replacement of a blown-out fuse in the basement of a great factory establishes the electric connection without which the

machinery cannot be made to turn. Jesus first *forgave*
the paralytic; then he gave him the power to walk.[43]
So by allowing the storm of Satan's unholy wrath
against God, and God's holy wrath against Satan, to
burst unhindered over his bowed, defenseless, sinless
head, he made the arch-fiend overreach himself, and
knock a great breach in the wall of guilt which had
cut off the sinful world from the *power* as well as the
favor of God.[44]

(3) *Jesus as Deliverer of the world (Weltvollender).*
The victory which Jesus won in principle on Calvary
remains to be consolidated in history. Heim sees the
history of the world from Calvary to the final consummation quite frankly in terms of a realistic eschatology
drawn from the New Testament, whose authority in
such ultimate questions utterly outranks that of all
secular, finite knowledge of the world. Four great
moments stand out in this cosmic drama: (a) the
resurrection and ascension of Jesus, who thenceforth
becomes the invincible Lord of History; (b) his public visible seizure of power; (c) the general resurrection; (d) the final consummation of this age of birth
and death, and the garnering of the fruits of world-
history in God's eternal storehouse.[45] Heim defends
this realistic eschatology against the Platonizing
eschatology of Barth's earlier writings, which represented the End as the perpetual lowering of Eternity
over Time, at every moment, and not as an event

[43] *Jesus der Weltvollender*, pp. 48, 63.
[44] *Ibid.*, pp. 109-127.
[45] *Ibid.*, p. 175.

toward which history actually moves.[46] The lightning
has flashed already, says Heim, in Christ's resurrection; we are still waiting for the thunderclap of
his public, cosmic Second Coming; but the two
events are actually one, and the thunder *must*
come.

In the period between the Resurrection and the
End, the Church of Christ, which possesses the first
fruits of the Spirit and lives in the hope of the New
Age, occupies a most important place. Responsible
ultimately only to her Lord, she renders practical
services to mankind, through the exercise of the healing and redeeming power entrusted to her, which even
the secular State is bound to appreciate. But though
she gladly serves the State, her conscience is not
bound by the State, and she holds herself free to
criticize evil economic and social conditions with that
same plainness of speech which Martin Luther—unlike many of his followers!—exercised on many oc-
casions.[47]

Both in his eschatology and in his political teaching, Heim is very close to another Lutheran theologian who seems exceptionally able to keep his head in
the confusion of the church conflict: Paul Althaus,
Jr. Not so directly allied as Heim with the Confessional Church, he represents that large section of the
German Evangelical Church which finds both extremes in the church conflict obnoxious, and tries

[46] *Ibid.*, p. 145. Cf. the essay on "Time and Eternity" in *The New
Divine Order* (English translation, 1930).
[47] *The Church of Christ and the Problems of the Day*, pp. 70 ff.

to stand aloof from them;[48] but his Lutheran principles lead him to conclusions similar to Heim's on many issues.

Althaus's views on the social responsibility of the church are clearly indicated in his *Theology of the Orders* (*Theologie der Ordnungen*, 1935), in which he takes sharp issue with Gogarten for subscribing to the proposition that the ethical law is "given to us in our capacity as members of a Folk," thus making it a purely rational and secular matter. He insists that the second or ethical half of the Hebrew Ten Commandments, when interpreted in the light of the Gospel, is relevant to social and political issues, and points out that wherever Christian missions go, they have a deep effect upon the social and political life of peoples.[49] Two errors are to be avoided in our Christian attitude toward the "orders" of family, State, etc. On the one hand, we must avoid the "Illusionism" which sees in them the pure original order of creation, and hears in the voice of the people the very voice of God. On the other hand, we must avoid the "Nihilism" which judges them so completely sinful that it either tries to withdraw from political

[48] Another theologian who holds aloof from all parties in the church conflict is my friend and former tutor, Georg Wünsch of Marburg. He has written two important ethical treatises, *Evangelische Wirtschaftsethik* (1927) and *Evangelische Ethik des Politischen* (1936). In the latter part of his political ethics (Part III, Chapters 3, 12, 13) he touches directly upon the delicate questions of race and nation, Church and State, and the relation between the Christian faith and the Nazi world-view; and his views on these subjects seem to me to resemble Althaus's, at least in their thoughtful discrimination and high, non-partisan perspective.

[49] *Theologie der Ordnungen,* pp. 34-39.

action or abandons all ethical judgment of better or
worse. It is our difficult duty to stand in an imperfect
social order and, admitting our participation in its
guilt, seek to cleanse it in the light of our vision of
its original divine intent. This may sometimes mean
disobedience and revolt; more often, patient toleration of evil because of the good with which it is bound
up, and which we seek to disentangle.[50]

Althaus's greatest contribution has been to *eschatology*—a branch of theology which has flourished amazingly in the apocalyptic atmosphere of post-war Germany. His book on *Die letzten Dinge* or *Last Things*
is probably the most important eschatological work
that has appeared in our time; and the development
the book has gone through in its various editions re-
flects and epitomizes the whole development of contemporary German theology. In his first edition
(1922), Althaus was very close to Karl Barth's "upward-looking" eschatology. Like Dean Inge in England, he was concerned to recall men from the illusory
faith in progress, and set them to living "the eternal
life in the midst of time" ("axiological eschatology").
All "teleological" eschatology that places the Judgment or the Second Coming ahead of us in history is
illusory; *every* generation is directly under God's judgment, directly in touch with eternity. The last generation has no special privilege. This view was attacked
by many as a substitution of idealistic philosophy for
real Christian eschatology; and in his third edition
(1926), Althaus formally admitted that his emphasis

[50] *Ibid.*, pp. 65-68.

upon a purely upward-looking, "axiological" hope had been very one-sided. This act of candor was very influential, and started a flood of discussion on the proper relation between the temporal and eternal element in the Christian hope.

Heim's essay on "Time and Eternity, the main question of present-day eschatology" was a landmark in this controversy. Heim found the temporal element in the Christian hope ineffaceable, but different both from the purely temporal hope of modern apostles of progress, and the purely eternal hope of the Platonists. An end *of* history will come *in* history, whereby the time-form of our fallen creation will be abolished; but the whole meaning of time will be gathered up and fulfilled in the eternal life which then will begin for all the world. This discussion of time and eternity, in which many writers participated, is reflected both in Althaus's later position and in Barth's recent *Credo*, where his Platonism is abandoned for a purely Scriptural theory of "times," beginning with fallen "world-time," and moving through the "time of grace" initiated by the Incarnation, to a coming "time of glory" that is unimaginable for us since it is God's time—"the time of that God with whom we shall live in unbroken peace in eternal life."[51]

Althaus's final position on eschatology is summarized in the second edition of his recent book on *Dogmatics* (1936).[52] Since the form of this present world is determined by the prevalence of sin, and

[51] Barth, *Credo*, p. 171.
[52] *Grundriss der Dogmatik*, II, pp. 177-181.

Christ is our redeemer from sin, *Christ is the end of history*. His Second Coming is the *end* toward which all history moves, and at the same time marks the *fulfillment* of history, and the transfiguration of the world. There is both *connection* and *contrast* between history and eternity; the Second Coming, if it *fulfills* this world, is at the same time the *death* of this world —which makes any purely millennial hope of a reign of Christ *on earth*, impossible. We are not to expect the end to be approached by a gradual progress; to the very end, the Church will always have to strive with Antichrist, within her fellowship as well as without. While all this tends to center our imagination on coming events, we must not allow the thought of the "signs of the end" to destroy the *immediacy* of our relation to eternity. As every man is to remember that this day may be his last, and through the mystery of death feel the immediate nearness of eternity, so humanity must consider that every age may be its last, and through the imminence of the Second Coming feel eternity pressing upon each present moment. Thus Althaus retains his original emphasis upon eternity, while making new room for Heim's emphasis upon things to come. He avoids a certain Biblical literalism which sometimes alarms one in Heim, and which makes one wonder if all the lessons of modern history and science are to be thrown away. His mature conclusion, which represents contemporary German theology at its best, may be summarized in the words of Otto Michel: "God stands

above time and at the end of time, therefore faith looks up and ahead."[53]

To those who are losing faith in a Kingdom of God which unaided human hands can build on earth, this eschatology that has been tried in the fires of affliction has much to teach, and much comfort and courage to give. It is one of the contributions of contemporary German theology which will probably influence world thought most deeply, in the long run. Echoes of it are already to be heard in the Scandinavian theology to which we next turn.

[53] Otto Michel, *"Unser Ringen um die Eschatologie,"* *Zeitschrift für Theologie und Kirche,* 1932, p. 174.

CHAPTER IV

PROTESTANT THEOLOGY OUTSIDE OF GERMANY

1. AROUND THE EDGE OF THE MAELSTROM

WHAT the French Revolution did for the Roman Catholic Church, and the Russian Revolution for the Orthodox Church, the German Revolution is now doing for the Protestant Church. It is engulfing and grinding to bits, in its mighty maelstrom, whatever is crushable or sinkable in the Protestant faith, leaving only what is oaken-ribbed, indefinitely submersible, and absolutely water-tight.

It is impossible for the Anglo-Saxon world to look on unconcerned at the plight of the German Evangelical Church today—just as impossible as it is to look on unconcerned at the great political upheaval which is the immediate cause of that plight. "It can't happen here" is hardly a Christian sentiment, when uttered in a spirit of complacent self-congratulation; but even if we should utterly fail in Christian sympathy with our German brethren in their present afflictions, it would be difficult now to escape the uneasy surmise that our isolation from these events is less complete than we formerly supposed. When political liberalism and democracy are being destroyed in all parts of the world by a great ground swell of social change, it is folly to suppose that our

Ship of State is not going to be rocked by the same swell; and when Protestantism—more especially *liberal* Protestantism—threatens to go to pieces in the land of its origin, it is time for American Protestants to trim ship and call all hands on deck.

There are two ways in which great social and intellectual revolutions can benefit religion. (1) Those who are directly involved in the revolution are driven back upon essentials and ultimates, so that their faith and loyalty—if not utterly destroyed—become the means of rekindling the devotion of their co-religionists in all parts of the world. Hardly a man of us, in these last few years, has failed to be affected in some degree by the faithfulness of certain members of the German Evangelical Church, whose sufferings are thus a sort of vicarious expiation for the sins of us all. (2) Those who are close enough to the revolution to feel the imminent peril of being engulfed in it are powerfully impelled to set their own house in order, in the hope of solving constructively the questions which the revolution has settled by a destructive convulsion. In this they are eagerly helped by the exiles and emigrants that every revolution sets loose like antitoxins in the surrounding portions of the body politic, tending to immunize it against the spread of the disease. Remoter regions are thus given guidance and inspiration by those close to the center of disturbance.

While there is much to be learned directly from contemporary German thought, there is much also to be learned from the thought of those countries

that immediately *surround* Germany. In the political sphere, those of us who are concerned to save the values in democracy do well to keep an observant eye upon developments in countries like France and Czechoslovakia, which still remain democratic, but which have to struggle hard to keep their heads above water in the rising tide of dictatorship. In the economic sphere, those who believe there is still some good in Capitalism watch eagerly the experiments which countries like Sweden are making with a "middle way" that attempts to avoid the evils of Capitalism without plunging into State Socialism.

In some of these same countries, not only Protestantism but *liberal* Protestantism, which has practically become extinct in Germany, still flourishes. Since the future of theological liberalism is a very acute and important problem with us, I propose that we conduct our necessarily somewhat cursory survey of Protestant theology outside of Germany with that problem specifically in mind; and as the most convenient method for such a brief survey, I propose that we use Karl Barth as our instrument of precision. "What think ye of Barth?" is a question which elicits prompt reactions in every part of the theological field in Europe today—very much as "What think ye of Hitler?" elicits prompt reactions in the political field. If the reactions are wholly positive, we may infer that the revolt against liberalism has proceeded pretty far in that territory; if they are pronouncedly negative, one may presume that some vestiges of liberalism are still to be detected. In either

case, we may hope to learn something of the dangers to be avoided and the corrections to be made if the genuine values in the liberal Protestant movement—so widespread in America—are to be preserved for posterity.

Protestant Europe outside of Germany and German Switzerland may be divided into three principal areas, each of which is contiguous to German Protestantism at some point. Reading counter-clockwise in a great circle around the edge of the German maelstrom, we come first to *Scandinavian (and Finnish) Protestantism,* which is very strong, and overwhelmingly *Lutheran.* Next we come to *Dutch and French Protestantism* (including a few French-speaking Protestants in Belgium and a good many in French Switzerland), which is predominantly *Calvinistic.* Finally, sweeping around to the south and east of Germany, we come to *Central European Protestantism,* very scattered and mixed in character, including minority groups of many races and denominations in Hungary, Czechoslovakia, and Poland. While there are a few other Protestant groups in southern and south-eastern Europe, such as the Waldensians in Italy and small groups in the Balkans and Soviet Russia, the bulk of non-German Protestantism is included in this circle. We shall be obliged to take a small representative sample of theology from each area, and shall concentrate principally upon Swedish, French and Czechoslovak thought. Then, having examined our samples for traces of surviving liberalism and nascent Barthianism, we shall back off from

the Continent and cross to Scotland—which stands intellectually nearer to Continental theology than any other point in the Anglo-Saxon world—so as to get a broad perspective on the whole Continental scene, before drawing our final conclusions.

2. SCANDINAVIAN THEOLOGY: NYGREN, AULÉN, AND THE SCHOOL OF LUND

The solid Lutheran North—Finland and Scandinavia—is sometimes called "the quiet corner of Europe." Touching disturbed Germany at only one point—the brief southern boundary of Denmark—this is perhaps the stablest and most peaceful area in all Europe. Having preserved its neutrality in the World War, Northern culture has never been violently interrupted in its development, and has continued to forge ahead along nineteenth-century lines. It is no accident, but the steady continuance of peaceful work and study, which has given to the names of Sibelius, Melchior and Flagstad the leading place they occupy in present-day music. Scandinavian[1] theology, too, judging from such samples as commonly come to our attention, maintains something of that scholarly discursiveness and serenity which characterized German theology in the days before the War and the revolution. The Scandinavians seem to be carrying on both music and theology from the point where the Germans laid them down

[1] To avoid intolerable repetition of the words "and Finland," I am using the word "Scandinavian" from this point on to include the *four* Lutheran countries of the North, and not merely the *three* strictly Scandinavian countries.

in 1914. United with the Germans in their devotion to the Lutheran faith, interested and distressed by the present church controversy in Germany, they are themselves entirely free from conflict between Church and State. Four State churches, happily married to four exceedingly enlightened governments, which look after the material welfare of the people while gladly handing over the forming of their souls to the clergy: on the surface there is nothing rotten in the state of Scandinavia, and one might well pray for the privilege of being born and bred there!

Beneath the surface, however, there is a good deal of unrest. Ever since the days when Kierkegaard was hurling his philippics against the State Church of Denmark, there has been a growing alienation between the life of the Church and the life of the people, in all four Northern countries. General membership in the Lutheran Church and absence of strong rival denominations does not mean unanimous devotion, but only a lack of active revolt. A recent *Christian Century* article on "Revolt in the North," by Ezra Young,[2] quotes Jacob Lange of the Folk High School in Odense, Denmark, as saying, "Our attitude toward the State Church is one of indifference rather than opposition. You to the west expect much of your church; we expect little, and we are not, therefore, disappointed!" The same article mentions a number of active local reform movements, in addition to the widespread influence of the Oxford Group Movement: (1) the movement led by Niels

[2] *Christian Century*, Dec. 29, 1937, pp. 1621-1623.

Dahl of Liselund, Denmark, who stands for the ideal of "a free church where Christ is a living reality, and where brotherhood is the only creed," and proposes to anticipate the impact of Fascism and Communism by mobilizing "the Christian revolution"; (2) the movement emanating from the Sigtuna Folk School in Sweden, which unites hand workers and brain workers on a basis of "humanistic Christianity," and hopes to find a "common ground" in religion where "rightists and leftists, liberals and conservatives, farmers and workers" can take their stand together; (3) the Christian labor movement which has its headquarters at Brunnsvik in Sweden, and has been much influenced by Kagawa and E. Stanley Jones.

All three of the above-mentioned movements relate themselves in some way to what we in America might call a liberal Social Gospel—a movement whose greatest nineteenth-century exponent in Scandinavia was Bishop Grundtvig, founder of the "folk schools" which contribute so much to the life of the North today. What of the influence of Barth in such an environment? Adolf Keller reports that the reception of the Barthian message has been most diverse in the different Northern countries. In Norway, which is split into a conservative pietistic and a liberal party, Barth is rejected with equal unanimity by both groups: by the liberals on account of his reactionary tendencies, by the conservatives because of his freedom in Biblical criticism! In Sweden, Barth is sympathetically studied; but Swedish theology, hav-

ing always held to the Lutheran ideas of the mysterious majesty of God, does not feel the need of reëmphasizing it, and objects to Barth's stating it in a way that seems to obscure the other pole of Lutheran thought, the Fatherly love of God. In Finland, apparently, Barth's name is little known. In Denmark, however, where Kierkegaard's influence has always remained alive, and the influence of Grundtvig has become secularized and partly lost in a general atmosphere of pleasant middle-class conviviality, the Barthian theology has decidedly caught fire with a certain youthful group of "dissatisfied, excited radicals," who have used it as an engine of destructive criticism against the Church, and caused a split in the Student Christian Movement. Keller says that when Barth went to Denmark he "discovered to his horror what the Barthians there had made of him," and was led to emphasize the "positive and constructive principles of his theology" in contrast to their sheer negativism.[3]

For our example of Scandinavian theology, we shall go to the University of Lund in Sweden.

The Church of Sweden is in an exceptionally interesting position, theologically speaking. She is bound by her history to German Lutheranism, and by her government to the episcopal churches of England and the East. Recent advances in fraternal rela-

[3] Adolf Keller, *Karl Barth and Christian Unity*, pp. 111-123. It may have been on this occasion that Barth wrote to a friend, on a postcard, "There is more joy on earth than in heaven over the progress of the Barthian theology."

tions with Anglicanism and Orthodoxy[4] have stimu-
lated reflection among Swedish theologians upon the
possible points of contact between Luther's theology
and that of the Greek Fathers to whom the Anglicans
and Orthodox are accustomed to appeal. Although
the Danish and Norwegian churches have not held
wholly aloof from these ecumenical negotiations, it
was the Church of Sweden, under the late Archbishop Nathan Söderblom, one of the greatest ecclesiastical statesmen of modern times, which took
and has retained the lead.

While making friendly advances toward the "catholicism" of his fellow-episcopalians, Söderblom at the
same time maintained his connection with other Protestant churches; and he advocated as the goal of the
ecumenical movement the ideal of "evangelical catholicity." By this he did not mean a syncretistic mixture
of Catholic and Protestant doctrines, but a world
union of Christendom on non-Roman (i.e., *volun-
tary*) lines, similar to that which is now emerging in
the "World Council" for which the Oxford and
Edinburgh conferences cast their vote. While such a
reunion of Christendom would embody the Catholic
ideal of a world church, speaking with one voice to
the world of nations, it would also embody the
Protestant ideal in that it would recognize that

[4] On the history of the negotiations and friendly exchanges between the Swedish Church and the other episcopal churches, see
*Ekklesia: eine Sammlung von Selbstdarstellungen der Christlicher
Kirchen,* (edited by Siegmund-Schultze) Vol. II, No. 5, *Die Kirche
in Schweden,* pp. 151 ff., an article on the ecumenical relations of
the Swedish Church by Professor Brilioth of Lund, who himself
contributed much to this development.

schism is not always a sin, and schismatic churches may be part of the body of Christ while retaining separate organizations. The prophetic line of true Christianity begins (he points out) with a schism from Israel; and it is almost a universal rule of church history that whenever a great revival of spiritual power has come to the Christian church, it has either been confined to one *section* of the church (Augustinianism in the West) or to a monastic *order* in the church (Franciscan movement), or has led, against the will of its leaders, to literal schism (Lutheran reformation, Wesleyan revival), because of the opposition of the majority.[5]

Söderblom could point this out with great strategic effect, because the church he represented was not itself a schismatic church. Lutheran in theology, the Church of Sweden passed through the Reformation without any disturbance of that "apostolic succession" so dear to the hearts of Catholics. Her Catholic bishops simply elected to renounce allegiance to Rome, and teach the "evangelical" interpretation of the Christian faith. When such a church, in the person of its Archbishop, takes up the cudgels for the truth in Protestantism, it gains a hearing among high churchmen of East and West such as is accorded to none of the other Protestant churches. It might fairly be claimed that the Church of Sweden, since Söderblom, has begun to supersede the Church of England as the real "bridge church" between Catholicism

[5] Siegmund-Schultze, *op. cit.*, pp. 27, 28 (Söderblom's essay on "International Friendship Through Evangelical Catholicity").

and Protestantism. The very success of the Anglicans' drive for unity with the Orthodox churches has tended to tie their hands in all negotiations with Protestants. If the Protestant churches are to draw any closer to the England-Sweden-Orient bloc, it will be on Swedish initiative, I believe, rather than upon Anglican or Orthodox initiative.

Within the Church of Sweden herself, a high-church liturgical movement and a free-church evangelistic movement are proceeding side by side; and the leaders of the Church (strange to say) have so far shown themselves sympathetic to *both*![6] As in economics, so in religion, Sweden is showing the world a "middle way."

Twenty years ago, the theological center of Sweden was the University of Upsala (just north of Stockholm), where the influence of Söderblom and his colleague, Einar Billing, was then predominant. Since 1920, when Billing became a bishop,[7] and especially since Söderblom's death, theological leadership has passed from Upsala to Lund. While extremely significant work continues to be done at Upsala by Runestam and Bohlin,[8] the prevailing trend of contemporary Swedish theology has been set by the

[6] For example, the majority of Baptists and Methodists have not formed separate church bodies but remained within the Church of Sweden (*Ibid.*, p. 12).

[7] It is a remarkable fact, testifying to the close relationship of theology to the life of the church, that Söderblom, Bohlin, Aulén and many other Swedish theologians have become bishops.

[8] Runestam has concerned himself with the problem of relating theology to contemporary psychoanalysis and contemporary social problems; Bohlin, with a critique of Kierkegaard and the dialectical theology (*Ibid.*, pp. 82-88).

"Lundensian" school, led by Gustaf Aulén and his close associate, Anders Nygren.

The University of Lund, located as it is near the southern tip of Sweden—farther south even than most parts of Denmark—has always been closely in touch with German theology. In the nineteenth century, when Upsala was chiefly under the sway of an "orthodox-pietistic tendency," Lund yielded successively to the influence of Schleiermacher, Hegel and Ritschl.[9] While the close relationship of theology and church in Sweden prevented any swing to irresponsible extremes, and gave a "high-church" tinge to the Lundensian interpretation of German liberalism, the present trend at Lund represents a critical reaction against the recent liberal trend—*a reaction independent of Barth's and much more moderate*. While influenced considerably by German Luther-research and by Althaus—who perhaps of all contemporary German theologians is closest to Swedish theology— the work of Aulén and his colleagues at Lund has proceeded on quite original lines, and constitutes one of the most distinctive schools of Protestant thought in the world today.

It is no accident that the two books by which Aulén and Nygren are now known to the English-speaking world, *Christus Victor* (Aulén) and *Agape and Eros* (Nygren), are both *historical* studies. The history of doctrine has a special importance for them both. The task of theology, according to Aulén's great work, *The Common Christian Faith* (*Den allmanneliga*

[9] *Ibid.*, pp. 65-69.

Kristna tron, 1920; 3rd edition 1931) is not to prove
the truth of Christian faith, or engage in metaphysical
speculations, but rather to set forth this faith in its
simplicity and its unity, clearing it of all alien en-
tanglements. According to Nygren,[10] the task of the
philosophy of religion is to define the uniqueness of
the religious experience, and that of dogmatic theology is to define the unique and determinative motives
of the Christian faith—which cannot be done in the
abstract, without close attention to *history*.

It is evident that this point of view has a close
affinity with that of Schleiermacher, Ritschl and Harnack; and the Lundensians are glad to acknowledge
their immense debt to the historical work of their
liberal German predecessors; but they claim it was
largely vitiated by rationalistic and moralistic pre-
suppositions. Schleiermacher started out, rightly
enough, to describe Christian faith from within, after
determining its essence or center; but he fell back
unconsciously from a true historical appreciation of
Christianity into a general notion of religion as the
"feeling of absolute dependence," and allowed this
rational abstraction to determine a large part of his
description of the content of Christianity. Ritschl
and Harnack were right in reacting against Hegelian speculative theology; but they allowed their
hatred of "metaphysics" to extend to the whole transcendental side of the Christian faith; and in making
war upon "Hellenism" they threatened to reduce
Christianity to an undogmatic moralism, egocentric

[10] *Ibid.,* pp. 72-75.

and anthropocentric. What is required is not to abandon the nineteenth century's quest for a truly objective and scientific theology, but to correct and improve its methods—above all, the great method of *historical investigation* by which so many of its durable triumphs were achieved.

The historical method of Schleiermacher as applied to theology, was an endeavor to distinguish between doctrines derived from religious experience and those derived from logical thought; that of Ritschl and Harnack, to distinguish between moral or religious value-judgments and all merely theoretical judgments; that of the Lundensians (known as *Motivforschung*) endeavors to distinguish between fundamental religious *motives* and the concepts or figures of speech in which they are expressed. When a number of such characteristic motives have been discerned, and found to run through the history of Christianity, they are then related to one another and grouped around a "Ground-motive" in which the "center" or "essence" of Christianity is found to consist. The disentanglement of motives from concepts is best seen in Aulén's *Christus Victor* and in his untranslated work on the Christian view of God; the discernment of a Ground-motive, in Nygren's *Agape and Eros*.

In the writings of the early Greek fathers, a view of the Work of Christ finds frequent expression which is usually dismissed by modern Western theologians as unworthy of serious consideration. It is commonly known as "the ransom to Satan theory"; and it makes use of some very strange figures of speech. Gregory

of Nyssa, for example, says that "God, in order to render Himself accessible to him (Satan) who demanded of Him a ransom for us, concealed Himself under the veil of our nature, in order that, as happens with greedy fishes, together with the bait of the flesh the hook of the Godhead might also be swallowed."[11] This idea of a shrewd divine deception—often repeated under various figures in patristic theology—is so obnoxious to the modern mind that recent histories of the doctrine of the Atonement tend to pass over it hastily, as an unpardonably crude preliminary to real Christian thought on the subject, which begins with St. Anselm's *Cur Deus Homo?*.

Aulén believes that this much maligned view, when the mythological language in which it is clothed has been properly interpreted, and its underlying "religious motive" has thus been revealed, will prove to be far more than a historical curiosity. "It should be evident," he says, "that the historical study of dogma is wasting its time in pure superficiality if it does not endeavor to penetrate to that which lies below the outward dress, and look for the religious values which lie concealed underneath."[12] What are these religious "values" or "motives"? A discerning historian should be able to see them, even in the midst of apparent contradictions and absurdities in the language employed to express them. In this case, we have to interpret the apparent contradiction between two views of the devil's relationship to humanity.

[11] *Great Catechism*, ch. 24. Quoted by Aulén, *Christus Victor*, p. 68.
[12] Aulén, *Christus Victor*, p. 64.

On the one hand, it is said that the devil acquired rights over man when he fell into sin, and it is right that his Satanic Majesty should demand a "ransom" in exchange for man's deliverance. On the other hand, it is protested (for example, by Irenaeus) that man belongs by nature to God, and the devil has brought him violently into captivity.

The religious motive behind the first of these contentions is *"the desire to assert the guilt of mankind, and the judgment of God on human sin."*[13] The motive behind the second is the feeling that man's sin is only a part of a wider, cosmic apostasy from God's will, in which everything evil is included, and which forms a rival kingdom violently striving against God's. If the first of these two motives had been the only one, the fathers might have been content to represent the death of Christ as a fair legal transaction between God and Satan; if the second alone, they might have represented it as the heroic death of a Prince in victorious combat with a usurper who has enslaved his Father's subjects. Since the two motives were mixed, the result was the absurd but suggestive idea of a divine deception—an action half-way between negotiation and open combat, expressive both of the hostility between God and Satan, and of God's unwillingness to use violent means to overcome the Adversary.

The initial qualms of the rationalistic and moralistic mind having thus been set at rest, Aulén proceeds to a systematic description of the faith of the early

[13] *Ibid.*

Church in Christ's great victory over sin, death and the devil. When all misleading figures of speech have been properly interpreted, he finds in this "classic" view of the Greek fathers—and of the Latin fathers before Anselm—a view of Christ's Work clearly distinguishable from the mediaeval and modern views, and much superior thereto. This classic view is highly "dramatic" and at least provisionally "dualistic." "Its central theme is the idea of Atonement as a Divine conflict and victory: Christ—Christus Victor —fights against and triumphs over the evil powers of the world, the 'tyrants' under which mankind is in bondage and suffering, and in Him God reconciles the world to Himself."[14] But the dualism is not final, and this greatly complicates and enriches the picture. Evil is at once that which opposes God and that which (as part of his creation) is an instrument which he uses for good; he himself is both the One who reconciles the world to himself, and the One who is reconciled. This view differs from the Anselmic and all other "legal satisfaction" theories of the Atonement, in that it makes reconciliation a "continuous Divine work,"[15] whereas these other theories make it at best a "discontinuous Divine work"; i.e., "an offering made to God by Christ as man and on man's behalf,"[16] which may have been *willed* by God but was not, strictly speaking, done by him. In comparison with all modern "subjective" theories of the Atonement,

[14] *Ibid.*, p. 20.
[15] *Ibid.*, p. 21.
[16] *Ibid.*, p. 22.

from Abelard to Liberal Protestantism, the classic view is as truly, nay *more* truly, "objective" than Anselm's, for "it describes a complete change in the relation between God and the world, and a change also in God's own attitude,"[17] due to the passing of a great crisis in the cosmic combat between the Creator and his apostate creation.

While the greater part of Aulén's book is devoted to a purely historical study of the relations of the classic view of the Atonement with the mediaeval Latin and modern subjective views, he makes it very evident that he regards it as the truly Christian view. It is characteristic not only of patristic theology, but of the whole New Testament. The Catholic (Anselmic) view, which is usually regarded as a clarification and development of earlier views, is really "a sidetrack in the history of Christian dogma," which led inevitably to the "subjective" view by a process of reaction. Luther alone, of all the moderns, understood the classic view, and used its realistic imagery without fear. But under Melanchthon's leadership, Protestant theology reverted to scholastic legalism, and led at length to the equal and opposite excesses of liberal subjectivism. Both the legal and the subjective view are shallower than the ancient view they replaced, because more strictly rational; they artificially reduce to simplicity a mystery that in its true religious depth must express itself in paradoxes:

God is at once the all-ruler, and engaged in conflict

17 *Ibid.*

with the powers of evil. These powers are evil powers, and at the same time executants of God's judgment on sin. God is at the same time the Reconciler and the Reconciled. His is the Love and His the Wrath. The Love prevails over the Wrath, and yet Love's condemnation of sin is absolute. The Love is infinite and unfathomable, . . . justifying men without any satisfaction of the Divine justice . . . yet at the same time God's claim on men is sharpened to the uttermost.[18]

Fundamentally—and here we approach the subject of "Ground-motives"—the differences between these three historic types of Christian teaching are reducible to three different views of the relationship between God and man; for all really religious motives have their roots in some attitude toward this primal relationship. In the classic type, the Atonement is *"a movement of God to man,"* and God is felt to be "personally engaged in the work of man's deliverance." The Latin theory makes God "stand more at a distance; for the satisfaction is paid by man, in the person of Christ, to God." In the modern subjective view, "God stands still more at a distance; as far as He is concerned, no atonement is needed, and all the emphasis is on *man's movement to God.*"[19] The basic Christian idea of the "Divine initiative" is in this last view completely reversed and set at naught. In his book on *The Christian View of God*, Aulén finds the source of all modern theological aberrations in the gradual humanistic perversion of the idea of God's

[18] p. 172. By permission of The Macmillan Co., publishers.
[19] p. 171.

love, which passes through three successive descending stages: "mild Providence" (eighteenth-century rationalism), "naturalized love" (Schleiermacher), and "ethicized love" (Ritschl)—after which it runs out into pure humanism.[20] Though he is so opposed to the liberal *conception* of the love of God, Aulén does not follow Barth in making the Lordship of God replace the Love of God as the central point of theology. Indeed, in the third edition of his *Dogmatics*, the idea of love becomes more central than in the first; and the whole of theology is made to proceed from this "Ground-motive": Part I, "Divine Love"; Part II, "The Way of Divine Love"; Part III, "The Community of Divine Love."[21]

For the English-speaking public, this characteristic "Lundensian" emphasis upon active, self-imparting Divine love as the Ground-motive of Christian faith is best expressed in Professor Nygren's remarkable book, *Agape and Eros*. It is primarily concerned with the contrast between two kinds of love, easily confused in modern languages, but clearly distinguished in Greek: the "love" (*Eros*) of which Plato speaks in his *Symposium*, and the "love" (*Agape*) of which St. Paul speaks in the 13th Chapter of I Corinthians. In these two words he finds the Ground-motives of Greek religion and original Christianity concretely expressed; and in the process of interaction between these two Ground-motives he finds the key to the whole history of Christian thought, with its intertwining of Hebraic and Hellenic elements.

[20] Sigmund-Schultze, *Ekklesia,* no. 5, p. 79.
[21] *Ibid.*

We all know Harnack's general scheme for this process: a simple Gospel to begin with, of "God the Father and the infinite value of the human soul"; the door opened to Hellenism by St. Paul, and an "acute Hellenization" ensuing in the Eastern Church, complicated with Roman legalism and imperialism in the Western Church; housecleaning begun by the Reformation and completed by the liberal Protestants, who have at last gone "back to Jesus" and made a clean sweep of all foreign admixtures in their religion. Nygren rejects this whole scheme.

To begin with, he finds that Harnack's version of the original Gospel is more Greek than Christian. It is Eros, not Agape, that loves in proportion to the value of its object. By the pursuit of value in its object, Platonic love is led *up and away* from the world, on wings of aspiration, beyond all transient things and persons to the realm of the Ideas. Agape, as described in the Gospels and Epistles, is "spontaneous and 'uncaused,'" "indifferent to human merit," and "creates" value in those upon whom it is bestowed out of pure generosity. It flows *down from God* into this transient, sinful world; those whom it touches become conscious of their own utter unworthiness; they are impelled to forgive and love their enemies, not because they are inherently lovable, but because the God of grace imparts worth to them by the act of loving them.[22]

[22] Nygren, *Agape and Eros* (translated by Hebert), pp. 52-56, 165. It may be questioned whether this idea of the utter worthlessness of

If Harnack is wrong in supposing himself to have eliminated "Hellenism" from his own conception of the Gospel, he is equally wrong in charging St. Paul and the Greek fathers with having succumbed to it. Nygren is inclined to agree with Reitzenstein's conjecture that when St. Paul named "faith, hope and Agape" as the three abiding Christian virtues, he was consciously opposing a well-known Greek list of virtues: faith, truth, hope, and Eros. If the Alexandrian fathers did to some extent succumb to Hellenism, the general upshot of the Great Councils of the Eastern Church was a decisive rejection of it, in the interest of simple Christian piety. The union of Eros with Agape began with St. Augustine. It was his Neo-Platonism, with its double motion, from God to man as well as from man to God—so different from the original one-sided conception of Plato and Aristotle—that made it possible to unite Platonic love with Christian love in the new composite idea of *charity* (*caritas*). The union (or confusion!) was carried to perfection in the teaching of St. Thomas Aquinas; but his work was soon undone by Luther (who went back to primitive Christian Agape) and the Renaissance (which went back to Platonic Eros). Liberal Protestantism is not the heir of Luther, but of the Renaissance.

---

man is a genuinely Hebraic or Biblical idea, or a Protestant idea artificially read into the Bible. Certainly Judaism has never accepted it, and St. Paul is the only New Testament writer who can easily be interpreted in this sense. Compassionate, forgiving parental love is not inconsistent with some recognition of the latent worth of the child.

While it is Nygren's chief concern to distinguish the original Christian idea of love from all Hellenic modifications, we must not suppose that he sees no truth in the Greek idea. His English translator, Father Hebert, explains in an important prefatory note—with the author's approval—that Eros and Agape represent two elements which, despite their unequal worth, both have a place in Christian theology: Nature and Grace, or Creation and Redemption. "The God who created the world is the God of Agape. As Creator, He is the author of the natural world and of human life, with its upward movement which Aristotle describes in terms of Eros. . . . But it is only in Redemption, that is, by Agape, that He is personally revealed. . . . Christian theology always endeavors to maintain the balance of these two sides, Creation and Redemption."[23] This balance is badly lost by the Humanistic tradition in Christian thought —which includes Catholic Scholasticism along with other forms of rationalism—for in its glad recognition of the presence of God in Nature, it misses the deepest meaning of Grace, and interpret Agape in terms of Eros. Marcion and Barth, on the other hand, upset the balance in the opposite direction. They are more deeply Christian than Aquinas, for they have grasped the true Gospel of Agape; but they express this truth one-sidedly, neglecting the truth in Humanism.

Nygren himself proposes no formula for the correct

[23] Nygren, *Agape and Eros*, pp. xii, xiii (the words are Hebert's). By permission of The Macmillan Co., publishers.

balance. Every historic union of Nature and Grace, Eros and Agape, seems to him at best an "uneasy balance of contradictories, a compromise containing within itself the seeds of its own dissolution." Every formal truce between the two warring elements means the betrayal of Agape. So the history of Christian thought presents, inevitably, a "continual alternation of synthesis and reformation." After each reconciliation, "it becomes the task of a later generation to break up the synthesis, and bring back the minds of man to a deeper perception of the true nature of the Christian idea of love."[24] As between Barth and his opponents, Nygren thus clearly inclines to the side of Barth; and like Barth, he prefers to leave theological truth in the shape of an unresolved paradox, rather than to seek some completely rational formula by which the tension of the paradox would be destroyed. On the other hand, he defends the element of truth in Barth's opponents, and he does not *glory* in paradox as did Barth when he wrote his *Romans*. "There is coming to be a regular cult of the paradoxical and irrational," observes Nygren—with obvious reference to Barth—"as though irrationality and lack of clearness were a hall-mark of Christian truth. The idea of Agape is not paradoxical or irrational in any such sense; it contains no logical contradiction, it demands no *credo quia absurdum*. On the contrary, it is a singularly clear idea, simple, and easily understood."[25]

Aulén and Nygren, between them, make it evident

[24] *op. cit.*, p. 182.
[25] *Ibid.*, p. 162. By permission of The Macmillan Co., publishers.

that Swedish Lutheran theology, with all its sympathy
for the Barthian reaction against liberalism, refuses
inexorably to follow him all the way in his rejection
of natural theology. It sees in Creation a divine work
never completely undone by the rebellion of the creatures; and it sees in Redemption a great victory of
Christ over the powers of evil, made manifest in his
Resurrection, whereby his Church has already entered
into the Kingdom she will more fully enjoy hereafter.
The difference is sometimes expressed by saying that
the Barthian theology is a "theology of the Cross"
(*theologia crucis*), standing in tragic uncertainty
under the shadow of the Cross, beholding its salvation
only as a promised "impossibility"; while the theology
of Lund is a "theology of the Resurrection" (*theologia resurrexionis*), standing thankfully in the light
that streams from the risen and victorious Christ, rejoicing in present salvation while it looks for greater
victories yet to come.[26]

[26] The expression *theologia resurrexionis* is borrowed from the
title of Walter Künneth's *Theologie der Auferstehung*, a book which
has made an even greater impression upon Swedish than upon German theology. In an extremely able book by one of the younger
Lundensians, Folke Holmström's *Das Eschatologische Denken der
Gegenwart* (German translation by Kruska, Gütersloh, 1936),
Künneth's "Theology of the Resurrection" is treated as the climax
of the three dialectical periods through which modern eschatological
discussion has passed: (1) the period of Johannes Weiss's and Albert
Schweitzer's pre-war researches, when the eschatological outlook of
the New Testament was recognized as an indubitable historical fact,
but its *truth* was heavily discounted because of the prevailing "evolutionary optimism"; (2) the period of the Barthian reaction after
the War, when the optimistic faith in progress was suddenly destroyed, but when New Testament eschatology was unconsciously interpreted in the light of Platonic idealism, which sees in eternal life
something entirely supertemporal; (3) the period initiated by the

3. DUTCH AND FRENCH THEOLOGY: LIBERALISM, BARTHIANISM, AND CALVINISTIC SCHOLASTICISM

It might be foretold that in the prevailingly Calvinistic world of Dutch and French Protestantism, a Swiss Reformed theologian like Barth would meet with a friendlier reception than in the solid Lutheran North. The presumption is justified by the event. Barth has found many ardent disciples in Holland, and a few in France. If we pay less attention to his Dutch and French *disciples* than to his Dutch and French *critics*, it is not in order to minimize the influence and importance of his disciples, but only because we are seeking to judge Barth's position from every conceivable angle, and his critics view him from more varied angles than his disciples.

Certainly in Holland there is no lack of varied angles! Ever since the time of the Reformation, the religious life of Holland has been characterized by a multitude of sectarian divisions, each with a self-contained life of its own and a characteristic system of doctrine—political and cultural as well as theologi-

---

reaction against Althaus's *Last Things* in its first edition, culminating in Künneth's conception of the Resurrection as the beginning of the eternal "fulfillment of time," and the Second Coming as the completion of that fulfillment which the Resurrection has already begun (Holmström, *op. cit.*, 15-25, 382-88). The book is dedicated to Althaus and sees in his last edition an excellent *formulation* of the new eschatology; but it ascribes to Künneth the most important influence as a "corrective" of older views. Holmström feels that the genuine New Testament idea of the Resurrection restored by Künneth, literally opens up "*a new dimension of reality*" (italics mine) hitherto ignored by liberals and Barthians alike, and points the way to a genuine "Biblical metaphysic" (page 386).

cal. Most of these divisions are subdivisions of the
Reformed Church, and look to French Calvinism
rather than to German Lutheranism for their international affiliations; but there are also several sects
of Lutherans, an "old Catholic" church (now united
with the German church of the same name, but older
in origin), and an important Mennonite sect hailing
originally from Switzerland. Altogether, the picture
presented by Dutch Protestantism is that of a sectarian over-development surpassed only by certain
American states. Pennsylvania would be a close
analogy.

Sectarianism may in itself be intolerant; but a multitude of sects makes for tolerance, and tolerance
makes for liberalism. Religious liberalism has a long
history in Holland. It goes back to the influence of the
Dutch Christian Humanists, Desiderius Erasmus and
Wessel Gansfoort, whose teaching found favor with
the ruling oligarchy and the intellectual classes, while
the teaching of Calvin ran like wildfire among the
mass of the people. This original antithesis between
the Humanistic *Rekkelijken* (liberals) and the Calvinistic "Precisians" established a strong polarity in
Dutch religious thought which has endured to this
day. In the early seventeenth century, it reappeared
in the controversy between the Arminian Remonstrants and the strict Calvinists.

The synod of Dort (1618-19) gave the victory to
strict Calvinism, and forced the Remonstrants out of
the Dutch Reformed Church, which became in 1651
the recognized state church; but the Remonstrants

and other liberals were "tolerated," at a time when toleration was almost unknown in Europe; and a steady stream of refugees, persecuted for conscience's sake, trickled over the Dutch frontier throughout the seventeenth and eighteenth centuries: Spanish and Portuguese Jews, English "Pilgrims" (Brownists), ten thousand French Huguenots, and many of the despised Socinians from Poland (warmly received by the Dutch Remonstrants and Mennonites). Philosophers like Descartes and Spinoza found Amsterdam the best place to publish their "subversive" works. Spinoza, as is well known, found kind treatment among the Dutch Collegiants (an Arminian sect), and followers as well as condemners when his works were posthumously published. By the end of the eighteenth century, the liberal party had so gained upon the Calvinistic party that the Dutch Reformed Church was demoted from its position of special privilege, and a hospitable reception was given to the rationalistic teachings of the French Revolution.

During the earlier part of the nineteenth century, the liberal-conservative antithesis expressed itself in the contrast between the rationalism of the "Groninger Theology" (redolent of the teachings of Lessing and Herder) and the strict verbal inspirationism of the great revival movement which swept the country at the same time, and led to the formation of a conservative sect, the *Afscheiding*. In the latter part of the century, an important "Modernist" movement appeared, within several of the churches, which led to a schism in the Dutch Reformed Church. Abraham

Kuyper, himself modernistically trained, reacted so strongly against modernism that he founded a free school system, headed by the Free University of Amsterdam (est. 1880) where strict, sound Calvinism was to pervade the whole curriculum, from theology to the natural sciences, and a completely anti-modernist culture was thus to be preserved and propagated.[27] His followers joined in 1892 with the earlier *Afscheiding* movement to organize the "reformed Churches in the Netherlands" (*Gereformeerde Kerken*)—to be carefully distinguished from the old Dutch Reformed Church (*Hervormde Kerk*), which is still in the majority, comprising about 35 per cent of the population, against 8 per cent for the new conservative sect. Although so small, the conservative branch of the Reformed Church is very influential in theology. Among French and Swiss as well as Dutch Calvinists, no recent theological works are more frequently quoted than those of Kuyper and his associate, Dr. H. Bavinck, author of a massive four-volume *Dogmatics*.

In quite recent times (1926) a further split has taken place in the *Gereformeerde Kerken*. A group of young pastors under the leadership of Dr. Geelkerken claimed the right to a certain degree of freedom in Biblical criticism, the test question being the right to interpret the story of the Garden of Eden some-

[27] At a conference I attended recently (June, 1937) in Vienna, a Dutch delegate raised a laugh among the English-speaking delegates by declaring it was no use to appeal to "science" to solve the race problem; we should appeal to "Christian science." He was probably a follower of Kuyper, and might even have talked of "Calvinistic biology."

what figuratively. Against them the Synod of Assen formally decreed that every pastor in the *Gereformeerde Kerken* must teach four "particulars": that there were in the Garden of Eden (1) a tree of the knowledge of good and evil; (2) a tree of life; (3) a serpent, and (4) an audible speech addressed by the serpent to Eve, all to be treated as "realities perceptible by the human senses."[28] Ministers who did not subscribe to these four particulars were suspended and dismissed, together with the presbyteries that maintained them; and the suspended presbyteries have now organized a group of twenty-four congregations to constitute "The Reformed Church in the Netherlands in Restored Union." This new sect cooperates in the ecumenical movement along with the Dutch Reformed, Remonstrant, Lutheran, Mennonite and Old Catholic churches, whereas the intransigent "speaking-serpent" branch of the *Gereformeerde Kerken* refuses to have anything to do with other churches. Kuyper and Bavinck were conservative Calvinists, like the late Professor Warfield of Princeton; but the prevailing wing of their church has now become more ultra-Fundamentalist than Machen himself.[29]

In order to understand this extreme contemporary

[28] For these "four particulars" and other matters of much interest concerning Dutch Protestantism, see the "Report of the Committee of the Ecumenical Council in the Netherlands for the Study of Subjects Appointed for Discussion at the Edinburgh Conference of 1937." (Distributed to delegates at Edinburgh)

[29] The preceding sketch of the development of Dutch theology is mainly based on Siegmund-Schultze's *Die Evangelische Kirchen der Niederlande* (No. 9 in the *Ekklesia* series).

swing to theological conservatism, we must realize that it is in reaction against a recent swing toward the opposite extreme. Dutch Modernism—an exceedingly interesting movement to study—began earlier and went to far greater lengths than Anglo-American Modernism.[30] The three founders of the movement, which began in the fifties of the last century, were (1) Professor Opzoomer of Utrecht, who stood for an "empirical" theology based on religious experience (Schleiermacher) and natural science; (2) Professor Scholten of Leyden, who was a Hegelian monist, evolutionist and determinist; and (3) Professor Hoekstra of Amsterdam, a Mennonite, who defended free will and theism along neo-Kantian lines.

Though the "Old Modernism" of this first generation was radical enough in its denial of supernaturalism and its approach to agnosticism about ultimates, the "Ethical Modernism" of the second generation went far beyond it. The revolt began when one of Opzoomer's pupils, the brilliant and skeptical Allard Pierson, attacked the cosmic theism of Opzoomer and Scholten on moral grounds. God the Sovereign and Creator, he said, is an idea strictly incompatible with the religious idea of God the Father: "And if you call that natural necessity, in which the individual is counted as nothing, the unfolding of God's Fatherly love"—which is what the "Old Modernists" *had* called it—"then," said Pierson, "I answer you with

[30] *See* Vanderlaan's *Protestant Modernism in Holland,* Oxford University Press, 1924.

another blasphemy, that my father-heart knows better than your God, what fatherly love is."[31]

While Hoekstra's *ethical* theism did not fare so badly under this criticism as his rivals' *cosmic* theism, the "Ethical Moderns" presently abandoned all personalism in their thought of God. Hooykaas taught that men's efforts are supported by some sort of objective impersonal moral order—Matthew Arnold's "power not ourselves that makes for righteousness"—but Van Hamel, Bruining and most of the later leaders of the school taught that "the God of ethical religion is . . . a power within ourselves, the urge toward the moral ideal," and is "not ourselves" only in the sense that the ideal "stands above our will and rules it."[32] This trend toward religious humanism or Ethical Culture (as we should call it in America) was widely felt at the end of the nineteenth century, not only among uprooted intellectuals, but in the venerable and respectable Dutch Reformed Church, where the Biblical criticism of Kuenen and the studies of Tiele and Rauwenhoff in the history and philosophy of religion had prepared many minds for radical conclusions. Some, like Loman, van Manen and the volatile Pierson, came to the conclusion that Jesus and Paul never existed, and Christianity was a mere "Idea."

The twentieth century has not only seen fierce opposition to Modernism among the conservative followers of Kuyper and Bavinck, but revolt and con-

[31] Vanderlaan, *op. cit.,* p. 65.
[32] *Ibid.,* p. 75.

fusion breaking out in the Modernist camp. The reaction of the church-going public to the new Gospel was anything but encouraging. The Modernists had helped to introduce democratic autonomy and strong lay representation into the local church government of the historic *Hervormde Kerk*; they were the victims of their own reform, for the church consistories in all the large cities turned against the Modernist pastors, and drove them out of the Church. They had either to join the Remonstrants (who remained very liberal), or organize "free congregations."[33] Small wonder that many Modernists became skeptical and critical of their own "advanced" theology, seeing that it failed so abysmally to speak to the condition of their parishioners.

In 1909 Professor Eerdmans, a Modernist, signalized his dissatisfaction with certain features of the movement in some articles entitled "Reaction or Progress"; and his views found favor with a considerable group who became known as "the Malcontents." Basic in his criticism was a rejection of liberal optimism about human nature, and an assertion of the place of Christ as Savior from sin. "In him," says Eerdmans, "there comes to us a life that was full of God, in which the power of evil was broken. By entering into his spirit, our life is placed upon another foundation, it comes under another sign, the sign of God."[34] Since the World War, the leader of the Malcontents has been Professor K. H. Roessingh of Ley-

[33] *Ibid.*, pp. 90-93.
[34] *Ibid.*, p. 109.

den, a Remonstrant, whose influence still persists despite his premature death at thirty-nine, in 1925. Eerdmans expressly disavowed his faith in all miraculous elements in the Gospels; Roessingh is "less dogmatic about the absolute, unbroken continuity of all phenomena in one system of cause and effect," and in general represents a "reaction against the second half of the nineteenth century, 'the coldest and barrenest time . . . experienced in the last centuries, the frost and weariness of which, even today when it is gradually beginning to yield, still lies in our members.' "[35]

It is not surprising to learn that the teachings of Karl Barth have received a friendly though not uncritical welcome among the Malcontents, whereas the unreconstructed Modernists regard him with extreme aversion. Through their interest in Barth and their critical attitude toward modern civilization, the Malcontents appear to be drawing very close to certain moderate conservatives, especially to the so-called "ethical" school,[36] which has for a long time been trying to mediate (in the name of practical religion) between the dogmatic rationalism of the superorthodox and the speculative rationalism of the Modernists. Among the "middle of the road" Dutch Protestants—whom these "ethical" theologians well represent—Barth has met with great response; for he seems to meet the need of combining unwavering faith in God and His Word, with openness to modern

[35] *Ibid.*, pp. 110, 111. The quotation is from Troeltsch.
[36] Not to be confused with the "Ethical Moderns."

Biblical criticism and awareness of the contemporary crisis in Western culture. Barth's ablest exponent and interpreter in Holland, Professor Haitjema of Groninger, stands a little to the right of this middle group among the conservative "Confessionalists." In the ultra-Fundamentalist *Gereformeerde Kerken*, on the other hand, and among the adherents of Kuyper's theology in the *Hervormde Kerk*, Barth has met with criticism as severe as that which emanates from the Modernists.

It is interesting to compare the attitude of Barth's conservative and liberal critics in Holland. Both parties unite in one accusation: he is irrational and excessively paradoxical. It is not surprising to get this criticism from the Modernists: what needs to be explained is that the Kuyperian neo-Calvinists have as strong a rational basis for their theology as the Catholic neo-Thomists. "They do not tolerate a division of revelation and metaphysics and for Kantianism they substitute a Christian, epistemological Realism."[37] Like Father Przywara himself, they cannot approve any type of dialectical theology which pushes paradox to the point where the principle of contradiction seems to be violated. To this general emphasis on rational metaphysics, the extreme, "speaking-serpent" wing of the *Gereformeerde Kerken* adds a special metaphysics of Biblical inspiration: "Behind every letter of the Bible there stands a massive '*est*.' The serpent actually spoke Hebrew in Paradise. This biblical realism must protest, although not in an un-

[37] Keller, *Karl Barth and Christian Unity*, p. 131.

friendly way, against what has been called the irrationalism of Karl Barth, the hidden God Who, even in the Bible, shows a veiled countenance."[38]

Barth has been frequently to Holland, and is familiar with the criticisms. At the end of the lectures he delivered at Utrecht in 1935, on the Apostles' Creed, he made some very interesting comments in answer to questions:

All your questions [he says] betray to some extent that you are still able to pursue theology in comfort, with a certain calmness and detachment in regard to its problems, such as we once knew in Germany but today know no longer. . . . And now this Professor has blown in from Germany[39] and with regard to many matters has said something in a somewhat *binding* fashion, and you . . . are making a more or less cautious defensive movement. . . . It has been a great pleasure to me to see that it is still possible to have this kind of theology in the world of today, for I am convinced that there is need for theology of this type also. . . . But there is no denying that the situation of the *ecclesia militans* can show a closer kinship to the great times of the Church's past, to the times in which Church dogma arose.[40]

In other words, Barth seems to be saying, the accusation of irrationalism is relative to an age of detached, leisurely culture-building, which is rapidly passing away. The age into which we are moving is

[38] *Ibid.*, pp. 130-31. By permission of The Macmillan Co., publishers.
[39] This was before Barth's expulsion from Bonn.
[40] Barth, *Credo,* pp. 173-75. Quoted by permission of Charles Scribner's Sons.

an age in which Christianity must maintain itself *by pure faith in a transcendent God*, against a world which denies every assumption that makes it possible to reason together. Surely a point that must be solemnly pondered! As for his conservative critics in the *Gereformeerde Kerken*, Barth has for them a half-serious, half-humorous, and wholly friendly word. He defends the right of historical critics to analyze the Bible scientifically like any human document, provided they do not presume to deny its divine truth, as the "mythical" school does.

We must not be surprised [he says] continually to meet texts in the Bible that are not able to hold out in face of the conception of truth held by historical science, but that the historian will be able to classify only as "saga" or "legend" . . . a speaking serpent—now, indeed, I am as little able to imagine that (apart from everything else!) as anyone. But I should like to ask the dear friends of the speaking serpent whether it would not be better . . . to go on and interest themselves in *what* the serpent spoke? To me they appear to be very important and momentous words . . . "Hath God said?" Where this question is heard, there a man *must* have the idea of being as God. . . . The fact that we do not give it up proves very palpably that the serpent has really spoken, yes, indeed![41]

Why is it that Karl Barth, a devoted Calvinist, has found so few followers in Calvin's native land of France, and so few also in French Switzerland, which Calvin dominated in his later years from his pulpit in

[41] *Ibid.*, pp. 190-91.

Geneva? Adolf Keller attributes it to a persistent quality of the modern French mind:

> The Frenchman is an incorrigible rationalist. Descartes
> is part of his mental make-up. Irrationalism in any form
> is foreign to him. The very aptitude of the French mind
> for a clever antithesis makes the paradox of Barthian
> theology more incomprehensible to them. The French
> antithesis is more aesthetic than metaphysical and is
> therefore not suited to an expression of a deeper, irra-
> tional, inner disruption.[42]

There is undoubtedly much truth in Dr. Keller's
observation; but I am inclined to lay more stress upon
another factor in the situation: *French Protestantism
is not so divided nor so strongly "polarized" as Dutch
Protestantism.* Its liberal wing never went to such
skeptical extremes as did the Dutch "Ethical Moderns"; nor did it ever entirely lose its fraternal relations with the orthodox wing of the church. Hence
it has never felt the necessity of so sharp a reaction as
Barth's.

The French Protestants are for the most part—except in Alsace and French Switzerland—a tiny minority group in a country half Roman Catholic, half free-
thinking; and if only for mutual aid and protection,
they have always tended to stick together. When in
the latter part of the nineteenth century, German
liberal theology began to be disseminated in France
by way of Strasbourg—then spelled Strassburg, and
under German rule—it caused a temporary split

[42] Keller, *Karl Barth and Christian Unity*, p. 136. By permission of
The Macmillan Co., publishers.

among the French Protestants; but when the crisis
of church disestablishment struck France in 1905, the
Protestant leaders resolved to meet the crisis, if they
honorably could, together. At the Synod of Montpellier, the liberal Protestants made great concessions
in order to return to full fellowship with their orthodox brethren, and at the Council of Jarnac (1906),
after an impassioned plea for fraternity by Pastor
Wagner—whose generous nature had strong ties with
both camps—the National Union of the Reformed
Churches was consummated. While some of the conservative "Evangelical Reformed Churches" did not
enter this union, further steps are being taken this
year (1938) toward a practically complete unity.

In the principal theological faculties, the united
Reformed Churches now work side by side with the
Lutheran Churches, whose strength was greatly increased when Alsace returned to France after the
World War. Among the French theological faculties,
there is much variety of outlook. *Strasbourg* in the
east—close geographically and intellectually to the
French Swiss faculties of Geneva, Lausanne and
Neuchâtel, as well as to the German University of
Tübingen—represents on the whole a liberal type of
theology; *Montpellier* in the south represents a conservative Calvinism tinctured with revivalistic tendencies emanating from the region of the Drôme; while
Paris in the northwest feels all the contradictory cross-
currents of that changeable and excitable capital. Despite these differences, there is cordial understanding
between these faculties—furthered in recent times

by common interest in the ecumenical movement, and by the holding of "congresses" where their students meet each other.[43] All these centers of theological thought have responded to the stern exigencies of the post-war period by adopting a new orientation which is *conservative by comparison with pre-war theology, but usually not Barthian.* As I have personally witnessed this change of atmosphere at Paris and Strasbourg, I may be pardoned for concentrating my attention at these two points.

When I first came in touch with the Paris and Strasbourg faculties, during the academic year 1921-22, their orientation was distinctly liberal. Pastor Wagner had died during the War, but the influence of his broad human sympathy and his passion for unity between all men of good will was still to be felt in the Protestant churches of Paris.[44] His friends, Wilfred Monod and Élie Gounelle, were vigorously carrying on the *Christianisme Social* movement—analogue of the Rauschenbusch Social Gospel movement in America—along lines first struck out by Tomy Fallot and Wagner. In the Paris theological faculty, critical scholarship of the broadest and most thorough sort was represented by such teachers as E. de Faye, authority on the Alexandrian Fathers, and Maurice Goguel,

[43] The January, 1938, bulletin of the Paris faculty announces such a congress for the month of April, at which students from Strasbourg, Montpellier and the Swiss faculties are to meet with the Paris students.

[44] Wagner often said that his credo could be summarized in three words: "Be a man." *See* his biography by Wautier d'Aygalliers, *Un homme: le pasteur Charles Wagner*, Paris, Fischbacher, 1927.

New Testament critic.[45] In the Strasbourg faculty—
still partly German-speaking and only recently reor-
ganized under French auspices—the influence of German liberal theology remained predominant, and the
latest developments in German philosophy, such as
Husserl's "phenomenology," were eagerly discussed.
The Strasbourg *Revue d'histoire et de philosophie
religieuses* was the most scholarly review published
by French Protestants; in its pages all the most liberal tendencies in France and Germany found a voice.

The one theological tendency which seemed to me
at the time sufficiently representative of French Protestantism and sufficiently distinct from German liberal theology to deserve special attention was the
"symbolo-fideism" of Auguste Sabatier and Eugène
Ménégoz. Sabatier had died in 1901, shortly after completing his two famous books, *Outlines of a Philosophy of Religion* and *Religions of Authority and the
Religion of the Spirit;* but his works continued to
exert a great influence for fully a generation after his
death, not only in France but in Britain and America
as well. His colleague Ménégoz lived on for another
twenty years, and issued the last volume of his *Publications on Fideism* in 1921.[46] His general point of

[45] De Faye and Goguel were much concerned to master and answer
the works of anti-clerical writers like Guignebert, and radical
Modernists like Loisy. I remember an evening party at the seminary
when a student masquerading as Professor Goguel came in with a
huge carpetbag marked "Loisy, *Opera Omnia.*"

[46] Ménégoz's death occurred on Saturday, November 1 of that
same year, just as I arrived in Paris for the opening of courses on
the following Tuesday. Dean Allier, of the Protestant Faculty, at
the opening session on Tuesday, paid a tribute to Ménégoz as a

view, in its relation to Sabatier's, is clearly indicated in the following quotations:

For almost twenty years, now, I have been working with M. Sabatier in our faculty, and living in contact with his thought. I have followed his development; he has followed mine; we have progressed together. Although starting from different points of view, we met. My Lutheran education had led me to take my stand upon the material principle of Protestantism, at the heart of the dogma of justification by faith, and I finally arrived at the doctrine of "salvation by *faith*, independently of *beliefs*," to which I gave the name of *fideism*. On account of his Reformed training, my colleague found himself taking the attitude of those who emphasize the formal principle of Protestantism. It was questions of authority, of method, of principles relating to religious knowledge that preoccupied him; and, recognizing the essential difference between the religious substance of the Christian faith and its contingent and symbolic form, he reached, as his conclusion, what he called *critical symbolism*. Thus the formal principle and the material principle of Protestantism are reconciled in *symbolo-fideism*. . . .

We maintain in opposition to liberalism, the necessity

---

great leader of the Paris School, referred to the intimate terms of affection that had always prevailed between him and his chief theological opponent on the faculty, the late Dean Vaucher, and concluded with the remark that such relations between theological adversaries "create, for the successors of such men, the obligation to maintain the most Christian fraternity in a household where, along with fervent piety and in the interest of that piety, there should reign the most genuine scientific freedom." Dean Allier's address convinced me that of all recent French Protestant thinkers, Ménégoz was most worthy of study; and I later wrote an article on him for an American theological review: "The Theology of Eugène Ménégoz," *Journal of Religion*, Vol. VI, March, 1926, pp. 174-94.

of faith. It is not love, it is faith that saves us. Faith is as absolutely necessary as it is absolutely sufficient.

As for the necessity of adherence to official dogmas, we deny it, in opposition to orthodoxy. What saves us is faith, not the acceptance of this dogma or that, however true it may be; and what destroys us is not this or that erroneous belief, but faithlessness (*incrédulité*).

We affirm the *sola fide* in all its rigor. We oppose the *sola* to the Orthodox, the *fide* to the Liberals. . . .

Ah! how great is the joy of him who has arrived at the certainty that no error of thought can condemn him, and that God, in order to receive him into his favor, asks of him but one thing: his heart. . . . With peace of soul, he has found liberty of thought. He is delivered from the yoke of legalism and orthodoxy. He enjoys the precious liberty of the children of God. And now he can, with a calm and confident mind, without painful apprehensions, and without danger to his inner peace, turn to the study of the traditional doctrines of Christianity and those numerous critical questions which preoccupy the modern world. Whether he finds the truth or fails to find it, the salvation of his soul is assured.[47]

During the thirteen years which elapsed between my departure from France in the summer of 1922 and my next visit, in the summer of 1935, I became conscious that great changes were going on in French Protestant theology. The book which first made me aware of these changes was a book on *The Problem of*

[47] *Publications diverses sur le fidélisme et son application à l'enseignement chrétien traditionnel*, Paris, Fischbacher, 1900-1921. Quotation principally from Vol. I, No. i; translation copied from my above-mentioned article in the *Journal of Religion*, by permission.

Prayer,[48] by Fernand Ménégoz, Professor of Dogmatics at the Protestant Faculty of the University of Strasbourg, and nephew of Eugène Ménégoz. From his uncle and from Auguste Sabatier, Professor Ménégoz inherits the conviction that religion is the prayer of the soul, and prayer is the soul of religion; but he questions whether modern liberal theology, since the days of Kant and Schleiermacher, has ever made prayer logically possible or conceivable in terms of its characteristic teachings. The disease of modern theology is subjectivism, or anthropocentrism. Prayer, however, in its genuinely Christian form, cannot live without a conviction that it is more than subjective, more than human, and really reaches its Divine Object. An examination of the views of modern philosophers and theologians on prayer discloses the curious fact that they have generally expressed grave reservations on this cardinal point of faith. Kant's view of prayer is hardly to be distinguished from Feuerbach's illusionism—and logically so, for prayer addressed to a God who is only a moral postulate, only a great As If, can hardly be taken seriously. As for Schleiermacher and his successors, they have never effectually refuted the positivistic view of prayer, for the theology of "immanence" and "experience," strictly interpreted, confines us to the sphere of psychology and history, the sphere of relativity, whereas the praying man needs to believe that he is in some real sense in

[48] *Le Problème de la Prière, Principe d'une revision de la Méthode théologique*, Strasbourg, Istra, 1925; 2nd edition revised and augmented, Paris, Alcan, 1932.

touch with Absolute, transcendent Reality. If Herrmann, Sabatier and other modern theologians have
sometimes spoken truly and nobly of Christian prayer,
that was only *une heureuse inconséquence*; their theological principles would not logically have permitted
them to do so.

Professor Ménégoz sees hope of a more adequate
view of prayer in the "theocentric" trend of recent
German theology—Erich Schaeder, Karl Barth, Karl
Heim—and the "objectivistic" trend of recent German philosophy, as represented in the "phenomenology" movement. In the constructive part of his book,
he uses the phenomenological method to study prayer
itself; i.e., he describes the objective content of consciousness of praying men, especially of the great masters of Christian prayer, Jesus and Luther. In the
critical part, he speaks appreciatively of Barth and
Heim. I have to confess that the real justification of
their revolt against liberalism, and the possible significance of their theology as an antidote for the
ills of ours, first dawned upon me when reading
Ménégoz's discussion of their views. But our "prayer-
centered" French theologian has nevertheless some
grave objections to register against his German
guides, especially against Barth; and these reservations may serve to define the difference between the
Barthian theology and the Strasbourg theology.
Ménégoz finds that Barth, in the endeavor to assert
the absolute priority of divine revelation over human
"religion," exalts God above man to the point where
all ties of relationship appear to be broken; and apart

from the reestablishment of connection in the unique redemptive work of Christ, prayer to God becomes inconceivable and impossible. One might say that the Modernist's prayers are addressed to a God so immanent that they "never get beyond the ceiling"; the Barthian's, to a God so transcendent that they are lost on their way through the "immense inane." Barth, of course, believes that prayer is made possible, *for the Christian*, by God's special act in reaching out to men in Christ; but he seems to imply that pagan prayer—the great wave of tormented aspiration that has mounted toward heaven from men of all nations since the world began, and still does today—such prayer never reaches God at all! This conclusion is intolerable to Ménégoz. The reality of the unique revelation of God in Christ seems to him to imply the reality of a "universal revelation" implicit in every sincere act of prayer, however ignorant or misguided: "A testimony of the Spirit of the transcendent God, immanent in the spirit of man."[49]

Strasbourg felt the influence of the dialectical theology sooner than Paris, being much more intimately in touch with the Swiss and German centers where it originated; but Strasbourg has now made its adjustment, accepted the new theology as a "corrective," and preserved for itself an irreducible residue of liberalism; whereas Paris, where the "new orthodoxy" appeared more recently, has been through a sharper

[49] Second edition, p. 188. The phrase contains a quotation from Eugène Ménégoz, with whose more liberal theology his nephew still agrees at this point.

reaction and not yet reached a new equilibrium. So, at least, it seemed to me on my recent visits in 1935 and 1937. The theological students in Paris are growing more and more vehemently orthodox. They are separated from the liberal "symbolo-fideist" era in the history of French theology by an almost visible gulf; for there is no considerable group of theologians in middle life to mediate between the old and the new era. Those who might have filled such a rôle died in the trenches twenty-odd years ago. Surviving liberal leaders like Wilfred Monod—a man of great devotion, poetic imagination, and deep human sympathy, whose autobiographical work, *The Problem of Good* (*Le Problême du Bien*) reminds one in many respects of Studdert-Kennedy's heroic grappling with the darker side of life—such men find themselves suddenly out of place among the younger generation, and their counsels no longer accepted in church and seminary.[50] One very active younger group of Paris students and pastors, under the leadership of Pierre Maury, has accepted the Barthian theology, and propagates it in an able periodical, *Hic et Nunc*. Their critics say of them that they are "more Barthian than Barth"; and they certainly bring to the exposition of their master's views a terrible French lucidity which makes every stumblingblock in it stand out with brutal angularity. More influential than Barthian theology at present, however, is the scholastic Calvinism

[50] M. Monod has lately resigned his chair in the Paris faculty because of conscientious objections to the present trend of policy. And yet the Dean of the Faculty is a liberal, Maurice Goguel.

of the Dutch *Gereformeerde* theologians, Kuyper and Bavinck, which has been popularized in Paris by the new incumbent of the chair of Reformed Dogmatics, Professor Lecerf. Both Maury and Lecerf, as well as some of the surviving liberals, regard themselves as true continuators of the authentic Calvinistic tradition; so that their controversies revolve, to an extent that seems amazing to an American, about the question, "What did Calvin really teach, and what does his teaching imply?" This situation may be illustrated with reference to three recent publications: (1) Maury's article in the Calvin number of *Foi et Vie*, "Whence Proceeds the Knowledge of God?" (2) Lecerf's book on *The Nature of Religious Knowledge*; (3) Jean Boisset's "Essay on the Nature of Man in Christian Revelation."

Boisset, from many indications, seems to be under the influence of the moderate liberalism of the Strasbourg school. He declares that the Biblical doctrine of man does not support "the unchristian pessimism of certain 'Christians' "; and that Calvin, despite the darkness of his view of human nature, never went so far as Barth in cutting the bond between God and man, or denying to man any "little spark" of natural light by which to know God.[51] Maury, on the contrary, points out that Calvin never thought it possible to know God—not even as Creator, much less as Redeemer—by that "little spark" of natural light that

[51] Boisset, *Essai sur la Nature de l'Homme dans la Révélation Chrétienne*, Paris, Alcan, 1936, pp. 290, 293. For the comparison of Barth and Calvin, see the whole of section III, *"Deux positions de la théologie réformée."*

was left to man. Quite like Barth, Calvin maintained
that when man tried to know God by this natural
light, he fell into "idolatry and every sort of super-
stition." Neither Barth nor Calvin ever denied that
God's work is manifested in the world and in man;
but both Barth and Calvin say that man is *too blind
to see God where he is* without the special light of
revelation. Barth, then, is the true interpreter of Calvin, and no liberal can be a Calvinist.[52]

As between the liberal and Barthian interpretation
of Calvin, Lecerf is closer to the Barthian; yet in his
whole discussion of *The Nature of Religious Knowledge*[53] he seems deliberately to avoid all mention of
Barth; and he assigns to secular knowledge a surprisingly large place in the building of a system of theology. Beginning with a strong assertion that there is
no place in Calvinism for a natural theology, but only
for a theology based on faith in divine revelation,[54]
he afterwards applies the tri-square of revelation to
various secular theories of knowledge, and finds that
Cartesian rationalism, Baconian empiricism and
Kantian idealism are all to be rejected as bases for a
Christian theory of knowledge, in favor of a "moderate realism" reminiscent of Catholic scholasticism:
"we possess a faculty, an aptitude, a spontaneity which
is only potential in the child and develops along with

[52] *Foi et Vie,* April, 1935, pp. 286-300, *"D'où procède la connaissance de Dieu. (Notes sur la théologie naturelle d'après Calvin)* by
Pierre Maury.

[53] *De la Nature de la Connaissance Religieuse; Introduction à la
Dogmatique Réformé,* Paris, Je Sers, no date (but on internal evidence quite recent).

[54] *Op. cit.,* pp. 7-52, *Préliminaires.*

the organism, whereby the object tends to become realized in the subject; spatio-temporal sense objects, in sense images; intelligible objects, in concepts; supra-rational realities, in ectypal analogies."[55] Only to the man of faith, be it noted, are these "ectypal analogies" clear; but that they are *there*, laid down in the real relations that exist between God and his creatures, Lecerf maintains as stoutly as any Catholic scholastic. The "analogy of faith" to which he appeals, after Calvin, is therefore very close to the "analogy of being" to which Father Przywara points.[56] Over against the Kantian agnosticism to which Sabatier tended, and the pure empiricism of the pragmatists, Lecerf takes his stand frankly by the side of the Catholic neo-scholastics, for an epistemology which affirms that man's mind (when properly enlightened) can embrace *being*. The only serious objection he holds against the Thomistic theory is that "by reaction against a certain ultra-Augustinian mysticism, Thomism will have it that the *acquisition* of this knowledge of God comes exclusively by way of the discursive reason"; whereas "for us, the impression made directly by God upon the religious soul is a fact of experience."[57] This outcome brings Professor Lecerf, in spite of his quasi-Barthian beginning, and his conservative Calvinist predilections, very close to the position of Fernand Ménégoz and the American "religious realists." What he excludes from the "pre-

[55] *Ibid.*, p. 128.
[56] *Ibid.*, pp. 42, 223.
[57] *Ibid.*, p. 272.

ambles of faith," he brings back as a *logical implication* of the faith; so that his system, unlike Barth's, bears all the marks of a severely *reasoned* structure of thought. In this he resembles the Dutch Calvinists and the Princeton Calvinists whom he quotes appreciatively. Yet at the end of his argument as at the beginning, he reacts against every trace of liberal immanentism and synergism, quite like Barth himself; as against Professor Ménégoz, he declares that prayer does not presuppose an initial relation of co-operation between man and God, or any general capacity of man to reach out to God without a "transcendental decision" of God (predestination) which determines man to have faith.[58] If Lecerf is a good representative of contemporary French Protestant theology—and I think on the whole he is the *most* representative man we could choose—the trend of the times, though not toward Barthianism, is definitely away from liberalism. In American terms, we should say that it is away from Brown and Clarke, and back to Hodge and Strong.

I do not want to give the impression that liberal theology in France is altogether mute and apologetic, or on the defensive, or (as in Strasbourg) has made its peace with the conservative trend. There is one unabashed and unrepentant liberal in France who would give the lie to any such assertion: Albert Schweitzer. Whether he is really a Frenchman or a citizen of the world is a bit problematic; he does not "stay put" long enough to become a settled inhabitant

[58] For critique of Ménégoz, *see ibid.*, pp. 273-280.

of any land, and he has not forgotten that the French Government once interned him as an enemy alien during the War, taking him away from his medical work in Africa in flagrant violation of the maxim, "Reverence life." But whether he is a Frenchman or not, there is no doubt that Schweitzer is a liberal. Others have drawn conservative conclusions from his studies in the eschatology of the New Testament: R. J. Campbell in England, and many theologians on the Continent.[59] Schweitzer has never subscribed to these conclusions. Though he promised the mission board to be "dumb as a carp" on theological questions if they would consent to send him out to Africa, he has never been hesitant about expressing his heresies in print. Frankly, he believes that Jesus and Paul were entirely mistaken in their eschatology. What we moderns must do, he believes, is to "take the ethical religion of Jesus out of the setting of his world-view and put it in our own," and thus under the influence of the spirit of his ethical religion, to "make the Kingdom of God a reality in this world by works of love."[60]

This sounds very much like eighteenth-century humanitarianism; and Schweitzer would cheerfully admit the charge. He admires the eighteenth century. It was the last great age of idealism; that is to say, a

[59] For Schweitzer's influence on English theology, *see* my *Contemporary English Theology*, Chap. II, p. 40; for his influence on Continental theology, *see* the note on Künneth and Holmstrom at the end of section 2, above.

[60] *Christian Century*, 1934, p. 1484. (Cf. *Out of My Life and Thought*, chap. VI.)

period in which men formed ethical ideals by thinking, and dared to believe that they could bring reality into conformity with these ideals. "Then ethical
religion and thinking formed one unity. Thinking was religious, and religion was a thinking religion . . . undertook to represent reality as it should
be . . . had power over reality."[61] Napoleon and
Hegel introduced the age of realism in which we now
live; which means that we are now making our hopes
and dreams conform to the course of events, instead
of aspiring to transform the course of events by our
hopes and dreams. Karl Barth, whom Schweitzer personally knows, and admires as a religious character,
seems to him horribly representative, in his theology,
of the age of realism in which we live. Barth has
given up the eighteenth-century hope of realizing the
Kingdom of God on earth, and reverted to the old
pattern of dogmatic Christianity: redemption *out*
of the world instead of transformation *of* the world;
acceptance of Scriptural revelation, however irrational, and "contempt for thinking," however earnest
and straightforward. The terrible thing about Barth,
to Schweitzer, is that he encourages religion to "turn
aside from the world" and abandon civilization to an
inevitable decline; while by his love of violent paradox he promotes the disintegration of thought itself.

The spirit of the age dislikes what is simple [remarks
Schweitzer]. It no longer believes the simple can be profound. It loves the complicated, and regards it as profound. It loves the violent. That is why the spirit of the

[61] *Ibid.,* p. 1483.

age can love Karl Barth and Nietzsche at the same time. The spirit of the age loves dissonance, in tones, in lines and in thought. That shows how far from thinking it is, for thinking is a harmony within us.[62]

This is the voice of a Continental! Evidence enough that liberalism is not dead on the Continent, though it be reduced to the status of an infinitesimal minority.

4. PROTESTANT THEOLOGY IN CENTRAL EUROPE: THE JOHN HUSS FACULTY IN PRAGUE

Central Europe is now a difficult term to define with exactitude. When this book was begun, it included a country called Austria; so that it was possible to continue our counter-clockwise circuit of Germany by passing from our Dutch-French-Calvinist area through neutral Switzerland and independent Austria, thus reaching those parts of Central Europe lying to the east of Germany. Now, the German frontier has suddenly been extended to the Brenner Pass, and the Nazi-Fascist alliance has ended the possibility of any foreign "encirclement" of Germany. What *Mitteleuropa* will be within a few years, when the German *Drang nach Osten* has proceeded further, is very hard to predict. Just at present, we find a belt of small countries connecting the Balkan States on the south with Finland on the north, and constituting a much-

---

[62] *Ibid.*, p. 1484. Quoted by permission of *The Christian Century*. (This is from Schweitzer's own summary of his lectures on *Civilization and Ethics*.) It should be noted that by "thinking" Schweitzer means something higher than logical reasoning; he means an ethical wrestling with life's rationally insoluble mystery, not wholly unlike Kierkegaard's "existential thinking."

needed buffer between Nazism and Sovietism. Moving from south to north, along a straight axis drawn between the Jugoslav capital, Belgrade, and the Finnish capital, Helsingfors, we pass successively through Hungary, Czechoslovakia, Poland, Lithuania, Latvia, and Estonia. The three Baltic States, last named, are not, strictly speaking, part of Central Europe, but a kind of precarious northern extension of it, squeezed hard between Russia and Polish-German pressures. Latvia and Estonia have strong affinities with Finland; they might be regarded as the vulnerable southeastern tip of the solid Lutheran North. Catholic Lithuania, by the time this book is published, may have been swallowed up by Catholic Poland. The fate of Czechoslovakia, half-surrounded by Greater Germany, is a matter of hourly speculation and concern to all Europe.

Whatever may be the immediate political fate of the Central European countries, one feature of the situation in that part of the world is not going to change: there are always going to be *minorities* there.[63] Any map of Central Europe, whether drawn from the racial, national or religious point of view, is full of little spots and islands of many different colors: Teutons in Slavic countries, Magyars among the Slovaks, Protestants in the midst of Catholics, hunted Jews vainly seeking where to lay their heads. The refugee problem is no new problem in this area!

[63] At present it is customary to blame all the ills of Europe on the treaties of Versailles, Trianon and St. Germain. They have much to answer for; but they did not create the problem of minorities in Central Europe; on the whole, they diminished it.

Every great invasion from the steppes of Asia, every great political change in Europe, from the Wars of Religion to the Russian and German revolutions, has created some new minority group in Central Europe, and some new threat of persecution. It is not surprising, then, that Protestantism in this part of Europe presents a very "spotty" character, compared with the solid Lutheranism of the North and the almost equally solid Calvinism of the West; nor is it surprising that *liberal* Protestantism has a long history here. The Unitarians, for example, have secured a position in Hungary which they hold nowhere else in the world. Driven out of Poland by the Counter-Reformation in the seventeenth century, they at one time were actually the *majority* group in Hungary; and since the latter part of the eighteenth century, they are one of the three recognized churches of Hungary, along with the Roman Catholic and Reformed Churches. The same tenacious clinging to religious liberties and privileges which has preserved the Unitarians in Hungary, has preserved many other Protestant minorities throughout Central Europe, in the midst of a strong Catholic majority, and made liberty and toleration a much more emphatic note in their teaching than in other parts of Europe.

To American Protestants, the most interesting country in Central Europe is undoubtedly Czecho-slovakia. The Czechs are often called "the Americans of Europe." While the ideals of the American and French revolutions have exerted a wide influence in this whole region, they have nowhere struck home so

deep as in the little republic which was conceived and born with American aid and sympathy, and nurtured in principles deeply akin to ours. The American traveler arriving in Prague steps out of the Wilson Station, faced with a flower-decked statue of our wartime president, and proceeds up Hoover Street past Washington Park. He may even (as I can prove by photographs) be ushered into an American suite in his hotel, where a large wall tapestry of the American dollar dominates the bed-chamber—doubtless to assist pious worshipers thereof in their nightly devotions!

These are only outward and visible signs of an inward and spiritual correspondence between our two nations. The Czechs believe in science and humanity and progress as we do. They have the sturdy independence, initiative and self-reliance that we had before we grew rich and slack. It is a good country for the common man; there is no aristocracy; the old "American dream" seems to have gone there as an emigrant at the close of the War. If Czechoslovakia is ever swallowed up by a totalitarian State, the Liberty Bell in Philadelphia should be tolled in mourning, as at the loss of a piece of our own territory. Here is a country after Albert Schweitzer's heart, where liberalism still has a fighting chance. If liberalism collapses *here*, what comfort is there for American liberal Protestants, on all the Continent of Europe? Let us take our stand, then, at Prague, and view the contemporary theological scene in Central Europe from the vantage point of the John Huss Theological Faculty, at the ancient Charles University in that city.

The name of this faculty is in itself significant. John Huss is the national hero of a people still 73½ per cent Roman Catholic. All religious parties claim descent from him in some sense. Even the Roman Catholics can point to the fact that, after Huss's execution at the Council of Constance in 1415, his Bohemian followers forcibly resisted extinction, and at length, in 1433, the Hussite "Utraquists" (claiming the right of lay communion in both kinds) were recognized by the Pope as the national Church of Bohemia. The *chalice* is to this day a Czech national emblem; and Czech Catholics are less passionately Roman or Ultramontane than many other Catholics. There is, however, a more radical branch of the Hussite tradition which passes through the so-called Moravian or Bohemian Brethren (*Unitas Fratrum*). The first leader of this movement was Peter of Chelcic (Peter Chelcicky), who broke away from the Catholic Utraquists, because of objection to their warlike tactics, and in 1457 founded a fraternal community upon an almost Tolstoyan interpretation of the Gospel: no oaths, no bearing of arms. In 1467 the movement renounced allegiance to Rome, and had its bishop consecrated by the Waldensians. Its last leader and bishop was the great educator Comenius, who was driven into exile with his flock after the Battle of White Mountain in 1620. The Czech Protestants like to point out that they lost their religious liberty in the same year the Pilgrim Fathers landed at Plymouth to establish religious liberty in America. From that date until the World War, Moravia and Bohemia

were under an Austrian régime of forcible Catholicization; and the Moravian Brethren themselves came to be a German Pietistic sect, with headquarters at Herrnhut, on Count Zinzendorf's estate in Saxony. In the early part of the twentieth century, a strong anti-Roman movement (*Los von Rom*) grew up; and with the establishment of Czech independence this movement burst forth with great vehemence, in two forms: many enrolled themselves in the new religious census as "non-confessionals" or free-thinkers, while a considerable section of the Catholic Church split off from the Papacy, and organized the Czechoslovak National Church, with a new liturgy in the vernacular. These liberal Catholics, as well as the Methodists, Unitarians and many other denominations which Americanized Czechs brought back to the land of their birth when independence was established, all make their initial appeal to the Czechoslovak population by claiming to be in some respect genuine "Hussites."

The John Huss Faculty is significant in its *composition* as well as in its name. While it mainly represents the principal Protestant body, the Czech Brethren Evangelical Church, a union of Lutherans and Calvinists, it also includes representatives of the Czechoslovak National Church. This church, under the leadership of its first patriarch, Charles Farský, adopted a definitely Modernist orientation. For a while after severing its connections with Rome, it negotiated with the Orthodox and Anglican churches, and a section of it actually joined the Orthodox

Church; but the majority group preferred to affiliate with the Unitarians in the International Association for Liberal Christianity and Religious Freedom, while at the same time keeping in close touch with the Life and Work and Faith and Order movements—especially the former. It is a very democratic church in government, and claims the distinction of being "the only liberal Church the majority of whose members belong to the socially dependent classes."[64] While it aspires "to lead its members to an understanding of the pure religion of Jesus in the spirit of Huss and the Bohemian Brethren," it "tends from Catholicism to Christian humanism without the use of a temporary refuge within the Protestant fold."[65] The word "humanism" should not be taken in any anti-theistic sense. The leaders of the Czechoslovak Church appreciate the danger of emphasizing the human and ethical factors in religion "to such an extent that God becomes a mere unifying concept for various noble aims."[66] While their theology, as expounded by Professor Kovář, has a distinct tinge of Unitarian liberalism, and of naturalistic objection to the miraculous, they have lately been much influenced by the neo-Thomist and Barthian criticism of liberal theology, and have begun to ascribe a greater importance to "God's supernatural activity."[67] They continue to object, however, to "the eccentric stress upon tran-

[64] *The Czechoslovak Church,* by Professors Hrík, Kovář, and Spisar, p. 20. (Prague, 1937.)
[65] *Ibid.,* pp. 15, 31.
[66] *Ibid.,* p. 46.
[67] *Ibid.,* p. 47.

scendentalism, which separates God from the world,
building between God and man a bridgeless abyss in
the sense of Barth's theology of distance."[68]

It is undoubtedly to their colleague Dr. Hromadka
of the John Huss Faculty that these neo-Catholic professors owe their introduction to Barth. In a faculty
whose theological trend is mainly liberal, he has created a great interest in the dialectical theology as a
necessary corrective of liberalism in an age of crisis.
Wherever I traveled in Central Europe, I heard Dr.
Hromadka's name mentioned as that of the ablest
intellectual leader of Czech Protestantism. Since comparatively little of his work is available in English
or German, I feel fortunate to have had the privilege
of an interview with him, in which he made his attitude toward liberal theology and Barthianism quite
clear. He was originally a pronounced liberal himself,
a pupil and follower of Troeltsch; and when he first
returned from his theological studies in Germany,
feared he would be excluded from the church for his
unorthodox views. The War compelled him to go
through a complete regeneration of his faith, and Karl
Barth was the one through whom he at length found
the way out. The essential thing in Barth, for
Hromadka, is his insistence that there is only one
measuring rod for our thought of God: what God has
told us of himself in his Word. The Word is the central pillar in the temple of Christian faith, and on it
the whole structure must be made to rest for support.
Many other truths may be *brought into* the temple of

[68] *Ibid.*, p. 63.

our faith, provided nothing is made to *rest* upon them, and God is not *measured* by them. While Hromadka is thus deeply and basically indebted to Barth, he recognizes in himself some specifically Czech points of view which modify his position. Since the days of Peter Chelcicky, the Czechs have stubbornly believed in the possibility of realizing the implications of the Gospel in practically workable social institutions. They are, like the Swiss, the Scots and the Americans, born *theocrats*. But, as Hromadka puts it, Calvinistic theocracy, even in its Barthian form, is based upon the idea of God's sovereignty or power, while the Czechs draw from Chelcicky the ideal of a *theocracy of love*; and to this ideal they continue to cling, in spite of the present necessity of strong military preparations against German aggression.[69]

In his critical works on Masaryk, Dr. Hromadka touches upon another important influence which differentiates his thought from Barth's: that of the philosopher-president whom the modern Czechs venerate as the father of their country, and a second John Huss. There can be no doubt that Masaryk was a pronounced liberal, in religious as well as in political thought. Born a Catholic, he revolted against the dogmatism of the Roman Church and became a Prot-

[69] I am indebted to Mr. Josef Barton, an American-born Czech student, for translating some passages from Hromadka's lectures on Dogmatics. These passages generally confirm the impression I got in my interview. At one point Hromadka says, "The Word of God is above the Church as the final norm of truth, since it is not in the Church but acts as a measuring-rod for the Church; the infallible Church is an eschatological conception." This corresponds to the simile of the *one pillar in the temple.*

estant—less because he believed in the teachings of any Protestant sect than because Protestantism gave him freedom to continue thinking for himself.

In the course of his "Faustian efforts to understand the world,"[70] Masaryk explored and evaluated the whole European tradition: the Jewish and Greek heritages, with special emphasis on Jesus and Plato; Eastern Orthodoxy, Roman Catholicism and Protestantism, all of which he found wanting, and refused to synthesize in the fashion proposed by Palacký, the Czech historian; and last but not least, modern humanistic culture in its various forms and periods. Like Albert Schweitzer, Masaryk found his greatest inspiration in the humanitarianism of the eighteenth century, as expressed in the American and French revolutions, of which he believed the "World Revolution," in progress since 1914, was the logical continuation. Romantic idealism (Goethe, Hegel), positivistic naturalism (Comte, Marx), and the indifferentism or "liberalism" which drifts with the course of "progress," without thinking, all seemed to him spurious offshoots of the great Enlightenment. "Romanticism ruins the personality by isolating, overstraining and placing it on the throne of God. Positivism breaks down the personality by declaring it to be a product and the result of natural activity. . . . Liberalism is

[70] The phrase is Oscar Jászi's, in a Memorial address delivered at an Oberlin College Assembly. In the same address, Professor Jászi declares that Masaryk was "the greatest man of the war period"—greater than Wilson, because his idealism was tempered with a "keen feeling of reality"; greater than Lenin, because of his "craving for justice above class interests, his horror of bloodshed and violence."

the monstrous echo of all the contradictory tendencies of modern society."[71] True humanitarianism, in opposition to all these its illegitimate children, sets "reason and morality" against "instinct, biology and Nature," and calls for "the responsible and rational collaboration of responsible and rational individuals."[72] Hromadka sympathizes deeply with Masaryk's humanitarianism, but feels that he leans too much "upon his own understanding and human goodness," failing—although a professed theist—to "reach the deepest motives of theism," or to realize the necessity for "an absolute norm above the individual and the world."[73]

In his essay on "Masaryk and Dostoievsky,"[74] Hromadka defines his attitude toward Masaryk still more clearly. He finds that Masaryk and Dostoievsky were related by a deep attraction, a common problem and a fundamental repulsion. Masaryk was attracted to Dostoievsky by his love of the *people,* his love of the *poor and unfortunate,* his love of *children*; and he formed so high an estimate of Dostoievsky's importance that he projected his great work, *The Spirit of Russia (Russland und Europa,* 1913) with the sole design of seeing Dostoievsky in his true perspective, and evaluating his work. He found in Dostoievsky

[71] Hromadka, *Masaryk as European,* Prague, 1936, pp. 30, 34 ("International Philosophical Library"). By "liberalism," Masaryk evidently means what Schweitzer means by "realism": accepting events without criticizing or shaping them.

[72] *Ibid.,* p. 32.

[73] *Ibid.,* pp. 37, 38.

[74] Czech version in *Masarykuv sbornik,* I, 1924-25; German version in a special supplement to the *Prager Rundschau,* pp. 97-113.

one who, like himself, saw the root of Europe's whole problem in the conflict between Positivism and Titanism; between the voice that whispers to man, "Thou art a product of nature," and the voice that says, "Be thine own master." But Dostoievsky resolved this problem in so different a manner from Masaryk that at length the sympathy between them was broken; and at the grave of Poe in Baltimore the philosopher could write in his notebook, that Dostoievsky was a "decadent" of the same sort as our unhappy American author. Dostoievsky repelled Masaryk because he so recognized man's weakness and helplessness, so shuddered at the demonic abyss in human nature, that he was fain to embrace the mystical faith of the peasant, and accept the theocratic control of the Church as a defense against himself. Masaryk, on the other hand (thinks Hromadka), trusted human reason and conscience so much, found such comfort in daily *work* and human *sympathy*, that he never fully faced the question, "Where is the final truth and highest norm under which man stands?"[75]

In spite of this fundamental repulsion, arising from an opposite estimate of man's ability to obey his conscience and do his duty, the two thinkers were at one on many important issues. Both found the three great realities of the universe in the *soul*, the *neighbor* and *God*. Both had the same deep compassion for mankind, which made them repeatedly return to the dark mysteries of murder, suicide and cruel oppres-

[75] *Masaryk und Dostojevskij,* p. 106.

sion. Both found their two ultimate masters in *Plato* and *Jesus*.

> To be sure [says Hromadka] there is a twofold Plato, Plato the mystic and visionary, and Plato the critical analyst of human knowledge and society. There is also a twofold Christ: Christ the holy Mediator of human deification, and Christ the Teacher of love for God and man. We know in *which* Plato and *which* Jesus Dostoievsky and Masaryk respectively confess their faith. But the first Plato somehow hangs together with the second, as perhaps the two Christs also hang together. *Do* they hang together? Masaryk and Dostoievsky cannot be studied without a study of the points of comparison here hinted at. Only then do the depths of the abyss between the two appear, and the deficiencies in their religious thought; but also, their positive contribution to the spiritual struggles of the modern man.[76]

With this comparison between Masaryk and Dostoievsky, our investigation of contemporary Continental theology may be said to have come full circle. We began our study of Orthodox thought with an indication of Dostoievsky's importance as a discoverer of a "fourth dimension" in human existence. We end our study of Protestant thought with an indication of Masaryk's importance as the last great leader of liberal humanitarianism. In Masaryk's works, especially *The Spirit of Russia*, we see these two colossal figures face each other, bow and part. Can we in America be content to follow Dostoievsky, Bloy, Kierkegaard and Barth, if it means turning our backs

[76] *Ibid.*, p. 113.

upon Masaryk? Can we turn our backs upon him
without turning our backs on all that we love best
in America?

5. A LAST LOOK BACK AT THE CONTINENT, FROM SCOTLAND

Before returning across the Atlantic to draw our
own conclusions from a purely American standpoint,
let us pause for a moment in Scotland, to get one last
impression of Continental Protestantism as a whole.
Scotland is the natural bridge between Continental
Protestantism and the Anglo-Saxon world. Ever since
the days of John Knox, Scotland has been much nearer
to the Continent than England; and it is likewise
much nearer to the New World, where so many Scots
have found themselves at home among fellow Protestants. Scotland is a sort of three-way switch, through
which a current of new ideas is continually coming
from the Continent, to be slowly transmitted over
strong resistence to neighboring England, and quickly
transmitted by powerful cables to distant Canada,
Australasia and the United States. In the late nineteenth century, Scotland did a great service to the
whole English-speaking world by assimilating the results of German liberal theology and Biblical scholarship, and making them available in a form that min-
istered to Christian faith instead of shaking it. What
is Scotland doing with the new Continental orthodoxy, and with Karl Barth in particular?

It may be said that the Scots have done little with
Eastern Orthodox, Roman Catholic or Swedish Lu-

theran theology. It is the Anglicans who are attending to that. But the work of Barth, Brunner and Heim has nowhere received a more friendly welcome than in Scotland—not even in Holland. One able young theologian, George Hendry, introduced his recent "Hastie Lectures" at Glasgow with the remark, "I share the conviction with some others that Scottish theology has to find its true affinity with the theology of Continental Protestantism rather than with that of England or America."[77] Barth has found a zealous interpreter and apostle in John McConnachie, and has—marvel of marvels—been invited to give the Gifford Lectures on Natural Theology! At the University of Glasgow, just now, systematic theology largely consists of the discussion of his works. Brunner and Heim have found their best English translators in Scotland, as Schleiermacher and his school did of yore. All this does not mean, however, that the Scotch are giving up without a struggle what they so painfully acquired in the last generation. They are an economical folk, and they prefer to add and consolidate, rather than to subtract and cast away. Schweitzer lectures in Scotland, along with Barth; and the new orthodoxy, like the old liberalism, is accepted with critical reservations which make it assimilable and storable in the rich, well-packed cellars where the Scotch mind hoards up things old and new. What is being made of the latest importations from the Continent may be best inferred from the way in which two veteran Scottish theologians, the late Pro-

[77] Hendry, *God the Creator*, London, 1937, p. viii.

fessor H. R. Mackintosh of Edinburgh and Dr. D. S. Cairns of Aberdeen, have handled the teachings of Barth.

Dr. Mackintosh's last legacy to theology was his book, *Types of Modern Theology*, a splendid review beginning with Schleiermacher and ending with Kierkegaard and Barth. It is evident throughout that he has been greatly affected by the Barthian criticism of modern liberal theology. He accuses Schleiermacher, for example, of "psychologism," and says that "he has put discovery in place of revelation, the religious consciousness in the place of the Word of God, and the mere 'not yet' of imperfection in the place of sin."[78] While warning hasty readers that they will generally find what they miss in Barth as a "complementary truth . . . a few pages later," and warmly acknowledging that "Barth has faced more directly than any other Christian thinker of our time the menace presented to Christian belief by Humanism," Mackintosh finds Barth something less than the Biblical Christian he intends to be, in one respect: his "excessive actualism." By this is meant Barth's doctrine of continuous creation—"as if created things did not 'stay' created, but at every moment fell out of existence again"—and his doctrine that "faith and regeneration are not conditions into which grace brings men, but bestowals from moment to moment." The Bible, on the contrary, everywhere indicates that both aspects of God's work are equally real: he creates the world, recreates man, brings them into a certain

[78] Mackintosh, *Types of Modern Theology*, p. 100.

"state"; and yet he is constantly bestowing new power and grace on that which he has made. We rely on God's *promises*, as Barth demands; we also rely on what he has *done*, so that it stands firm.[79]

Dr. Cairns in his recent book, *The Riddle of the World*, thinks it natural enough that Barth should have been led to oppose "natural theology" by the necessity of combating the New Paganism in Germany, but thinks he has been led to intolerable extremes in the process. Like Ménégoz, this Aberdeen theologian finds it impossible to believe Barth's doctrine that there is no real knowledge of God among the heathen saints and prophets, and no natural goodness in man upon which divine grace can lay hold. "There does not seem to be any adequate ground for it in Scripture," says Dr. Cairns, "and it is plainly against the Logos teaching of the Johannine writings."[80] The best missionaries recognize that God has been at work in the heathen heart before their arrival, and the preaching of divine revelation is meaningless unless it answers to some need of the human heart. "Can there be revelation that is not corroboration? If we have no glimmerings within us of the knowledge of God, how can we recognize His Son as the fulness of His glory? Can the Divine Image in man really be destroyed without the destruction of essential personality?"[81]

Such objections and questions as these, uttered by

[79] *Op. cit.*, pp. 314, 315.
[80] Cairns, D. S., *The Riddle of the World*, pp. 365, 366. (Round Table Press, 1938.)
[81] *Ibid.*, p. 366.

soberly Biblical theologians, responsible Scottish
churchmen, cautious in their judgments as Scots are
reputed to be, ought to give us pause before we accept the extreme Barthian version of Continental
Protestant theology in its entirety; but the welcome
given to Barth in spite of these difficulties should warn
us equally against a too hasty rejection of it. Perhaps
—no, *probably*—we need Barth's services more than
Scotland needs them. Calvinism has never died there,
though it has passed through many permutations;
whereas in America it perished suddenly, far too suddenly to yield up to us its eternal message; and Barth
can make it at least conceivable and appealing to us
again.

CONCLUSION

IT NEEDS no argument, after our survey of so many and various Continental theologies, to prove that there is no such thing as a single "Continental theology," which might be compared—to either its credit or its discredit—with "English theology." In theology as in politics, Continental Europe is divided into sharply opposed blocs and parties; and there is little of that peaceful interpenetration which makes it hard to tell whether some Anglicans are High, Low, Broad, or all three at once. If it is permissible to speak of an "Anglican," "English," or even "Anglo-Saxon" point of view in theology, it is much more problematic whether one ought ever to speak of a "Continental" point of view.

What is most commonly meant by the "Continental" point of view is the Barthian point of view; or else, more broadly, the new Protestant orthodoxy which Brunner, Heim, Aulén, and Lecerf all share with Barth in spite of their differences. This is the way in which "Continental" theology is conceived in Mr. Denzil Patrick's excellent essay on "The Great Misunderstanding," in the "œcumenical" number of *The Student World*.[1] The causes of misunderstanding between Anglo-Saxons and Continentals are here reduced to two: (1) the Anglo-Saxon preference for *inductive* method, which leads to a high estimate of science, reason, and natural theology as pathways to

[1] *The Student World,* 2nd Quarter, 1937, pp. 129-141.

the knowledge of God, *versus* the Continental preference for *deductive* method, which leads to a severe
disparagement of all pathways other than divine
Revelation; (2) the Anglo-Saxon faith in an "onto-
logical" presence of God in church and sacrament
and Christian life, *versus* the Continental insistence
that God's presence with man is only "eschatological,"
a promise rather than a realized fact. In these two
great contrasts Mr. Patrick rightly sees reflected the
long-standing controversy between the Catholic and
Protestant formulations of Christian doctrine; and
he warns Anglicans (who have long since lost sight of
the boundary between Catholicism and Protestantism) that they cannot hope to settle their differences
with the Continent by any conciliatory "both . . .
and"; for it is the very genius of contemporary Continental thought to take its stand upon an uncompromising "either . . . or," with Luther, Calvin, and
Kierkegaard.

Mr. Patrick's interpretation of contemporary Continental theology calls attention to a vitally important factor in the situation: the emergence, Phœnix-
like, from the ashes of a defunct liberal Protestantism,
of a new militant Protestant orthodoxy, which has
restored life and vigor to all the most uncompromising slogans of the Reformation: Scripture alone, faith
alone; revelation, not reason; God's grace, not man's
works. But if we take this new uncompromising
Protestantism as the one clear expression of the "Continental" point of view, it becomes necessary to
classify all Orthodox and Catholic theology as un-

Continental, and many Scottish Presbyterians and English Nonconformists as un-British—which is substantially where Mr. Patrick comes out!

I believe that the Eastern Orthodox and Roman Catholic churches of the Continent have made sufficiently vital contributions to contemporary Christian thought so that our concept of "contemporary Continental theology" should include Orthodox and Catholic theology. While it is difficult to frame a concept which will apply equally to a rejuvenated Protestantism and a rejuvenated Catholicism, it must be insisted that Continental theology *as a whole* has certain qualities which are lacking in British and American theology, and *vice versa*. To put the contrast briefly and summarily: what Continental theology lacks in *balance* it makes up in *depth*; while Anglo-Saxon theology tends to push its practical good sense to the point where it endangers the sense of the sublime, without which theology becomes as prosaic as arithmetic. The quality here hinted at is difficult to describe, but it is vitally important, so important that no contemporary Christian preacher should fail to expose himself to its influence, however far he may be from accepting any of the specific theologies in which it is embodied, and however wise he may be in preferring to follow the general direction of British theology in preference to that of the Continent.

We have repeatedly referred to this quality as *the sense of an extra dimension*. In the nineteenth century, when Anglo-Saxon science, invention, industry, democracy, and practical Christianity achieved such

an ascendancy throughout the habitable globe, prophetic voices were raised upon the Continent, protesting against the self-complacency and premature finality of the prevailing world-view. Kierkegaard from the North, Dostoievsky from the East, proclaimed the tragic depths of the human heart to a generation content with creature comforts, and heralded a new heaven and new earth to a world that could imagine nothing better than what it had. These prophets of the fourth dimension were regarded then as fanatics; today their works are being avidly read, under the conviction that their dream of divine heights and diabolic depths is our best clue to reality, while the "real" world with which our recent ancestors were so superlatively content was but a thin crust over a volcanic abyss. It is, of course, the recent cracking of the crust and uprush of molten lava, in the period since 1914, that has given general currency to this *sense of depth* on the Continent of Europe. All the creative religious thought of the period since the War gives evidence of it: Rudolph Otto's *Idea of the Holy*, Léon Bloy's *Pilgrim of the Absolute*, Berdyaev's *Meaning of History*, most explicitly, Martin Buber's *I and Thou*. The generality of this sense on the Continent is proved by the simple fact that Otto was a Protestant, Bloy a Catholic, while Berdyaev is Orthodox and Buber Jewish. *Every* great tradition in religious thought has been quickened into new life by the apocalyptic crisis which has come upon Western civilization in our time; and it is only Continental Europe, so far, that has felt the full force of that crisis.

Let us attempt to list some specific contributions which contemporary Continental thought, rich in the dimension of depth, may be expected to make to the whole movement of Christian thought in our time:

(1) *The dimension of depth in the Bible.* Karl Barth, whatever may be the fate of his theology as a whole, will surely be recognized by future historians as the one who opened up again, for Christian faith, that "strange new world within the Bible" of which he has so eloquently written—the world of *God*, which is not to be reduced to the world of *man*, however moral and religious man may be. Before Barth, the Bible was to many liberal Protestants only a great piece of historical literature, behind which they were dimly aware of "something like the tremors of an earthquake or like the thundering of ocean waves against thin dikes";[2] since Barth, there is a breach in those dikes, and the Bible has once more become to us what it was to our fathers, a personal Word from a living God, speaking directly to our present state. Others may wish to supplement Barth's exclusive emphasis upon God's self-revelation in Scripture with a corrective emphasis upon tradition, reason or Christian experience; but there will be growing agreement. I think that the Biblical revelation is *classic* and *normative* for Christian thought; or, to adopt Professor Hromadka's simile, the central pillar on which the whole structure of Christian theology must rest.

[2] Barth, *The Word of God and the Word of Man* (Pilgrim Press, 1928), p. 29.

(2) *The dimension of depth in the relation between God and the world.* "God is in heaven and thou upon earth"—this renewed emphasis upon the majestic transcendence of the Creator and the deep abyss which separates him from all his creatures will be as characteristic of Christian thought in the twentieth century as was the emphasis upon divine immanence in the nineteenth century. The idea of God's immanence, in the sense of his *pervasive, sustaining, overruling activity,* is a necessary part of the Christian idea of God; but in the nineteenth century this was sometimes pushed to the point where God and the world were pantheistically confused. Against all such pantheistic confusion, which deprives the creation of its independence and spontaneity as truly as it deprives the Creator of his majesty and eternity, the doctrine of divine transcendence is a great protection. It guarantees the separate existence of transient things and the validity of the natural laws which govern their behavior, while maintaining their ultimate dependence upon the divine Creator who drew them out of non-being and fixed their nature.

Not only Barth and Heim, but Przywara and Berdyaev also can be quoted in support of this fresh emphasis upon divine transcendence. These Continental writers represent the same general drift as that of English theology since Baron von Hügel and Dean Inge began their protest against "immanentism." On the whole, the moderate form of this reaction, as exhibited, for example, in Przywara's doctrine of the "analogy of being" or in Archbishop Temple's

"dialectical realism," is to be preferred to the extremist tendency to dissolve *all* sense of analogy between the Creator and the creation; but there is nevertheless much to be learned from the extreme transcendentalism of Barth and Heim. It presents the divine majesty in its awful overpoweringness, its mysterious "otherness," with such overwhelming force that no one who has been exposed to it can ever succumb to the idolatrous tendency to identify God with any natural object, process, or institution. This, in a time when pagan idolatry is again becoming a powerful rival of Christianity, is no small recommendation. To steel our determination to obey God rather than man, and our confidence that if God be for us it matters not though the whole world be against us, we might well take Barth and Heim for our constant devotional reading, even while we take more moderate men for our theological guides.

(3) *The dimension of depth in the soul of man.* Here it is the Russians who are our great guides. Barth's doctrine of total depravity is as artificial and unreal as Calvin's; he seems to be talking about a theological lay figure rather than about actual men. Not so with Dostoievsky and Berdyaev. They portray convincingly the dread abysses into which men may and actually do sink, while keeping a discerning eye for those divine possibilities which link men with their creative Source even in the midst of their iniquities, and open the way for their eventual reclamation and "deification."

The doctrine of Divine-Humanity, as taught by

the Russian Orthodox, is in many respects the antithesis of Barthianism, and exposed to dangers of an
opposite sort—excessive idealism about man's capacity for overleaping the gulf that separates him from
God, and becoming literally a co-creator—yet this
doctrine is as truly characteristic of contemporary
Continental thought as is Barth's transcendentalism.
The dimension of depth is nobly evident in this Russian sense of the presence of Hell and Paradise in
every human soul, this appreciation of the divine
gift of *freedom*, which can equally well lead men to
fraternize with demons or with angels, before at last
the gift is used as God intended it. Only so much of
Barth's transcendentalism is to be seriously accepted
as is compatible with the deep truth in this Russian
doctrine of Divine-Humanity. Perhaps the reconciling
theory will be found in Brunner's doctrine of Man.

(4) *The dimension of depth in the mystery of
iniquity.* The problem of evil is being plumbed to
its depth in Continental Europe today; and all facile
solutions of it are being rejected. In particular, the
insufficiency of human freedom as a full explanation
of the evil in the world is being realized; and the idea
of Satan is having an amazing revival, in the writings
of Karl Heim, Otto Piper, and many others.

The idea of a personal devil, as advocated by Heim,
has great difficulties. There are devilish forces, conscious and well-organized, in our world; yet for all
their power and ingenuity, there is always something
pluralistic and something *unconscious* about their
behavior. Their name is "legion"; they are always on

the point of falling out with one another, like boot-leggers and hijackers, at the very moment when they begin to succeed; and the greater part of the damage that they do is ascribable rather to unconscious selfish-ness than to deliberate malevolence. What this new emphasis upon the "Satanic" may leave as a perma-nent residuum in tomorrow's theology is perhaps best suggested by Paul Tillich's concept of the "demonic." All things tend to become demonic, says Tillich, through a natural exaggeration of some attribute of their being—as a nation becomes demonic when, as a consequence of having achieved a strong sense of internal solidarity, it begins to prey upon and exploit its neighbors—but if anything became completely Satanic it would destroy itself and cease to be.[3] No literal "devil" can be conceived to exist in God's world; but the world is full of "demons" of many sorts, whose power is most real. If the existence of this realm of darkness is a stumbling-block to the neat and orderly scientific intelligence of the nineteenth century, it has no ultimate terror for the Christian, who learned long ago to contend with "principalities and powers," and "the world rulers of this darkness."

(5) *The cosmic dimension of depth in the work of Christ.* One of the great theological events of our time is the reopening of the problem of Atonement by Bishop Aulén. This is closely connected with the rediscovery of the reality of the demonic. So long as "the devil and his angels" were taken to be mere

[3] Tillich, *The Interpretation of History,* chapter on "The Demonic."

figures of speech for human sinfulness and natural evils, the work of Christ was necessarily supposed to be exhausted in the great task of the reconciliation of man with God. So soon as these dark realities begin to take on cosmic proportions, it becomes evident that the problem of world-deliverance is a three-cornered affair, involving the rescue of man from the cosmic powers of darkness as well as from the darkness in his own nature and the resulting alienation from God. It is surely not too soon to predict that the "classic" theory of the Atonement, revived by Aulén, and amplified by Heim and Althaus, is destined to make a profound effect upon the whole Christian world in the next generation.

(6) *The dimension of depth in the Church and the State.* Here the great contributions are being made by the Orthodox and Catholic doctrines of the Church, and the German Protestant doctrine of the State. Out of the contemporary struggle between Church and State there has arisen a conviction that both of these institutions have divine depths beneath their obviously human surface. Catholics such as Maritain are presenting an idea of the Church much more spiritual than the mediæval theocratic idea: the idea of a Christian Society, divine in its root and human in its fruits, destined to spread out from strategic "cells" or "centers" and transform civilization from within rather than from without, so soon as our present humanistic civilization has been liquidated. Still more appealing, from our Protestant point of view, is the Orthodox idea of the Church as a vast communal

(*soborny*) fraternity, where the dead and the living are made one in Christ and the foundation is laid for the spread of "sociality" throughout the social order. If we grant the possibility of such a pervasive influence of Church upon society, we must seriously consider the German Christian view that God reveals himself in the call of the State upon the citizen. If the doctrine of the divine "orders" (*Ordnungen*) is highly objectionable in the form it assumes in Gogarten and Hirsch, it has real force as defined by Brunner and Althaus; and with its aid there is some prospect of a Christian social ethic more adequate than any the previous generation has known.

(7) *The dimension of depth in the mystery of the future.* Here indeed all mysteries and depths are compounded, and piled one upon another; for here, in the struggle with its apocalyptic destiny, the Continent has experienced its severest intellectual birthpangs, and struggled through to a new hope, fit to endure through all possible catastrophes. As we have seen in our review of the various editions of Althaus' book on *Last Things*, Continental thought has pushed back from modern idealism (idea of progress) through Platonic idealism (idea of a timeless eternity) to a fresh appreciation of the truth in New Testament eschatology. While I cannot personally believe that this truth is to be taken so literally as Karl Heim seems to suggest, and would much prefer to take it symbolically or "mythically," as does Berdyaev in *The Destiny of Man*, I believe it to be genuine *truth*, to which we shall all be driven in the end

by the endeavor to understand the tragic events of our time. Thus far, the Anglo-Saxon world has either continued to clutch convulsively after the slipping idea of inevitable progress, or if it has loosened its grip upon that idea, it has replaced it with the Platonic hope of a timeless eternity, as Dean Inge has most conspicuously done. While the third step, back to New Testament eschatology, is by no means a clear or unambiguous step in contemporary Continental thought, it is a step of the greatest importance, which we must all take if we are not to abandon our Hebrew heritage and our Anglo-Saxon "activism" for that very "quietism" of which we are still accusing the Continent, but from which it has now been delivered. Nothing in contemporary Continental theology better repays careful study than that great controversy over "time and eternity" in which Althaus and Heim have played such conspicuous parts, and of which Folke Holmström has given such an excellent review in his book, *Das Eschatologische Denken der Gegenwart*. "Both upward to eternity and ahead in time"—this must be the double direction of our religious aspiration if we are to have the *tempered optimism*, the *patient activism*, which our hard times require.

If we thus follow the trend of Continental thought, shall we not be led to abandon all liberalism in theology, and fall victim to some form of "theological Fascism"? That is bound to be a serious question for British and American theology. The Anglo-Saxon world remains one of the last strongholds of political liberalism; and political liberalism has more than a

verbal association with theological liberalism. It is no accident that the nations which produced the Declaration of Independence and the Reform Bill of 1832 have also produced theological liberals such as John Locke and Bishop Butler, Channing and Emerson, Kingsley and Maurice. Unless we are prepared to abandon our whole democratic heritage, we must not turn our backs completely upon the principles and achievements of theological liberalism.

But it is becoming every day clearer that neither form of liberalism can be defended in our time by purely negative tactics. Democracy cannot be defended by doggedly clinging to its privileges while neglecting its obligations. Only "disciplined democracy," as the Czechs call it, can stand against Fascism. Theological liberalism's openness to new truth cannot be preserved unless it is combined with a more decisive and resolute loyalty to truth already revealed. This generation cannot tolerate that species of "quest" which never arrives anywhere because it never commits itself to what it discovers. As Dean Inge puts it, a loyal Christian may be a liberal *Protestant* or a liberal *Catholic*—loyal, that is, to the truth already apprehended by one of those two great traditions, while holding that truth subject to correction and amplification—but he can no longer be simply a *liberal*. In other words, liberalism cannot persist as an independent noun, but only as an adjective modifying a noun.[4]

If we accept this position, we shall be led at once

---

[4] Cf. the discussion of this point in *Contemporary English Theology*, chap. IV, section on Dean Inge.

to inquire, *"Which* noun—Catholicism or Protestantism?"* Paradoxical as it may sound to American liberal Protestants, I feel bound to say that my study of Continental theology leads me to answer, "Catholicism." It is only in Catholic circles that liberalism still thrives on the Continent. Reason and philosophy have a recognized standing in classical Catholic theology (both Eastern Orthodox and Roman Catholic) which they do not have in classical Protestant theology. Origen and Aquinas were both pronounced intellectualists, who believed that divine revelation was finally harmonious with the best human knowledge; Luther and Calvin were pronounced anti-intellectualists, who perpetually insisted that the wisdom of man is foolishness with God. The truth in liberal Protestantism is much better conserved by Berdyaev and Maritain than by Barth and Heim. The Catholics and not the Protestants are the natural allies of liberalism, since they perpetuate the Greek philosophic tradition, which original Protestantism tried hard to overthrow out of exclusive devotion to the Biblical, Hebraic tradition.

As a believer in the need of a transformed, reinvigorated liberal Protestantism, I am therefore led to declare myself a liberal Catholic. This does not mean, of course, that I propose to leave the Protestant fold. The form of Catholicism to which I adhere is what John Frederick Oberlin and Archbishop Söderblom have called "Evangelical Catholicism." It is consistent with a large appreciation of the continuing mission of the Protestant churches (as a correc-

tive to the traditionalism and pride of the Catholic churches) and a special love of that most Protestant of all Protestant bodies, the Society of Friends. While I cannot declare myself a follower of Barth's new Protestant orthodoxy, I am far from regarding it as a mere reversion to dogmatism, and hope that all our thinking may increasingly be seasoned with his "spice."

Whatever may be true of some of his younger followers (who do seem at times to be headed toward a blind authoritarianism which simply denounces and excommunicates its opponents, instead of reasoning with them), Barth himself is no Fundamentalist. He is a man trained in the liberal theology, retaining many of its virtues while reacting against its defects. His new Calvinism does not reproduce all the difficulties of old Calvinism; his recent tract on Predestination, for example, while coming out boldly for "double predestination," makes the line between the elect and the reprobate pass, *not* between two groups of people, but between two conflicting tendencies in every human soul; and the atoning sufferings of Christ are said to be the greatest example of what reprobation means, as well as what divine love means![5]

Still more than from Barth, I am prepared to welcome contributions to our American theology from other Continental Protestants, whose anti-intellectualism is less extreme. Through the work of the

---

[5] See in the *Theologische Existenz* series, the pamphlet entitled *Gottes Gnadenwahl*.

Niebuhr brothers, the American mind had for some years been prepared to appreciate the work of Paul Tillich, before political events drove him from Germany, and brought him to his present position at Union Theological Seminary, New York. The striking analogy between Tillich's philosophy and Berdyaev's makes him an excellent interpreter to us of that "Protestant Catholicism" which is fundamentally at one with the main trend of Orthodox and Catholic philosophy, while retaining a distinctive Protestant emphasis and flavor. The same may be said of the work of Emil Brunner, whose recent acceptance of an appointment at Princeton Theological Seminary is perhaps the beginning of a career as significant for American theology as Professor Whitehead's has been for American philosophy. As Tillich's speculative philosophy parallels the "Orthodox Gnosticism" of Berdyaev, so a certain *scholasticism* in Brunner's thought parallels the scholasticism of Maritain and Przywara. Union and Princeton seem likely to become important ports of entry for all these tendencies in the next generation—and so to be drawn closer to each other than one would have dared to hope a dozen years ago.

While I thus welcome to our shores the influence of Continental as well as British theology, and have written these two books to help further it, I do not think our American theology should become merely imitative. Our theology needs exposure to Continental thought to give it *depth*, and to British thought to give it *balance and wise moderation*; but

inasmuch as our American situation differs widely from that of all European thinkers, all attempts to follow them precisely would be foolish. We have to think our way much more *consciously* than the British, much more *cautiously* than the Continentals—for we have still much to lose, while the Continentals have lost all save honor! In the three centuries since the Pilgrims landed in Massachusetts, we have developed a distinct theological tradition of our own, in which the names of Jonathan Edwards, Horace Bushnell, and Walter Rauschenbusch stand out as landmarks. The distinguishing mark of this tradition is the dominating influence of the "evangelical" movement upon American Christianity. Since the "Great Awakening" under Edwards, no part of the Christian world has been so deeply stirred by evangelical "revivals of religion," nor so active in missions of mercy growing out of these revivals, as North America. The liberal theology of Bushnell and Rauschenbusch was essentially a *liberal evangelicalism*, designed to correct the excesses of the evangelical movement and provide wider outlets for its energies, not to destroy or discourage it. From the evangelical appeal to "religious experience," this liberal theology derived a type of argumentation less drily logical than that of the Catholic and Protestant scholastics, and closer to the practical life of the Church. If today our liberalism has fallen into the doldrums and lost its religious urgency, the first resort for those who would rejuvenate it should not be to any figures so remote as Luther and Calvin, but to Whitefield and Ed-

wards, Finney and Moody. If *we* do not go back to these great evangelists, no other part of the Christian world is likely to; for they belong principally to us. However just may be the present reaction against Schleiermacher's theology of experience, it does not deeply touch their message. The "experience" of which they spoke was not Buber's "I—It" relationship of mere objective contemplation; it was a thoroughly responsible "I—Thou" relationship. It was closely akin to Kierkegaard's "existential thinking." The recent anniversary of John Wesley's Aldersgate experience was observed by many American Christians with a wistful sense of longing that the current of life which it symbolizes might again begin to stir in our veins; and it was not only the Methodists who felt their hearts strangely warmed at that thought!

One final observation needs to be made, however. There is nothing more characteristic of America than *the tendency to look forward rather than back, when facing an emergency*. The God of the pioneer is not only the God of his fathers, but even more truly the God of his sons and grandsons, to whom he entrusts their incalculable future. America has always looked westward, to unsettled land and untried experiments, for her visions of the New Jerusalem: communities such as Oberlin, New Harmony, Salt Lake City were typical of multitudes of radical experiments in Christian Utopianism. In spite of all disappointments, these experiments have left in the American mind a strong conviction that God is a Great Adventurer, engaged in carving out a better future for the human

race than anything that could be inferred from traditional precedents; so that if all sacred books were to be burned, and all holy traditions destroyed— even the evangelical tradition which has meant so much to America—God might yet be rediscovered tomorrow by some bold pioneer pressing westward. Something of this forward-looking mood is characteristic of American religious thought—notably of Professor E. S. Ames and Professor H. N. Wieman. Truncated as their religious philosophies may seem from the European point of view, they are nevertheless truly religious and genuinely inspiring in their certitude that God lives and works today and tomorrow, and his handiwork is recognizable in fresh creative activity, transforming the world before our eyes. This is not a book about American theology; but I should like to express my belief, in closing, that when the great religious crisis of our time has been passed through, it will be found that the faith of Christendom has been saved not only by the effective rear-guard action of the Continentals, falling back upon impregnable strongholds, and the stubborn tenacity of the British, holding the center against all attacks, but also by the bold advance-guard action of the Americans, pushing ahead to new victories through blithe indifference to all the precedents that required them to retreat!

BIBLIOGRAPHY

INTRODUCTORY CHAPTER: THE CONTINENTAL SENSE OF AN "EXTRA DIMENSION."

Buber, M., *I and Thou*. Scribners, 1937.

Dostoievsky, F., *The Brothers Karamazov*. Modern Library.

Kierkegaard, S., *Philosophical Fragments*. Princeton University Press, 1936.

Otto, R., *The Idea of the Holy*. Oxford University Press, 1923.

Pfleger, K., *Wrestlers with Christ*. Sheed & Ward, 1936. (Best general introduction.)

CHAPTER I. EASTERN ORTHODOX THEOLOGY.

Baillie and Martin (editors), *Revelation*. Macmillan, 1937. Chapter by Bulgakov.

Berdyaev, N., *Dostoievsky*, Sheed & Ward, 1936.

The Meaning of History. Scribners, 1936.

The End of Our Time. Sheed & Ward, 1935.

The Fate of Man in the Modern World. London, Student Christian Movement Press, 1935.

Freedom and the Spirit. Scribners, 1937.

The Destiny of Man. Scribners, 1937.

The Origin of Communism. Scribners, 1938.

Bulgakov, S., *The Orthodox Church*. London, Centenary, 1935.

The Wisdom of God. Paisley Press, 1937.

"From Marxism to Sophiology," *Review of Religion*, Vol. I, pp. 361-368.

Social Teaching in Modern Russian Orthodox Theology. Hale Memorial Sermon, Seabury-Western Seminary, Evanston, 1934.

Pfleger, K., *op. cit., Dostoievsky, Soloviev, Berdyaev.*

Visser't Hooft, W., *Anglo-Catholicism and Orthodoxy.* Chap. II. London. Student Christian Movement Press, 1933.

CHAPTER II. ROMAN CATHOLIC THEOLOGY.

Aubrey, E. E., *Present Theological Tendencies.* Chap. IV, "Neo-Thomism." Harpers, 1936.

Dawson, C. (editor), *Essays in Order.* Macmillan, 1931.

Gilson, E., *The Philosophy of Saint Thomas.* Cambridge, Heffer, 1924.

The Spirit of Mediæval Philosophy. Scribners, 1936.

The Unity of Philosophical Experience. Scribners, 1936.

Horton, W. M., *The Philosophy of the Abbé Bautain.* New York University Press, 1926.

Maritain, J., *The Angelic Doctor.* Dial, 1931.

Freedom in the Modern World. Scribners, 1936.

Three Reformers: Luther, Descartes, Rousseau. Scribners, 1929.

Introduction to Philosophy. Longmans, 1930.

Humanisme Intégral. Paris, Aubier, 1936.

Pfleger, *op. cit., Péguy, Bloy, Soloviev (an Orthodox thinker who turned Catholic).*

Przywara, E., *Polarity,* trans. by Bouquet, A. C. Oxford University Press, 1935. (See also Bouquet's summary in *Theology,* Dec., 1934.)

"Religionsphilosophie Katholischer Theologie." (Printed in *Handbuch der Philosophie.* Munich, R. Oldenbourg, 1926. Bouquet's *Polarity* is a translation of this.) Oxford University Press, 1935.

Analogia Entis. Metaphysik I. Prinzip. Kösel & Pustet, Munich, 1932.

Zybura, J. S., *Present-day Thinkers and the New Scholasticism.* St. Louis, Herder, 1926.

Chapter III. German Protestant Theology.

Althaus, P., *Theologie der Ordnongen*. Gütersloh, Bertelsmann, 1935.

    Die Letzten Dinge. Gütersloh, Bertelsmann, 1926.

    Grundriss der Dogmatik. Erlangen, Merkel, 1936.

Aubrey, E., *op. cit.*, Chap. III. "Dialectical Theology."

Baillie and Martin, *Revelation, op. cit.*, Chapter by Barth.

Barth, K., *The Word of God and the Word of Man*. Pilgrim Press, 1928.

    The Christian Life. London, Student Christian Movement Press, 1930.

    Epistle to the Romans. Oxford University Press, 1933.

    The Resurrection of the Dead. Revell, 1933.

    God in Action. Round Table Press, 1936.

    Credo. Scribners, 1936.

    The Doctrine of the Word of God (Prolegomena to Church Dogmatics), Edinburgh, T. and T. Clark, 1936. (Second volume of this *magnum opus* is already out in German.)

Brock, W., *Contemporary German Theology*. Cambridge University Press, 1935. (Excellent for background of contemporary theology.)

Brunner, E., *The Theology of Crisis*. Scribners, 1929.

    The Word and the World. Scribners, 1931.

    The Mediator. Macmillan, 1934.

    Natur und Gnade. Tübingen, Mohr, 1935.

    God and Man. Macmillan, 1936.

    Philosophy of Religion. Scribners, 1937.

    The Divine Imperative. Macmillan, 1937.

    Oxford Conference Books, *The Christian Understanding of Man*. Chapter by Brunner.

Ehrenström, N., *Christian Faith and the Modern State*. Willett, Clark & Co., 1937 (esp. Chapters VII-IX).

Gogarten, F., *Politische Ethik*. Jena, Dierderichs, 1932.

Hauer, W., *Deutsche Gottschau*. Stuttgart, Gutbrod, 1935.

Heim, K., *The New Divine Order*. Harpers, 1930.

 The Church of Christ and the Problems of the Day. Scribners, 1935.

 God Transcendent. Scribners, 1935.

 Jesus der Herr. Berlin, Furche-Verlag, 1935.

 Jesus, der Weltvollender. Berlin, Furche-Verlag, 1937.

Hirsch, E., *Die Gegenwärtige Geistige Lage*. Göttingen, Bandenhoeck und Ruprecht, 1934.

 Deutsches Volkstum und Evangelische Glaube. Hamburg, 1934.

 Die Alte Testament unde die Aredigt des Evangeliums. Tübingen, Mohr, 1936.

 Der Weg der Theologie. Stuttgart, Kohlhammer, 1937.

Keller, A., *Church and State on the European Continent*. Willett, Clark & Co., 1936 (sections on Germany).

Künneth, W., *Theologie der Auferstehung*. Munich, Kaiser, 1934.

Piper, O., *Recent Developments in German Protestantism*. London, Student Christian Movement Press, 1934. (Best general introduction.)

Rosenberg, A., *Der Mythus des 20. Jahrhunderts*. Munich, Hoheneichen-Verl., 1935.

Tillich, P., *The Religious Situation*. Holt, 1932.

 The Interpretation of History. Scribners, 1936.

 Oxford Conference Books, *The Kingdom of God and History*. Chapter by Tillich.

Other important writings of Barth, Brunner, Tillich, et al., will be found in the periodical, *Zwischen den*

Zeiten, and the series of pamphlets, *Theologische Existenz Heute.*

Wünsch, G., *Evangelische Ethik des Politischen.* Tübingen, Mohr, 1936.

CHAPTER IV. PROTESTANT THEOLOGY OUTSIDE OF GERMANY.

Aulen, G., *Christus Victor.* Macmillan, 1931.
Chapter in Revelation, ed. by Baillie and Martin.

Holmström, F., *Das Eschatologische Denken der Gegenwart.* Gütersloh, Bertelsmann, 1936.

Horton, W. M., "The Theology of Eugene Ménégoz," *Journal of Religion*, Vol. VI, 1926, pp. 174-194.

Hrík, Kovar, and Spisar, *The Czechoslovak Church.* Prague, 1937.

Hromadka, J. S., *Masaryk as European.* Prague, 1937.
Masaryk und Dostojevskii. Prager Rundschau. Special number.

Keller, A., *Karl Barth and Christian Unity.* Macmillan, 1933.

Kraemer, H., *The Christian Message in a Non-Christian World.* London, Edinburgh House Press, 1938.

Kuyper, A., *Calvinism.* Grand Rapids, Eerdmans, 1931.

Lecerf, A., *De la Nature de la Connaissance Religieuse.* Paris, Je Sers, 1931.

Ludwig, E., *Defender of Democracy: Masaryk of Czechoslovakia.* McBride, 1936.

Mackintosh, H. R., *Types of Modern Theology.* Chapters on Kierkegaard and Barth. London, Nisbet, 1937.

Ménégoz, E., *Le Problème de la Prière.* 2nd edition. Paris, Alcan, 1932.

Nygren, A., *Agape and Eros.* Macmillan, 1932.

Patrick, D., "The Great Misunderstanding." *Student World*, 2nd quarter, 1937, pp. 129-141.

Schweitzer, A., *Out of My Life and Thought*. Holt, 1933. *Philosophy of Civilization*. Macmillan, 1922. *Civilization and Ethics*. Macmillan, 1922.

Sigmund-Schultze (editor), Ekklesia, No. 5, *Die Kirche in Schweden*, and No. 9, *Die Evangelische Kirchen der Niederlande*.

Vanderlaan, E., *Protestant Modernism in Holland*. Oxford University Press, 1924.

INDEX

Origen, 228
Orthodoxy, 31, 39, 152, 154
  "Action Orthodoxe," 6
  new Protestant, 215, 216, 229
  renaissance of, 1 ff.
  see also Russian Orthodox
  Church
Otto, Rudolph, 218
  "wholly other," 91
Oxford Conference, x, xiii, xv,
  152
Oxford Group Movement, 149

Patrick, Denzil, 215, 216
Pfleger, Karl, 53
Pierson, Allard, 174, 175
Pilgrim of the Absolute, 218
Piper, Otto, 222
Pius X, 44
Plato, 74, 80, 81, 82, 165, 209
Poland, 147, 198, 199
  see also Central European
  Protestantism
"Positive" theology, 23-24
Protestantism, *see* German Prot-
  estantism, Central European
  Protestantism, etc.
Przywara, Erich, 65 ff., 178, 230
  Analogy of Being, 66-68
  Barth criticized by, 77, 105 f.
  contrasted to Barth and Rosen-
  berg, 66-67
  Gottgeheimnis der Welt, 69
  metaphysics of, 74-83
  notion of an analogy of being,
  70-82, 220
  *Philosophy of Religion Presup-
  posed in Catholic Theology*,
  69-70
  Thomism of, 79, 81-82

Rauschenbusch, Walter, 231
Ritschl, 86, 87, 88, 155, 156, 157
Roessingh, K. H., 176 f.

Rosenberg, Alfred, 66, 67, 95, 96
  contrasted to Barth and Przywara, 66-67
  *Myth of the Twentieth Cen-
  tury*, 114
  prophet of Aryanism, 113 ff.
Rousseau, 59
Russian Orthodox Church, 4 ff.
  see also Orthodoxy

Sabatier, Auguste, 184, 187, 188
St. Anselm, 158, 160, 161
St. Augustine, 80, 81, 82, 165
St. Paul, 164, 165
St. Thomas Aquinas, 44, 52, 67,
  70, 71, 74, 165, 166, 228
  Classic exponent of the "anal-
  ogy of being," 79, 81-82
  see also Thomism
Scandinavian theology, 148 ff.
  Aulén, Gustaf, 155 ff.
  compared with Barthian, 168
  influence of Barth, 150 f.
  Lund, University of, 151, 154 ff.
  Nygren, Anders, 155 ff.
Schelling, 44
Schiller, 95, 118
Schirach, Baldur von, 95
Schleiermacher, 86, 87, 88, 101,
  155, 156, 157, 187, 232
Scholten, 174
Schweitzer, 206
  as a French liberal, 194-197
  criticism of Barthian theology,
  196-197
Scottish theology, reception to,
  and criticism of Barthianism,
  210-214
Sigtuna Folk School, 150
Sketches from the Underworld,
  10, 11
Sobornost, 36-38
Society of Friends, 229

<small>PRAISE FOR MATT BURGESS'S</small>

Dogfight, A Love Story

"Absorbing . . . rich . . . Burgess lives and dies by the credibility of his dialogue and details, and his portrayal is clearly the product of much close study."   —*Time Out New York*

"Matt Burgess serves up a savory dish with his new novel, but the meat of the story is his writing . . . [an] exciting and really-tough-to-put-down novel. . . . The plot is fun, original, [and] addictive."
                                                  —*Minneapolis Star Tribune*

"Every once in a while you come across a book that completely captures a place. Even if you've never been there yourself, it's like you can see it, smell it, taste it."   —NPR's *Weekend Edition*

"Sharp wit and enormous heart fill the pages of *Dogfight, A Love Story* . . . intense, emotional and funny . . . a dazzling debut."
                                                                          —*MetroMag*

"Matt Burgess's debut novel is a beautifully made, street-smart novel. . . . Written with an almost furious energy, *Dogfight* has an amazingly well-rounded cast of characters and a plot that leads up to a violent and probably inevitable climax."
        —Charles Baxter, author of *The Feast of Love* and *The Soul Thief*

"Burgess has created full-bodied characters with on-the-mark dialogue, and he evokes his hometown of Queens. . . . An impressive debut, bristling with energy, from an author to watch."   —*Booklist*

"Burgess turns in a wonderful debut that honors his native Queens and its people with richly drawn characters. The colorful writing of this nuanced, layered story will no doubt bring attention to a talented new fiction writer from whom readers will want to see more."
                                                        —*The Las Vegas Review-Journal*

Matt Burgess

Dogfight, A Love Story

Matt Burgess is a graduate of Dartmouth and the University of Minnesota's MFA program. He grew up in Jackson Heights, Queens.

www.mattburgessbooks.com

Dogfight,
A Love Story

A Novel

Matt Burgess

Anchor Books
A Division of Random House, Inc.
New York

For Georgia Banks

FIRST ANCHOR BOOKS EDITION, SEPTEMBER 2011

The Library of Congress has cataloged the Doubleday edition as follows:
Burgess, Matt.
Dogfight, A Love Story / Matt Burgess.—1st ed.
1. Hispanic American youth—Fiction. 2. Drug dealers—Fiction. 3. Brothers—Fiction. 4. Street life—Fiction. 5. Queens (New York, N.Y.)—Fiction.
I. Title
PS3602 U746D64 2010
813'.6—dc22 2009041885

Anchor ISBN: 978-0-307-47643-2

Book design by Michael Collica

www.anchorbooks.com

Printed in the United States of America
10 9 8 7 6 5 4 3 2 1

When the crack of doom arrives . . .

man will flee from his brother.

—The Qur'an

Contents

Acknowledgments

"I'd like to thank my mother" is something my mother's been whispering in my ear since I started this book, and so, straightaway, I'd like to thank my mother, Sandy Burgess. And my father, George Burgess, the best man I know. I'd also like to thank Charles Baxter, Julie Schumacher, and Ethan Rutherford, who all read multiple drafts of this novel and offered invaluable feedback; my friends and my siblings, without whom I wouldn't have any stories; my agent, Leigh Feldman, for her generosity, enthusiasm, and support; Andrew R., who answered countless questions about the Queens underworld (and who asked that his full name not be used); and all the wonderful people at Doubleday, especially Bill Thomas, who made this book better in innumerable ways, and Nora Reichard, who put every word of every sentence on trial for its life. Finally, I'd like to thank Georgia Banks, to whom I have dedicated this book, along with my love and my life.

Dogfight,
A Love Story

Part One

1

Little Round Pills

In the middle of Alfredo Batista's brain there is a tall gray filing cabinet, frequently opened. The drawers are deep, the folders fattened with a lifetime of regrettable moments. There is, tucked away toward the back, a list of women whose phone numbers he never asked for. There are the debts accrued. In the bottom drawer, in separate folders, there are the things he never learned to do: drive an automobile, throw a knuckleball, tie a knot in a cherry stem using only his tongue. What else? In the top drawer, there is a file recounting the evening he left the Mets game early, thinking the run deficit insurmountable. There is the why-didn't-I-wear-a-condom folder. There is—this one's surprisingly thin—the crimes-against-my-brother folder. Alfredo is only nineteen years old, and already his cabinet overflows with files, none of them collecting dust, each one routinely inspected. All it takes is a random word, a face in passing, and a memory blooms, a cabinet drawer slides open. An intracranial research librarian—Alfredo imagines him bespectacled, with frayed pant cuffs and dandruff on his shoulders—waddles over to the open drawer, plucks out the appropriate file, and passes it on to the brain's well-staffed and efficiently run Department of Regret. Here, unable to help himself, Alfredo scrutinizes the folder. He re-creates the event's sensory details. He goes over, with sick and

meticulous precision, exactly what was said and, of course, what was not said. He relinks the chain of events.

A new folder is to be added. It will be labeled with today's date, June 14, 2002, and above that, in blocky capital letters, a name: SHIFRIN, VLADIMIR.

"Who's Vladimir Shifrin?" Alfredo says.

Winston—a dark-skinned Haitian with long, delicate fingers—pulls down on the brim of his Spider-Man hat. He looks over his shoulder. Drops his voice to a conspiratorial whisper. "From what I understand," he says, "Vladimir is a drug dealer."

"This is why you call me?" Alfredo says. "Why you wake me up? Drag me over here?"

They sit close together on a wood-slatted bench in Jackson Heights' Travers Park. There are other parks in Queens—like Astoria Park or Flushing Meadows—where you can snooze under a tree or stick your nose in trumpet-shaped flowers. These parks are pastoral, as the guidebooks might say. They've got grass you can yank right out of the ground. But here in Jackson Heights, the parks, like Travers, are asphalt parks, blacktop playgrounds. There aren't any flowers or butterflies, and that keeps exactly nobody away.

It's two o'clock in the afternoon right now—it's a nice, unseasonably cool, late-spring Friday—and Travers is packed. Everyone is out. Everyone and their mother is out. There are games of soccer, handball, freeze tag, skilo, and skully. Look around. Shirtless men play netless basketball. A father snaps pictures of his little girl, while a Chinese woman dances to the water-like rhythms of tai chi, while teenagers bum cigarettes off the neighborhood schizo, while bees, drunk with pleasure, swarm the bottoms of trash cans. The swings squeak. An old Jewish man—Max Marshmallow, Alfredo's friend—checkmates another old Jewish man whose body deflates like a popped bag of potato chips. A little white boy, oddly calm, has his head stuck between the vertical bars of a fence, and Alfredo can't help but think of his own brother, the newly named Tariq, spending his last hours up at the Fishkill Correctional Facility. On Travers's softball field, Pakistanis play cricket. On a bench in the sun, the Mexicans who didn't get picked up by this morning's work truck take swigs from their brown paper bags. And in the middle of the park, over by the sprinklers, squats a giant and inexplicable stone tortoise, as if for thousands of years he's been making the

trip north from the Galápagos, and he's decided to stop here, in the middle of a park in western Queens, so much does he favor the company of little children and the intermittent splash of sprinkler water. Alfredo understands. He likes it here too. He feels a particular affinity for the father snapping pictures of his daughter. But, all things considered, Alfredo would rather be home, asleep, his face in a pillow.

"Vladimir's a drug dealer," he says. "That's great. Good for him. But hey, sorry, why do I give two shits?"

"Wow," Winston says. He scoots over on the bench, puts some extra space between them. "I guess you give two shits because you *told* me to go find a drug dealer who—"

"I asked you to find a *dog,* actually." Well, to be fair, Alfredo asked Winston to find both, a dog and a new neighborhood drug dealer, maybe even a two-for-one, a new neighborhood drug dealer walking a dog. But Alfredo is going to outlay some shit here anyway because he's tired, because his feet are blistered, because—most of all—Winston is wearing that red and blue Spider-Man hat. Alfredo keeps looking at it, his eyes narrowing. "But instead of a dog, you're talking about—"

"Vladimir."

"You're talking about Vladimir. Any chance he's a drug-dealing dog?"

"He is a drug-dealing fifteen-year-old boy. Slinging outside the Catholic school on Thirty-first Ave—"

"McClancy's?"

"Please. Don't get too interested. He slings outside McClancy's. He *attends* McClancy's. Him being a fifteen-year-old boy and all. And maybe he's holding down exactly the kind of package we need to pick up for Jose."

"Tariq," Alfredo corrects.

"Sorry. Maybe he's holding down exactly the kind of package we need to pick up for Tariq. Oops. I'm sorry. Maybe he's holding down exactly the kind of package *you* need to pick up for Tariq."

"So?"

"God damn, you're in a bitchy mood. Maybe I should just go over to Gianni's." Winston stays right where he's at. He's about to walk away like that stone tortoise is about to hop over the fence. "Do you have any idea how rude you're being right now?" he asks. "I'm telling a story here, and you're not even *trying* to listen. You're looking all over the

park. At God knows what. And I can't get into a good storytelling rhythm, you know what I mean?"

"Where's your Mets hat?" Alfredo says.

Winston looks away. "Oh."

Either due to stress or drug abuse, Winston suffers from alopecia, a condition that causes his hair to fall out in clumps. Coils on his pillowcase. A nest in the drain. Alfredo feels bad for him, genuinely sorry, and he makes all the requisite clucking noises of sympathetic friendship, but he does not downplay the problem, does not tell Winston that it ain't that bad or that it's nothing to worry about. Business is business, and Alfredo considers Winston's quilt-like scalp to be a professional liability. The poor guy—overweight, bulging eyeballs, ashy skin—is already eminently punkable, and the alopecia just makes it worse. *Shave your dome*, Alfredo argues. *You're a big black Haitian. This is a post-Jordan era.* But Winston says nah. He thinks he has dents in his skull. He thinks he got dropped too many times as a baby and he'd look ridiculous now with a completely bald head. He thinks he maybe doesn't have alopecia at all, and the patches will grow back starting tomorrow, or possibly the next day. In the meantime, he wears his red and blue web-speckled Spider-Man hat. The only problem, however, is that the superhero endorsement makes Winston no less vulnerable. The red antagonizes the Crips; the blue, the Bloods. (Winston's skin—black—does him no favors with the Latin Kings or the Vice Lords or the Netas or MS-13.) So Alfredo buys him new, more imposing, and yet more color-neutral hats. Wool knits in the winter. Baseball caps when it's warm. But within days these hats get misplaced, left behind on a rooftop somewhere, or lost under the cushions of a customer's couch. On Monday, Alfredo gave Winston one of the new black Mets hats, and now, on Friday, Spidey's back.

"I think maybe I left it on the subway last night."

"On the subway," Alfredo says. "Let me ask you something—"

"I don't know," Winston says. He picks at the splintered wood of the bench. "You buy these hats for me, and I appreciate them. Seriously. And I swear to God I'm not trying to lose them. It's just, I don't know. I don't know what's the matter with me."

On the lam from the handball courts, a Sky Bounce blue ball skips past their bench. Alfredo bends over, scoops it up. Doesn't even bobble it. He feels tempted to bring it up to his nose—he loves the sharp,

summery, rubbery smell—but that might look awfully strange, and so he tosses it back toward the courts unsniffed. The ball sails over the heads of the players, but park etiquette demands that they shout out thanks anyway.

"It was a cool hat, too," Winston says.

"It's okay," Alfredo says. "Tell me about Vladimir."

"All he sells is Ecstasy. Nothing else. No pot, no coke, no heroin. Just E. Just a straight-up E pusher. Like this is 1997 or something."

"Is that the end of the story?"

"You're mad about the hat still? Ask me how much he sells the E for."

Alfredo asks.

"Ten dollars," Winston says. He leans back on the bench, stretches his legs out in front of him. "Ten dollars for an *entire pill.* That, my friend, is what he's *selling* it for."

"Terrible," Alfredo says. "You can't even get crack for ten dollars anymore. Me and Isabel wanna go see a movie, it costs us *twice* that. A *movie.*"

"Ask me who his connect is. His brother. That's who. I don't know his name, but let's call him Boris." Winston's feet tap out a happy rhythm as he talks. "This so-called Boris? He's a chemist. Boris the Chemist. You can't make this shit up. The two of them are fresh off the boat, Boris and Vladimir. Been here like three weeks. Maybe more—I don't know. Boris, from what I understand, makes the X right in the apartment. The kitchen, I guess. That's not factual, though. That's just us speculating. The rumor is that he gets in his lab coat, rocks out with his beakers, and however many hours later he's brewed up some X. Doesn't even know he's supposed to stamp it, so the pills go out logoless."

Alfredo shakes his head. He says, "They're not branding their product."

"They don't know *what* they're doing. So then Boris gives the pills to Vladimir, and little bro stands outside the school gates at three sharp every day. And he *under*sells the whole fucking neighborhood. Because what do they care?" Winston's ass is now hovering above the bench. "There's no middleman. From the kitchen to the street. Ten-dollar Ecstasy."

"You've tried this Ecstasy? It's good shits?"

Winston grimaces. "I haven't done E in a serious minute. You hear about those lab monkeys? Going brain-dead?" He picks at the cuticle around his thumb. "Matter of fact—not that I want to make a big deal or anything—but I am quitting all drugs. Including weed. Starting tomorrow."

"Starting tomorrow," Alfredo says. He watches two little Indian girls march past the bench. With their shoulders hunched forward, they clutch dollar bills in their little brown fists.

"But the preppies," Winston says, elbowing Alfredo. "Over at that Catholic school? They're buying Vladimir out. Rolling on X five, six, seven days a week."

"Those poor nuns," Alfredo says. He hears a familiar jingle coming from around the corner: the patented, crazy-making *doo-doo-dee-doo* of Mister Softee, the ice cream man. Kids run into one another, grab at their parents' wallets, snap their heads back and forth in a lactose frenzy. The ice cream truck pulls up in front of the park's entrance. The jingle is louder, the children palsied. Alfredo takes off his glasses and breathes fog onto the lenses. When he puts them back on, he grins—pleased to see those two little Indian girls at the front of the ice cream line.

"You got any of that money you owe me?" Winston says. "I could really go for a cone."

"How much of this is fact?" Alfredo says. "You know what I mean? This Vladimir kid. The kitchen. The ten-dollar E. Boris. How much do we know for sure?"

"Nothing," he says. "Never even seen the kid. These are things I've heard over at Gianni's. A couple of times. From different people. But still." He puts his hands in the air, exposes for inspection the cool whites of his palms. "This is just shit I've heard."

Alfredo turns away and looks around the park for his favorites. The picture-snapping father is gone. And the little boy—where'd he go?—has somehow slipped his head free from the metal bars. At least the tortoise is still here. And Max Marshmallow over by the stone chess tables, harrumphing and kvetching toward another checkmate. He'll be here as long as I will, Alfredo thinks—forever. And ah, here come the numero supremo favorites, the little Indian girls, walking past Alfredo's bench now. They hold their ice cream cones high, the first children to return with bounty.

"How'd you know Mister Softee was coming?" he calls out to them. "You got his schedule memorized?"

They hasten their steps. Don't talk to strangers, their mothers have warned. Don't go into vans, or pet somebody's dog, or accept candy from an outstretched hand, or discuss ice cream with strange men sitting on park benches. It disturbs Alfredo to see himself through their eyes: a menace. He fingers his mustache, wondering if it makes him look like a child molester. His jeans begin to vibrate. It's his phone, humming inside his pocket—it's either Baka, his drug connect, looking for the money he's owed, or it's Isabel, his girlfriend, calling to confirm that Alfredo will have his Boricuan ass home by four o'clock, so they can walk over to Elmhurst Hospital together. She may cap this reminder with a threat—*If you're late, expect a frying pan upside the head*—or she might hang up with some sweetness, sing him a snatch of whatever Spanish love song she just heard on Mega 97.9. Could go either way. Isabel is seven months swollen with the tentatively named Christian Louis Batista, and Alfredo, while trying to be a sensitive guy about the whole thing, is having some migraine-inducing difficulties negotiating the minefield of her moods. Pregnant! Third trimester! Alfredo wants to chase those Indian girls down and shove his phone in their faces. You see this? This is my girlfriend calling. My baby's mama. A woman who loves me. See? I'm not some scary chester. I am a Puerto Rican, an American citizen, a father-to-be. But Alfredo also understands that chasing two little girls in a city park is not the best way to prove one's own innocent intentions. He stays on his bench and lets the phone vibrate. If Isabel needs him home by four, then he doesn't have time to be taking calls. He doesn't have time to hear about frying pans or Enrique's "Experiencia Religiosa" or little Christian karate kicking the walls of her uterus or the latest shit Alfredo's mother pulled. Alfredo's got work to do.

"Look at you," Winston says. "You're deliberating on this Vladimir situation. You're saying, 'Hey—*hey*.' You're going, 'My man came through with some info that's not too shabby this time.' "

"This kid. He's going to have much drugs on him?"

"You know what today is? Today is the last day of school for all the private-school kids. Get out a week early so they can beat the traffic out to the Poconos. Remember when we was in high school? Last day before summer vacation? Kids *lining up* for drugs. Dealers coming correct."

"And Vl—"

"And our man Vladimir is gonna have his pockets full of pills. Make his money for the long summer ahead. Know what I mean?"

Alfredo stands up and feels dizzy. "Okay," he says. He punches his timecard, clocks in for the day. "Let's go rob him."

Back in the day, when Alfredo and Winston were little shits and new friends, they chanced upon the Alleyway. Too narrow for a car, but wide enough to accommodate a couple of teenaged boys, the Alleyway succeeded an earlier discovery—marijuana—and provided an ideal venue for the smoking of those first, poorly rolled blunts. No police, no old ladies, no moochers asking for a real quick hit. Nobody but the two of them. The Alleyway is T-shaped, and Alfredo and Winston got blazed at the bottom of that T, behind a gate door closed to the street. On either side of them they had stores—a Laundromat and a nail salon—both of which produce their own olfactory, marijuana-masking chemicals. At the top of the T are two- and three-family homes, far enough away that crinkle-nosed neighbors rarely called the cops; close enough that when they did, Winston and Alfredo ran right at the houses, choosing among multiple escapes, this one's driveway or that one's backyard, and slipping safely to the street with the ease of THC coursing through capillaries. This went on for years. Winston and Alfredo would duck into the Alleyway and come out fifteen minutes later, giggling and red-eyed, a cloud of smoke blooming behind them.

When Tariq went to prison, all that stopped. Because when Tariq went to prison, Winston and Alfredo went to work, using the Alleyway now as their base of operations. What made it so well suited to recreational purposes—low exposure, multiple exits—made it equally well suited for professional ones. But no more smoking, Alfredo said. Can't shit where we eat. Can't toke where we sling. It was one of many rules, and today he's allowing it to be broken.

"Fifteen years old?" Winston says. Pinched between his fingers he holds what was supposed to be a courage-fortifying blunt. "I mean that's just a little kid. You know?"

Alfredo sits on the ground, his back against the wall, his hand on his chest. He counts his heartbeats. The big dark pillow hasn't materialized yet to smother his face, but he knows that it's coming.

"And it's the middle of the day," Winston says. "And it's like a really nice day, too. Hey, Jesus. Do you need like a paper bag to breathe into?"

Alfredo shakes his head.

"Well, let me know," Winston says. A glass bottle lies on the ground, and Winston kicks it, sends it clattering, helicoptering down toward the other end of the Alleyway. "The kid's gonna be outside a *school*," he says. "That's what worries me. They've got cops in schools nowadays. Right? Aren't there like cops in the *hall*ways?"

"I don't know about cops," Alfredo says. "There might be some nuns." Winston extends the blunt toward Alfredo, and Alfredo waves it away. He's already taken two, three hits, hoping to dilute the panic filling his chest. It hasn't worked. He leans forward, away from the wall, and puts his head between his knees.

"Why don't we just go over to Gianni's," Winston says. "Cop a few slices. Chill out a bit." As he inhales another lungful of weed, the cherry at the tip of his blunt glows red. He passes it back toward Alfredo, but again Alfredo waves it away. "You serious?" Winston says. Confused, he looks down at his hand, as if to make sure this is still a blunt he's offering, that it hasn't turned into something else entirely, a cup of tea maybe, or a big brass tuba. "You don't want any *more* of this?"

"It's all yours," Alfredo says. Keeping Winston smoking keeps Winston quiet. As long as he's got that blunt bopping between his lips, he can't prattle on about everything he's worried about, and he can't, in turn, sharpen Alfredo's own secret fears. God knows Alfredo's not above breaking the law, but he hates to steal. He wishes he were more like the recently deceased John Gotti, a gangster who saw the pleasures in thieving, who'd hijack a truck full of fur coats just for the thrill of getting away with it. But that's not Alfredo. To talk about it, sure. To sit on a park bench and scheme. But to be in an alleyway about to go do the thing—that, for Alfredo, is a chest-seizing nightmare. He closes his eyes and carefully, carefully breathes in through his mouth. It was more than two years ago, while sitting next to his older brother in the backseat of a Camaro at three thirty in the morning, that the hairs on Alfredo's arms stood up, and he discovered he was a hyperventilator.

Earlier that night, Virgil's Catering Hall in East Elmhurst had hosted the sweet sixteen birthday party of a Miss Rashida Katabi. There had been a DJ spinning records, shawarma in warm buffet trays,

an elaborate cake-cutting ceremony. The privilege of using Virgil's for this special occasion had cost Rashida's father, a walleyed Lebanese man, $2,800, which sum he paid in cash. How did Alfredo know all this? Because his brother told him. And his brother knew because the guys in the front seat of the Camaro—Gio and Conrad—told him, and *they* knew because they worked at Virgil's and had closed down the catering hall only a couple hours previous. They were driving back now, still wearing their polyester uniforms, with friends in the backseat, with intentions: they were going to break in and rob the place. The plan had been formulated weeks in advance over late-night bottles of Corona. Keys had been copied, combinations scribbled down. They'd just been waiting for someone like Mr. Katabi to walk into Virgil's with an envelope stuffed full of cash.

Alfredo had begged his way into the car and now he was asking to get out. Bent over on the sidewalk, his skinny legs quivering like a dog's, Alfredo could take deep breaths but he couldn't breathe any of it out. December's cold air poured down his lungs. His fingertips felt numb. A hive's worth of bees seemed to buzz in his ears. In his haste to get out of the car he left the back door open, and the Camaro's internal system beeped and dinged. The ceiling light glowed above his conspirators' heads. Alfredo watched them watch him. Outside, exposed in the street, choking on air, certain he was going to die, Alfredo felt that it was the tears falling out of his eyes, more than anything else, that disqualified him as a criminal badass. With shouted apologies from the front seat, the car drove away, left him behind. They drove toward Virgil's Catering Hall, and—although they didn't know this at the time—they also drove toward their eventual arrests, toward court dates and public defenders and years-long imprisonments.

That first panic attack, and the ones he's had since, the palpitations he feels now, might have something to do with the sacred prohibition against stealing. Alfredo wonders if he's crazy to credit his breathing difficulties to a fear of supernatural retribution. And yet it *is* a commandment, number seven, *Thou shalt not steal*, right after don't kill nobody or commit adultery. And while he doesn't go to Mass anymore on Sunday mornings, or melt the paper-tasting wafer onto his tongue—it has been five years since his last confession—he still walks the streets afraid. He peeks up at the clouds, fearful of somehow giving offense. He has rules: he won't take the Lord's name in vain, he says a

quick grace before dinner, he can't pass a church without making the sign of the cross. Sometimes before he falls asleep, he'll send God a silent prayer in which he offers a general thanks for the life he's been allowed to create for himself and asks only that God do nothing to snatch the pleasures of that life away (Isabel mainly, and now Christian Louis too). Alfredo respectfully prays for noninterference. No lightning bolts, okay? Please don't burn down New York. You leave me alone, I'll leave You alone.

Alfredo stands up off the ground, but that only seems to make it worse. His arms are goose-pimpled, his tongue coated with anxiety. All this trouble, and he won't even get to keep the pills for himself. He intends to give them to Tariq, who returns home tomorrow after an absence of two and a half years. A drug package being the standard reentry-day gift. Alfredo hoping to impress upon his brother that he is a weight-slinging gangster with resources to spare. *Well, that changes everything,* his lungs say. *If you're not going to keep the pills for yourself . . .* Yeah, right. Stealing is stealing. He can ask for Vladimir's E, he can put in a request—what is religious scholarship if not the prying open of loopholes?—but if Vladimir says no, nah, nyet, go fuck yourself, then Alfredo, the weight-slinging gangster, knows he won't be able to just reach out and take it, hit this stranger, this ninth grader, right in the mouth.

Winston, who's never thrown a punch outside the world of two-dimensional video games, blows a gray stream of sticky-smelling smoke into the sky. The smoke rises, drifts toward the two- and three-family homes, toward a clothesline with pinned-up jeans and T-shirts and orphan socks. It curlicues into an open pant leg. Alfredo expects the smoke, now hidden, to ascend even farther up the jeans and come out the waist, maybe in the shape of a man's chest, and this thought is quickly replaced by another: two, three hits of that blunt and I'm already blazed, waiting on some gray-skinned savior to come out of the sky.

"What's the matter?" Winston says. "What you looking at?"

"Maybe for this Vladimir thing," Alfredo says, and, as always, talking relaxes him: better to be pushing words out of his mouth than drawing air in. "I'm saying if it'll make you feel better. Stop your crying. Maybe we can call the Alphabet Brothers."

"Why? So they can rob Vladimir while we stand in the background and cheer them on?"

"So *you* can stand in the back. So *I* can stop hearing you bitch."

"Sure," Winston says. Having smoked the blunt down to roach size, he stubs it out on the brick wall of the Alleyway. There was still some pot left, the best part actually, but Winston doesn't do roaches. He doesn't like burning his valuable fingers. "Whatever. Do your thing. Call up the Alphabet Brothers."

The Alphabet Brothers—Alex, Bam-Bam, and Curtis Hughes—are a trio of tough black guys from Corona, Queens: Jackson Heights' neighboring neighborhood. The brothers don't look too tough, though. Each of them is over six feet tall, but not one of them weighs more than 145 pounds. (Their mother, Mrs. Hughes, calls them a bunch of skinny belinks.) They've got the long lean bodies of blacktop basketball players, and if you saw them out on the court you'd think they were pure shooters, the guys who spot up behind the arc and put up J's, who are squeamish about running through screens, who don't like to bang in the post for rebounds. The Alphabet Brothers, however, don't do any of that. Sports aren't really their thing. Their thing is punching people in the face.

It starts in the hands. Due to some genetic quirk, the Alphabet Brothers have arthritic-looking fists, with bony knuckles as big and as round as walnut shells. If Vladimir refuses to hand over his goods, the brothers will act. Each one punches from the shoulder and hits like a mule.

But, unfortunately for Alfredo, the Alphabet Brothers don't work for free. The negative aspect to their involvement is the negative of any merger, corporate or piratical: splitting the spoils. But like the Comcast/AT&T merger recently announced in the papers—Alfredo's a proud reader of the *New York Post*—without the collaboration, there ain't no profits. The two parties need each other. Alfredo provides the information; the lump-fisted brothers, the violence. The brothers, God bless 'em, do the actual stealing. They also cover Alfredo's ass retribution-wise. If the young and inexperienced Vladimir cops a postrobbery, pride-stung hard-on, if he gets all horny for revenge, then he'll have to come after two separate crews, and—seeing as how the poor kid's unaffiliated—he'll have to come after crew one (Alfredo and Winston) and crew two (Alex, Bam-Bam, and Curtis) all on his

own. "And to make moves like that," Winston suggested, "guy would have to be drunk on some mad vodka."

But as is Alfredo's wont, he worries still. The concern isn't that the Alphabet Brothers will, after robbing Vladimir, turn around and rob Winston and Alfredo, too. They've got too much history together, too much mutual business: they've got a dogfight going off tomorrow night in Max Marshmallow's basement. But what if the Alphabet Brothers try to press their man advantage? Intimidation artists, they might lean over Alfredo with their cumulative height advantage of twenty-one inches (Alfredo's five foot six and a half) and loudly insist the spoils be split according to man, and not crew, thereby giving the brothers the majority of Vladimir's E and cash. What if they gang up and . . . oh, never mind. Alex and Bam-Bam's cell phones go directly to voice mail. Only Curtis answers Alfredo's call.

A good thing, too. Pulling the string on one Alphabet Brother is easier than marionetting all three, even if that one is Curtis Hughes, seventeen years old, the youngest of the trio and the most belligerent, which is a little like ranking last in a leper colony beauty contest.

"You're not serious," Curtis says when he arrives. "*That* is your drug dealer? The little white boy across the street? With his hands in his fucking *pockets*?" Curtis hocks up a loogie and spits it onto the sidewalk, just far enough away from Alfredo's Timberland boot. "Tell me that the real boss hog is round the corner. Slinging X by the fistful. Tell me, Alfredo, that you're fucking with me."

Alfredo and Winston had Curtis meet them here, on the sidewalk across from the Catholic school, and he's shown up scowling. He climbs off his bike, a twenty-four-inch Schwinn built for children. Face doused, shirt stuck to his chest, Curtis, despite the cool weather, is sweating like Patrick Ewing at the foul line. Little bikes are his preferred mode of transportation—they advertise to the world that he's an original gangster, not above taking a bicycle away from a child—but it isn't easy for a grown man to ride a boy's bike, it's especially hard on the knees, and Curtis agreed to pedal the twenty blocks over here because he thought he was robbing a drug dealer. Not some wannabe, his thumb up his ass.

"Because I don't need to come all the way out here to rob white people. I can do that at home."

"Don't worry," Winston says. He pops a piece of General Tso's chicken into his mouth. On the way over here, Winston, his eyes red and his stomach grumbling, stopped in the Wok 'n' Roll on Seventy-third for some Chinese takeout. He eats the chicken straight from the container, pork fried rice sticking to his chin. "Trust me," he says.

Curtis stares, his face contorted as if somebody just smeared a dollop of fecal matter under his nose. "Now I know I'm a fucking idiot," he says. "I know there's nothing I can do about being so obviously stupid. But over in Corona, the drug dealers? They look like me. And the kids that look like *that*? Over there, across the street? Those are the wiggers playing dress-up for Halloween. Punk bitches just trying to look hard. And nobody gets fooled, starts thinking these kids are for real, worth anybody's time, except, you know, the jerk-offs. But hey. That's Corona."

"We wanna know if he's a drug dealer," Alfredo says. "Let's go ask him."

They make their way across the street. Monsignor McClancy High School is a graffitiless, freshly painted three-story building, with large windows and grass lawns and big, shadow-casting trees. This could've been Alfredo's school. Without his father's accident, without the subsequent loss of Jose Sr.'s store and the soaring costs of his medical bills, Alfredo might have ended up here, carrying books and notebooks through McClancy's heavy doors. He went to grammar school at the nearby Our Lady of Fatima and the all-boys McClancy would have been the next logical parochial step. Oh well. Alfredo went from Fatima to I.S. 145 to Newtown High, where he lasted a little under two years before dropping out. Had things broke differently—had lightning bolts not been tossed—Alfredo might've found himself in McClancy's smaller classrooms, learning from ear-yanking nuns who don't take any shit. Who knows? He might have gotten that cap and gown after all. Might've been in seminary school by now, on his way to wafer-dropping, thurible-swinging priesthood.

As a preemptive measure, Alfredo takes off his glasses and stashes them in his pocket, next to his baggie of Internet-purchased prescription pills. The edges of trees, windows, people—it all goes fuzzy. He squints. What else can he do? These glasses are his only pair and he

doesn't need Vladimir landing a lucky punch and cracking a lens. Although a battle royal seems increasingly unlikely. Alfredo wants to believe Winston's story, but Curtis's doubts match his own. There's no question the kid they're walking toward is Vladimir—his is the only Slavic face in a sea of Hispanics—but is this Vladimir a drug dealer holding down weight? He's certainly trying to *look* like a drug dealer. Over his McClancy-mandated shirt and tie, he wears a purple and gold retro Lakers jersey. On his head he's got on a straight-billed black baseball cap, turned around backward. His pants are baggy and slung low. But the problem is that the kid's trying too hard. It's as if Moscow's version of MTV just recently started playing Snoop Dogg and Dr. Dre videos, and Vladimir—anticipating his own American debut—took notes. He's even got an old-school pager clipped to the waist of his wool pants. And it's all wrong anyway. Not only does the hip-hop outfit clash with Vladimir's pale skin and above-the-lip peach fuzz, but it's a pusherman ensemble from a different time and place: the early nineties, the West Coast. There is, however, one cause for hope. A group of kids float around Vladimir. A promising sign—split the nucleus of a teenaged atom and you'll often find drugs—but in the five minutes Alfredo and Winston were across the street, waiting for Curtis, they didn't see one hand-to-hand. Not a single money-for-pills exchange. Either the kids have already copped, or they're waiting to cop, or—Alfredo hates to even think it—this little Russian's got nothing to sell.

"Hey, Vladimir," Alfredo shouts as he gets closer. "What's good with X? Let's talk about some E."

Vladimir's face goes blank. His pink lips don't twist or curl or bend; his mouth is a dumb slot set into the bottom of his face. His eyes move from left to right, scan his interrogators: one black guy; another black guy, heavier and shorter than the first; and a Hispanic, the one who's talking, and the shortest of the three. Vladimir's eyes move without fear or excitement or confusion, as if he were a third grader reading a quadratic equation. As if he were staring at a pile of bricks. He blinks often.

"You speak English?" Alfredo whispers.

"Jesus Christ," Curtis says.

"Ecstasy," Alfredo says. For Vladimir's benefit, Alfredo pantomimes

dropping a little round pill onto the tip of his tongue. He makes his eyes go wide, smiles with all his teeth. "You eat them and dance to techno? Start feeling fantastic? No? Doesn't ring a bell?"

Curtis punches Vladimir in the chest. He falls backward into the chain-link fence. The metal squeaks and strains as the fence flexes to keep Vladimir upright. His mouth hangs open. The air has jumped from his body.

"Those are Air Jordans?" Alfredo says, pointing to Vladimir's shoes. "I haven't seen those in a while. What year are they?"

Vladimir rubs his chest, chews on the air around him. Winston, Alfredo, and Curtis are circled around him, and around that circle a larger one has formed: the onlookers, the Catholic schoolboys with leather bookbags slung over their shoulders. These kids watch in profile, their bodies half turned in case they suddenly need to run for their lives.

Curtis drags his tongue across his upper row of teeth. He leans in close to Vladimir and breathes softly onto his face. "Run your shit," he says.

Vladimir moves as if submerged in honey. From his pocket he takes out a money clip—a thin wad of tens tucked into the fold—and hands it to Curtis. Vladimir reaches back in, roots around, and pulls the pocket inside out. A white tongue outside his pants, the tip flecked with fuzz. That's all he's got: a money clip and some lint.

"This jersey expensive?" Alfredo says. He pinches the fabric between his fingers. "You get it off eBay? How much those Air Jordans cost?"

"Take off your shoes," Curtis says.

To untie his sneakers, Vladimir crouches down into a catcher's stance. Blond hairs uncurl from the bottom of his hat. The back of his neck needs a shave, Alfredo thinks. He grabs the kid's shirt and eases him back up. Poor Vladimir. It's his first ball, and he doesn't know whom to listen to, when to sit down and when to stand up.

"I'll get my own sneakers," Alfredo whispers. "But the Ecstasy. Can you please give one of these black guys your Ecstasy?"

Vladimir turns his other pocket inside out. A set of house keys—attached to a dirt-smudged rabbit's foot—falls to the ground. Toppling out after them is a silver-and-black cell phone, and some loose change, too. The coins jangle as they hit the sidewalk. Vladimir looks

down at the ground. He smells faintly and sweetly metallic, like a can of soda opened and left out overnight. His hands are steady, but his eyes have gone moist.

"Oh jeez," Winston says.

Curtis throws a left hook, punches Vladimir in the ribs. There's a dull *phttht,* the sound of a bowling ball getting dropped in the sand. Vladimir falls to his knees. Hunched over, his forehead kissing the sidewalk, he holds the side of his rib cage with one hand, and with the other hand he slaps at the pavement beneath him.

"Come on," Winston says. "Maybe we should go." In a circular, unconscious movement, he rubs his chest, inadvertently wiping chicken grease all over his shirt. "Maybe we should just get out of here."

"Shut up," Curtis says. He sticks his hands in Vladimir's back pockets. He looks in his hat, and, finding nothing, tosses it into the street. He bends over and crooks a finger into Vladimir's socks, feeling around the kid's ankles and heels. The futility of the search, not to mention its intimacy, its skin-on-skin contact, seems to embarrass Curtis. As he straightens up, he gives Vladimir's shoulder a shove. "Take off your pants," Curtis says. "And squat."

"Come on," Alfredo says. "It's not up his ass."

Curtis smiles. "See? I'm so incredibly stupid. I don't know these things. Tell me, Alfredo. Please. Where's the E at?"

They look around. While nobody was paying attention, the high school rubberneckers have vanished. Those kids have money, they've got parents who can spend six thousand a year on tuition, but they are still an urban crowd—they knew how long they could watch and they knew when to slink away. Only a matter of time before the skinny black kid with the all-bone fists turned his interrogation toward them, and so they took off. Maybe to go get the wheezing Vladimir some help.

"Hey, Winston," Curtis says, still smiling. "Where's this E at?"

Alfredo considers putting his glasses back on, but it doesn't seem necessary. He squints and sees nothing. This long stretch of sidewalk is wide open, without sharp corners or alleyways. And because it's outside a school, in front of a tow-away zone, there aren't any parked cars nearby. No tires or front bumpers where a supply of X might be stashed. If Vladimir doesn't have the drugs on him, then he doesn't have any drugs at all. Alfredo rubs his overstrained eyes.

"I think we should get out of here," Winston says.

Again, inside Alfredo's pocket, his phone begins to hum. "What time is it?" he asks no one in particular, and perhaps accordingly, no one answers him. It's gotta be pretty close to four, he thinks. He could check his phone for the time, find out for sure, but he doesn't want to see his home number flashing and chastising, Isabel on the other end of the line, her knuckles turning white. *Incoming* . . . a frying pan to the head. He reaches for Vladimir's waist and unclips the kid's pager. Vladimir recoils, collapses his body inward.

"Don't worry," Alfredo says. "Hey, listen. Tilt your head back. Breathe in through your nose." Alfredo holds the pager up to his eyes. He puts his glasses back on, checks again, and sees that the pager is off, the LCD screen dim, blank save for the ghost outline of digital eights.

"What time is it?" Winston says.

"Three twenty-seven," Alfredo says. Vladimir begins to push himself up off the sidewalk. He opens his mouth, and Alfredo kicks him right in the neck.

The last time Alfredo's *tias* visited from Puerto Rico, they reached in for a cheek pinch and then stopped. Straightening their backs, they eyed his mustache with suspicion. It can't be, they said. This is Alfredito? The third grader who used to memorize license plates? He had changed beyond recognition. Sometimes he can't even recognize himself. There are old family photographs in shoeboxes, in albums, in frames on the walls of the Batista house, and when he sees the kid in these photographs—the little boy with the bow tie, standing with his nursery-school classmates; the little boy who's got his arm around his brother's shoulders at Coney Island; the little boy holding a stuffed duck or a baseball, or sitting on the kitchen table eating cake with his hands—when he sees this kid in unremembered clothes in unremembered rooms, playing with unremembered train sets, he can't quite believe that the picture person is him, one and the same, Alfredo Batista.

It awes him to see Vladimir gag. On all fours, red-faced, Vladimir crawls on the sidewalk, away from Alfredo. He doesn't get far.

Curtis hooks his hands under Vladimir's armpits. He yanks him up, braces him against the chain-link fence. Vladimir's eyes are open and white. His feet pad at the ground as if slipping on ice. Close to his face,

Curtis pants with an almost sexual excitement. He's been taken off his leash. He snaps his hips, deals from the shoulder, and hits Vladimir in the mouth. Vladimir's head smacks the fence. Perhaps because of that head-on-metal clang, no one hears the soft tear of his lower lip. His eyes are closed. A tooth—a lower canine, yellow rimmed—punctures the lip and pops clean through to the outside of his face. Around that tip-filled hole, blood swells, drips down his smooth white chin.

Winston walks away. Alfredo, seeing his friend leave, gives pursuit.

"Hey," Curtis says. "Where you guys going?"

"Keep the money clip," Alfredo says without turning around. "It's all yours."

"But hey. Hold on. Are we still doing that thing tomorrow?" He's a little boy whose pals have just gone home for supper and taken their ball with them. "We're still doing that dogfight, yeah?"

Alfredo doesn't answer. Winston, elbows out, is hustling down the block, and Alfredo needs to jog to keep pace. "Hold up," he says. His boots aren't made for running; they pound preexisting blisters. "Slow down, wouldya?"

"I gotta go home." Winston, like Alfredo before him, does not turn around to answer. He rounds the corner, putting Curtis and the boy out of sight.

"Winston."

"I've gotta go home, okay?"

Alfredo grabs him by the elbow and turns him around. "Would you just hold on, please?"

Winston won't look at him. Half his forehead is streaked with sweat; the other half, dry. A preexisting condition. When hot or anxious, the right side of his face perspires; when eating samosas or Sammy's halal or KFC spicy chicken or pizza slices overflaked with red pepper, the left side beads up. Alfredo blames the drug abuse. The pot, the coke, the E, the everything else—somewhere along the way a switch got flipped, Winston's glands derailed.

"Please," Alfredo says. He pulls Winston by the elbow, steers him toward the pay phone on Seventy-second Street. They have a history with this particular phone. When Alfredo and Winston were ten years old they used it to make prank calls; at eleven they tagged the side of it with a black Magic Marker, "Yap" for Alfredo, "Sagat" for Winston; at

thirteen, and working off the instructions of Jose Batista, Sr., they cottonballed the phone and others in the neighborhood; and now, at nineteen years old, Alfredo picks up the receiver and dials 911. When asked what his emergency is, Alfredo looks at Winston and tells the operator a little kid has been hurt, knocked out on Seventy-first Street, between Thirty-first and Thirty-second avenues. He's surprised by the evenness of his own voice. He didn't expect to be so calm, to ask for an ambulance in the same easy tone he'd use to order a gypsy cab or a pepperoni pizza. The operator asks for Alfredo's name, and he answers by hanging up. He sticks his finger in the coin return slot, just to make sure.

"All those kids saw us," Winston says. "They saw our faces."

A red and yellow bodega squats at the end of the block. Signs advertise the store's wares, but for whatever reason the plurals have been lopped off. The bodega promises its customers cigarette, magazine, sandwich, bus ticket to Atlantic City. Alfredo points his chin at the place. He tells Winston, "Come in here with me. I want to show you something."

Bells clatter as Winston and Alfredo push through the door. Behind the cash register, the Pakistani proprietor jabbers Urdu into his headset, talking to some long-distance relative in Islamabad or Peshawar or someplace Alfredo's never heard of. The man smiles at them as they walk past his counter. They pass the coconut ices, the ramen noodles, the mousetraps and ant traps, the single rolls of toilet paper, the dusty packages of Indian rice, and they keep going till they reach the back of the bodega, where giant refrigerators rise up out of the ground. Behind the frosted-glass doors sit six-packs of Budweiser and forties of malt liquor, each can and bottle individually priced.

"We're gonna get drunk?" Winston says.

Alfredo reaches into his pocket and pulls out Vladimir's pager. With his thumbs, he pushes the top off the plastic case. He slides it carefully along its grooves. Inside the pager, where one might expect wires or microchips or triple-A batteries, are little round pills of Ecstasy. Neatly stacked in three rows of—the numbers burst in Alfredo's head—nineteen pills each, minus five that Vladimir must have already sold that afternoon. Fifty-two pills in a hollowed-out pager.

"Abracadabra."

Winston looks at the pills. "I told you," he says, but there's no swagger in his voice.

"How tough was that kid?" Alfredo says. "Took a beating and wouldn't give it up. Know what I mean? I tell ya, I'd like that kid to work for *me*."

"You don't pay enough."

I don't *make* enough, Alfredo thinks. But right now, in his hand, he holds fifty-two pills, with a street value of $25 apiece. Talking about— Alfredo's math is immediate—$1,300. That's Christian Louis money. That's money that could help pay for cribs, cradles, high chairs, humidifiers, mobiles, titanium strollers, diapers, plush giraffes, breast pumps for Mama, clothes the baby will grow out of, and the endless parade of pediatrician visits. Of course $1,300 can't cover all that. All by itself a crib with a waterproof mattress can cost close to a G. But $1,300 would help. At the very least it could buy more drugs, which could be converted into more cash for more drugs for more cash for more drugs and on and on and on. But this package ain't for me, Alfredo reminds himself. It ain't mine, it ain't mine.

Winston licks the tip of his finger and plucks out a pill. Instead of swallowing it whole, he chews on it, so the MDMA can zip into his bloodstream.

"You gonna give my brother twenty-five bucks for that?" Alfredo asks.

"Take it out of what you owe me," Winston says.

Again, Alfredo's phone hums, and he feels the tug of its telecommunicative leash. Time to go. He fits the cap back onto the E-beeper and slides it into his pocket. It's got to be close to four o'clock, if not later, and Alfredo is nine blocks from home. He and Winston make moves toward the front of the bodega. The Pakistani behind the counter cups his hand over his headset's mouthpiece. He wants to know if he can help them find anything they need. Oh sure. Alfredo needs a time machine, stronger lungs, a pit bull, a healthy baby, a Lotto ticket for his father, a more mentally balanced brother. Actually what Alfredo really needs right now is one of them Ecstasy pills. After watching Curtis punch a hole in Vladimir's mouth, Alfredo would love to swing open a neurological floodgate and get a brainful of serotonin howling through his body. He could take just one pill, he tells himself, and give

Tariq the remaining fifty, a nice round number. Outside the bodega, the sun is shining.

"I don't hear any ambulance sirens," Winston says. "Where's the whoop-whoop?"

Alfredo decides to keep the E in his pocket. He doesn't need the guilt. He doesn't need another file for the cabinet: *Ecstasy, June 14, 2002, afternoon, another drug I shouldn't have taken.* Besides, Alfredo has a long day ahead of him. He can't show up at the hospital with his pupils all dilated, his teeth grinding. Isabel would be pissed. Or worse—she'd be disappointed in him.

2

The Incredible Floating Fetus

The denizens of the clumsily named Elmhurst Hospital Emergency Room Waiting Room—the wounded, the pregnant, the hypochondriacs, the sneezers and coughers and terminally ill, the insured and uninsured, the kids who need stitches, the careless bagel cutters who gashed open their hands—they all sit on the edges of their chairs, their ears cocked toward the nurses' station, waiting for their names to be called. Not Isabel Guerrero. Alone among these waiting room waiters, Isabel is happy to wait. Happy to lean back in her shit-brown metal folding chair and put down roots.

On the inside of her eyelids, Christian Louis floats. He's in a diaper. He's got a wine-splashed birthmark on his cheek. In a voice that's somewhere between a baby's and a man's, he tells Isabel he has spina bifida. Where does he learn such words! Yesterday he told her, smiling, that he had Down syndrome. The day before, cystic fibrosis. There are hundreds of birth defects, diseases where the nervous system shuts down and kidneys collapse, where babies get hooked up to machines and never come off—and with her unborn child whispering these diseases in her ear, Isabel is shook. She believes Christian Louis. She knows Jose's—sorry, *Tariq's*—return is a bad omen, a black crow on the health of her child. Leave this waiting room? No thanks. Isabel stays right where she's at, undiagnosed.

Not that she's comfortable or anything. I'm sweating like a pig, she thinks—and she doesn't even know if pigs sweat. Babe? That animated oinker in *Charlotte's Web*? They seemed pretty dry. She thinks of the pigs she's seen in real life, like the ones over at the churrascaria on Northern Boulevard, but they were all dead. So, okay, she has no idea if pigs sweat or not, but goddamn, she's sweating, that's for sure. And it's not even hot outside. And they didn't even walk here. Alfredo had said his feet hurt, and Isabel took a step back and spread out her arms. Twenty-nine weeks pregnant. One hundred and sixty-two pounds. With breasts that were already big but have gotten bigger, more tender, sensitive it seems to changes in weather, and hanging off her like sacks of potatoes. Isabel said, "*Your* feet hurt? You gotta be kidding." He wasn't. He insisted they take the Q32. From that air-conditioned bus to this air-conditioned waiting room, Isabel hasn't even had a chance to work up a sweat. And yet . . . she sweats. Like (maybe) a pig. She pretends to scratch the back of her neck and gives her armpit a covert sniff. Nothing horrible. Fabric softener, salt, a little something earthy. On the inside of her eyelids, Christian Louis drifts by, doing the backstroke. He says, *Hey Mama. Maybe this anxiety you're feeling has less to do with my potential spina bifida and more to do with . . . oh I don't know . . . Uncle Tariq? Let's talk about that!*

Isabel says, *Nah. Let's talk about how hot I am.* She wishes she were the kind of woman who could just peel off her sweaty shirt and stuff it in a garbage can. Imagine? Not giving a shit like that? That's a Sigourney Weaver in *Aliens* move. That's some *Thelma and Louise* action. Imagine Alfredo coming back—from the bathroom, the parking lot, the water fountain, the operating room, from wherever the fuck he's at—and finding you here, in the front row of the waiting room, wearing only your sneakers, your sweatpants (elastic waistbands!), your bra, and that's it, nothing else, just your big tata pregnant breastesses swinging in this AC-generated breeze.

She turns to look at the people directly behind her: a white couple in their thirties. The woman, like Isabel, is pregnant. (The other day Alfredo showed her an article in the *Post* about the boom in babies, nine months after September 11. *I guess Osama sets the mood,* she'd said.) But unlike Isabel, the woman is probably not here for her prenatal checkup. They're here, Isabel assumes, for the man, who's got a bloody towel pressed to the back of his head. They pay Isabel no atten-

tion. It is, she thinks, one of the better things about hospital waiting rooms. Invisible, she hears no hey mama, no teeth sucking, no hiss hiss hiss. Waiting rooms are, for her, the next best thing to movie theaters. This one is even set up like a movie theater: long rows of chairs all face the same direction, and the people in them stare straight ahead at the TVs bolted prison style to the top corners of the wall. The television on the right plays national news (priests going to jail, Enron cronies on trial), while the one on the left shows telenovelas (gemelos malos, pelea entre hermanos). No one talks to anyone else. Thank God. Usually she'd be up in the OB-GYN section of the hospital, but a burst water pipe kicked her down here, to the ER waiting room, where Isabel worried there'd be more men, more maniacs, more ogling catcallers, but so far, so good. Everyone adheres to the subway contract. Keep your eyes glassy. Build up your own protective bubble of thoughts.

Isabel leans forward in her chair. She puts her hands behind her back and folds up an inch of her shirt. The skin is hot. With the bottom of her shirt hiked up, she presses the exposed small of her back to the cool metal of her chair. Jesus Cristo! Santa Maria! She angles herself in the chair to feel as much of the metal as possible. All ball busting aside, Isabel's feet don't hurt that bad. She expected her calves and ankles to cankle; she expected her feet to swell up and feel as tender as her boobs. But they've been all right. (A hereditary thing, maybe. Her mother the puta always had strong legs and feet, and Isabel should know—she's absorbed many a kick.) So the feet are fine, no problem at all, but her back? Particularly her lower back? Forget about it. There's some Boy Scouts and sailors in there, tying up knots. Lately, at the Manhattan video store where she's worked part-time since she was fifteen years old, Isabel has had nightmare days restocking tapes onto the bottom shelves. She's started stashing them on the top, hiding *The Warriors* behind *The Bad News Bears, Youngblood* behind *Anaconda.* She'd work at the cash register, but she has to pee every ten minutes. Run to the employees-only toilet, squat over the bowl, squeeze out a pathetic trickle. Then go back to work and bend over so some jerk will be able to find *Xanadu* when he wants to rent it. Fuck the whales, Isabel thinks. Forget about the manatees and the troops in Afghanistan. Save my back! Put me on one of those wooden boards like Hannibal Lecter and wheel my ass around.

But this metal chair cooling her off? Beautiful. Let other people go

see doctors. Hear about Tay-Sachs and Huntington's chorea. Isabel is fine right here. She's recently decided to build her happiness out of things just like this: buttered popcorn, the click of a movie projector, Alfredo's mother leaving the house, putting on underwear straight from the dryer, getting into a bathtub surrounded by candles (Isabel's never actually done this, but she will, as soon as she and Alfredo get their own apartment), the smell of Magic Markers, riding the subway into Manhattan, the monkeys at the Central Park Zoo, the café at the Museum of Natural History, the increasingly rare delight of taking a good and solid shit, and, just now added to the list, cold metal on hot skin.

Alfredo plops down into the seat next to hers. "We're next," he says. He wiggles the eyebrows. "I've been schmoozing the nurses. Bribing them with Starbursts." He slips a pink one into her hand. "I told them, 'Listen. We've been here an hour and a half. I work for Channel Seven news, and I'm gonna come in here with a camera crew, expose everyone in this dump of a hospital.' They didn't buy it. I get Starbursts from the vending machine. I tell the nurses, 'Listen. What can you do for us? Here's some candy.' I said, 'But not the pink ones. The pink ones are for mi amor.' " He slips another one into her hand. " 'They're her favorites.' "

"Are you crazy?" Isabel says. "You think just because you give the nurses some"—In the movie version of her life, it would be at this exact moment that a nurse would lean into a microphone and call out Isabel's name. "*Ms. Guerrero. The doctors can see you now.*" Cut to Alfredo grinning. Cut to Isabel with her mouth open. But for maybe the first time ever, she is glad this isn't the movie version of her life. A nurse doesn't call out her name. Isabel gets to finish her sentence and stay in the waiting room—"candy, that we're gonna be next in line or something?"

For another hour she and Alfredo wait in their chairs. Alfredo gets up once to buy more Starbursts. He brings the whole package back to Isabel this time, not only the pinks, but also the reds, yellows, and oranges. He slides the candy into her palm one by one, as if he were bribing a maître d'.

"What do you think he's gonna say?" Alfredo asks. "When he sees you?"

She doesn't know if he means Tariq or the doctor. She takes his

hands. They're smooth and uncalloused. With his fingernails bitten down to the quick, raw and sensitive skin is exposed. She kisses a knuckle. More items for the list! Put it down between Magic Markers and candlelit baths: the pleasures of unwrapping a Starburst, the softness of her boyfriend's hands.

When she was fourteen years old Isabel got her arm broken, and she sat in this waiting room for over three hours. She was more than eager to see a doctor that time. Prior to that she'd been to this hospital only once, to escape from her mother's womb, and after her arm broke, she didn't come back until she was pregnant herself and had to pee in a cup and apply for Medicaid and schedule prenatal appointments like the one today. Just once! Her arm got broke, and her mother called a cab and took her to the hospital. Her only visit between ages zero and nineteen. But did she have more than that one opportunity to come to the hospital? Could she have benefited from consistent medical attention? Would it have been helpful to talk to a staff psychologist, or a sympathetic social worker? *Oh boy!*

She was twelve years old when she lost her virginity. She was pulling back the shower curtain—the one with the map of the world—and she already had one foot out of the tub, when her mother's boyfriend came into the bathroom. His name was Raul Diaz. With his hand covering his mouth, so that his words came out muffled, he told Isabel she was beautiful. He stepped into the bathtub with her. The room smelled like soap. Water dripped off her body. His belt buckle clattered against the wall of the tub. Afterward, when she saw the blood on the tiles, she wondered if this was her first period, and if the rest of her menstruating would always be this bloody and painful. Raul wouldn't look at her. He whispered, *Lo siento. Lo siento.* He helped her clean up the blood. They used paper towels.

Raul was a Cubano. He wore a gold watch too big for his wrist. In the mornings he read *El Diario* with his feet up on the kitchen table, but he never looked comfortable doing it, probably because his legs were too short. He started coming into her bedroom at night. *Isabel? You awake?*

One afternoon, with Raul out of the house, Isabel's mother whipped her with a surge protector. She called Isabel a whore. She held

the outlet end of the surge protector, with its empty, unsmiling faces, and she hit Isabel with the cord, attacking from close range. Snake-like welts rose to the surface of her back. They were bulbous-headed, with slithering, three-pronged tongues.

Like a cartographer she drew borders in her bed. A third of the mattress, the part right next to the wall, was hers. This was her safe zone. When Raul snuck into her room, she moved over into the other two-thirds. When Raul left, she moved back. Columbus returning to the New World! She'd press her body against the wall and go back to sleep.

Urinary tract infection: the diagnosis at thirteen. The school nurse told her she was going to have to start peeing right after sex. Isabel imagined this, getting up when Raul got up, following him out of the bedroom. Later that day, the nurse called Isabel back into her office and gave her a bottle of cranberry juice she'd picked up on her lunch break. *Cranberry juice is good for UTIs,* she explained. She told Isabel she was also going to have to get herself some antibiotics. *And don't let any of these boys peer-pressure you into being sexually active,* she said. She waited for Isabel to nod, and so Isabel nodded. *Is everything okay at home?* the nurse asked. Isabel scratched the side of her nose. *Everything's fine,* she said. *Thank you very much for the cranberry juice.*

Sometimes, when Raul climbed on top of her, she pretended to be asleep. She became an expert at pretending to be asleep. Sometimes, when Raul climbed on top of her, she got out of bed and watched from across the room. Or she'd watch from the ceiling, see things from up high the way people can do right after they've been struck by lightning. She'd watch that man, Raul, rape that girl, Isabel. She'd see his hand jammed into the pillow, next to that poor girl's face. Sometimes, however, Isabel couldn't make the leap out of her body. Sometimes, for whatever reason, she'd be stuck in that bed, listening to the *tick-tock* of his enormous gold watch. He always smelled and tasted like mouthwash.

When she was fourteen years old, Raul moved out. Isabel's mother slammed a door on her arm. Then she called a cab, took her to the hospital.

Frankie, her mother's new boyfriend, moved in. He moved out. New guys moved in, moved out, moved in. Isabel slept in her safe zone and waited for these men to tiptoe into her bedroom, but they never did. Not one of these men raped her. But unfortunately no one from

the future ever traveled back in time to tell her that, and so she was always afraid. If Frankie didn't grab her in the kitchen today, he'd get her tomorrow. If one boyfriend moved out without touching her, the next boyfriend would. She could take quicker showers and get dressed in the bathroom and wear two pairs of pants to bed and not clean her privates and try to avoid the apartment on lazy weekend days, but in the end—Raul taught her this—if they wanted to get her, they would. While she waited for it to happen, she took a serrated knife and cut up her arms.

While her mother was between boyfriends, she and Isabel ate tons of spaghetti with butter and parmesan cheese. They played a game where they'd pretend it was pesto gnocchi, baked ziti, fettuccine Alfredo. Her mother would ask what she wanted for dinner, and Isabel would say, *Linguine with clam sauce.* And her mother would say, *Excellent! Just what I planned on making!* Sometimes, on her way home, Isabel stopped to look at the menus of Italian restaurants, so that she could bring new, more exotic pasta names into the apartment. Penne puttanesca, rigatoni carbonara. Her mother would ask her to explain what they were. Carbonara: pancetta, scallions, black pepper, and egg. *Coming right up,* she'd say. And then she'd serve Isabel a steaming bowl of spaghetti with butter and parmesan cheese. *Bravo, Mama! Perfecto!*

A new boyfriend moved in. Isabel waited. She cut her legs. Blood wriggled into her socks.

Daring escape! At fifteen years old Isabel got a part-time job after school at a video store in Manhattan. She showed up early, left late, covered other people's shifts. The manager praised her work ethic. Isabel went to school less often. In her free time, with the money she made at work, she hit up the movie theaters. Always alone, always in the back row, where no one could see her. She'd unzip her purse, take out a can of soda, and cough loudly as she popped open the tab. In the movie version of her life she didn't work at a video store and she didn't see so many movies, unless the movie version of her life was *Clerks* or *Cinema Paradiso* or *The Purple Rose of Cairo.*

One day at the store she put on *Casablanca.* It was her first time seeing it. At the end of the movie, when Rick and that lady are hugging at the airport, Isabel stood behind the counter, ringing up a customer, staring at the TV screen, and she actually said out loud, *What are you doing, girl? Get on that fucking plane.*

"That's us!" Alfredo says. They're calling Isabel's name, and Alfredo hurries toward the nurses' station, moving through people as if this were a deli and he's got a ticketed number in his fist, his right to roast beef. "That's us," he says again. "Excuse me. Perdón, señora. We're coming! Hold on!"

Up at the front desk, he turns and waves Isabel over. She is not moving fast enough apparently, and so his waving intensifies. She is an airplane, and he is the man on the runway with the orange wands, his hands chopping through the air. Alfredo says something to the nurse. He holds up one finger. He takes a few cautious steps away from the desk before spinning around and dashing over to Isabel.

"You okay?" he says.

An old white man sits in a chair, his hands folded over his cane. Isabel accidentally clips him, bangs his ear with her hip. She steps on a woman's foot. The floor tilts away from her. The bottoms of her shoes have been replaced by ball bearings. She has the sensation of going down stairs and expecting there to be one more step than there actually is. Again and again, Isabel steps through that phantom step and has to catch herself. She leans against the backrest of an empty chair.

"What's the matter?" Alfredo says.

A blue-scrubbed nurse pushes an empty wheelchair toward Isabel. Miraculously, in a city-run hospital of God knows how many employees, the nurse is the same one who met with Isabel and Alfredo on their first visit. She helped them fill out the forms, enroll in PCAP and Medicaid. She counseled Isabel on HIV protection and the benefits of a nutritionally balanced prenatal diet. The nurse has, as she did then, a long braid of black hair snaked over her shoulder. It has been six months since Isabel has seen this woman, and her reappearance now feels ominous. As if the hospital already knows about the diseases baby Christian's been whispering in her ear. As if the hospital can tell just by seeing her bang into chairs that there is something wrong wrong wrong. So they send the O.N.—the Original Nurse—and tell her to bring a wheelchair. The nurse tilts her head toward the chair. Her thin lips smile.

"I can walk," Isabel says.

"Yeah, but why? If you don't have to?"

"This is a nice ride," Alfredo says, running his hand over the armrest. He expertly depresses the wheel brakes and flips open the metal footrests. Holding Isabel's arm, he eases her into the chair. "Let me at those handlebars," he tells the nurse.

Two large doors wheeze open, and Isabel is pushed into a new area of the hospital where the lights are brighter and the sounds noisier. Sneakers squeak as nurses and doctors hustle from the ruptured appendix in 104 to the stabbing victim down the hall. The smell of the place—rotting skin and pink antibacterial soap—lingers like a punch in the neck. Worst of all: while Isabel is wheeled around corners and down corridors, through this Elmhurst bazaar, the nurse straggles behind, walking in step with Alfredo. This is not an ideal position for Isabel, who always sits in the back of movie theaters and sleeps pressed against the wall and insists on taking whatever seat faces the door in restaurants. When people loom unseen over her shoulder, when voices float behind her head, Isabel's scalp tingles and her arms tighten. The nurse offers Alfredo directions: go there, make a left here. Maybe she tilts her chin. Maybe she points. Maybe, when a turn approaches, she touches the small of Alfredo's back.

"I'm coming from a job interview," he says. He isn't talking to Isabel. "I think it went okay. The interview. I felt like I asked some good questions. I was on point, I think. Thing is, I'm hoping to make some professional breakthroughs. But who knows, right?"

He must remember the nurse from that first PCAP visit—which doesn't surprise Isabel; he misses little—and he is trying, for reasons Isabel only vaguely understands, to atone for something. Six months ago on the Q32 bus coming back from the hospital, Alfredo complained about having to pretend he was unemployed. He had looked down at the clipboard in the nurse's hand and said he was temporarily between jobs. Spitting the words out like they were curdled milk. As if he expected the Medicaid enrollment form to have an employment status box marked "Drug Dealer." "Do you know how hard I work?" he asked Isabel. "How I'm out there every day? Busting my ass like a dog?" He went on. He complained about how sick he felt, how miserable, how low that hospital experience had dragged him. Until Isabel, in an attempt to put things in perspective, said, "*Your* hospital experience? I had a hand shoved up my vagina." On the bus a surprisingly high number of people (three) turned around to look at them. For the rest

of the trip home Alfredo said nothing. He stared out the window, watching as Elmhurst gave way to Jackson Heights.

"I forget," Isabel says. "What kind of job were you interviewing for?"

"Sales," he says. "Cell phones and pagers. That kind of thing."

Isabel smiles, not knowing where he gets this shit from. If he anticipates the questions and plans what to say ahead of time, or if he just digs right in and pulls it straight out of his ass.

"Well, I think you'll probably get that job," the nurse says. "You seem *very* personable." The chair stops in front of an empty examination room. Despite being small and windowless, a considerable draft blows out of the room, prickling Isabel's legs. The nurse comes around to the front of the chair and bends forward at the waist. "You think maybe you'll be able to stand up now?"

"I never needed to sit down."

The nurse smiles in Alfredo's direction. Isabel has one ally in this world—when Christian Louis is born, she'll have two—but until then, it is Alfredo, and Alfredo only. Do not, you blue-scrubbed bitch, try to turn him against me. In the movie version of Isabel's life, she steps to this nurse and scratches her face.

Isabel walks into the examination room. She is greeted by a sink, a blood pressure cuff, a computer monitor, and a box of rubber gloves with five rubber fingers sticking out of the top as if waving hello. The metal scale, the metal cabinets, and the metal footstool all seem to have been waiting for her. The only grouchy holdout is the examination table, with its unwelcoming strip of white paper. And the nurse, of course. She sticks a small cup in Isabel's hands and asks her to leave.

"The bathroom is next door," the nurse says. She winks. "You probably have to tinkle anyway, am I right?"

With both hands wrapped tight around the cup, Isabel walks out of the room, leaving Alfredo and the nurse behind. The nurse takes her ponytail and drapes it over her other shoulder. She tells Alfredo to sit tight and make himself comfortable. She says the doctor should be with them shortly. And then, like Isabel before her, she walks out of the room.

Abandoned, Alfredo fiddles with the sink. Turns it on and off. He taps on the door to the metal cabinet, which makes a solidly tinny sound, like rain on a rooftop. He wonders if there are some prescription pills inside this cabinet. Some painkillers maybe. He taps on the

metal again, as if expecting any Percocets or Vicodins to tap back. With a steady hand, he fingers the handle to the cabinet door. His breathing is disconcertingly calm.

Maybe he's been cured. Maybe now that he stole that E-beeper and got away with it, he will never again hyperventilate. Maybe—oh Lord—maybe he should've kicked the air out of someone else's throat a long time ago. He doesn't like thinking about it. He'd felt like one of Winston's video game street fighters: somebody hit a button, and Alfredo's foot flew forward. It was something his brother might have done—hurt a stranger on instinct, like an animal—and Alfredo long ago promised that his brother's methods would never be his own. He sold coke, so Alfredo sells weed. He made deliveries, so Alfredo stands on a corner, lets the duff buyers come to him. He got pinched robbing a catering hall, so Alfredo doesn't even walk past catering halls. He treated Isabel poorly, so Alfredo treats her—or at least tries to—in the way she deserves. But what about Vladimir? The kid's eyes were bulging. His face flushed red. He may have swallowed his own tongue. He may . . . oh fuck this. Alfredo can stand in this examination room by himself and feel guilty, or he can open the cabinet door, add some prescription pills to the clear plastic baggie of scrips he already has in his pocket, get caught by Isabel, get caught by the doctor, and then watch the Medicaid form get torn in half, forcing Isabel to give birth on a wood-slatted bench in Travers Park, Santeria priestesses easing Christian Louis's head from her womb. Or Alfredo can follow Isabel and the nurse and bounce on up out of here. Go looking for a rest-room of his own.

The first bathroom door he finds is locked. Maybe he didn't give the knob a good-enough turn. Maybe if he just—nope, it's locked. Because he doesn't want to just stand outside the door and wait, his arms folded in front of his chest; because he does enough of that at work, on the corner; because the whole idea right now is to keep mov-ing and stop thinking—Alfredo goes in search of another restroom.

Doctors zip past him. Nurses, too. Everyone wears sneakers, and everyone, it seems, gives Alfredo a look. It's not quite a disapproving look, but it's close, and Alfredo gets the message: *You know, son, you can't just wander around a hospital, and* (clutching clipboard to chest) *if I weren't so busy* . . . Maybe they're right. Alfredo in the wrong place at the wrong time might cause mortal damage. Say he trips over a plug

to one of those *beep-beep* machines, or bumps into a perfectly calibrated microscope. But give me a break, Alfredo thinks. Not like he's going to slip on a banana peel and send high-priced hospital equipment toppling down one after another like so many dominoes. No, what really worries Alfredo is making a left at the end of this corridor and witnessing someone's private misery. A woman's mastectomy consultation. A little girl shiny pink with third-degree burns. Because what Alfredo sees now is more than enough. Patients in gurneys, exposed, pushing away turkey sandwiches, crying, calling out for help. Alfredo hastens his steps. If he weren't so far gone already, he'd go back to Isabel—if he even knew how to get back. He has arrived at this point in the hospital by making end-of-corridor turns indiscriminately, without reason to his lefts and rights, and while he won't exactly admit he's lost, he's as close as a man can get. Ah, but what's that? He passes a ladies' restroom, and the feminized glyph on the door gives hope. She's all dolled up in her triangle skirt, and so her stick-figured boyfriend must be close by. And here he is, the old pimp. End of the hall.

Intragender modesty has little virtue in a place with bedpans and sponge baths, with male doctors asking female patients to disrobe and nurses sliding catheters into the heads of penises. Alfredo walks into one of the hospital's few men's rooms, one of the few lavatories with multiple stalls and multiple urinals. A guy stands hunched over the sink and washes his hands. Alfredo hurries past him, unzipping as he goes. His bladder—which had been considerate enough to keep quiet on the long journey over here—now belts out an aria. He takes aim at a little blue urinal cake. It is not as much fun as pissing into a urinal full of ice cubes, but at least Alfredo has the gratifying pleasure of seeing his pee turn green. He gives himself a couple of perfunctory shakes, flushes the lever with his elbow, and makes his way back to the sink where that guy is still—still!—scrubbing away.

"Oh man, I hate this fucking place," the guy says. "The diseases? You kidding me? I'm not OCD or anything, but I must've come in here five times already. Just to wash my hands. You know how many germs are floating around here?"

No, but Alfredo does know that men shouldn't talk to other men in the men's room. The two of them stand at the sink, which is a more acceptable conversational district than the urinals or (God forbid) the

stalls, but *still*. This is the *bathroom*. Alfredo wouldn't talk to his father in the bathroom. Maybe it's a hospital thing—they have a way of breaking down people's boundaries. And actually, Alfredo feels a little desperate to talk to someone himself. He points to the sign above the sink and reads the words aloud. " 'Washing hands saves lives,' " he says. "Well there you go. You're doing a service."

"I been here ten minutes. I should get a fucking Medal of Honor."

"You wanna hear something? My girlfriend—she's eight months pregnant, okay?" She is, of course, only seven months pregnant, but Alfredo tells meaningless lies to stay in practice. "She's got these monthly prenatal checkups. I don't have to come, but I come. Nothing for me to do except hold her hand. Which is fine. I love her. But I gotta take off time from work to get down here. And I really need to be at work right now, know what I mean? Because, like everyone else, I've taken a big financial hit since nine-eleven and when this fucking baby comes, God bless him, you know how much it's gonna cost me? For diapers alone? You know how much I'm paying *already* for things? You know how much I'm gonna *have* to pay?"

"Everyone pays," the guy says. He splashes water on his face. He is in his mid- to late twenties. An obvious fake tanner enthusiast, he has turned his white skin orange, probably thinking it makes him look healthier, more vivacious, and maybe it does, but not today. Today his head sags. On his face he carries a day's worth of beard—a cluster of hair on each artificially tanned cheek, shadows on the chin and upper lip. Worst of all, an arrowhead of stubble pokes out from the center of his hairline. Alfredo guesses the guy is the reluctant owner of a widow's peak, and part of his daily routine is shaving it off with a razor. Just one more thing he didn't get to do today. Alfredo knows tired, and this dude is *tired*. The guy looks in the mirror and scowls. "Insurance, no insurance. Kids, no kids. Doesn't matter. Everyone pays. Right out the ass."

Alfredo pulls out his bag of prescription pills. He leaves it on the edge of the sink, while he goes to the paper towel dispenser. He needs to dry his hands thoroughly before touching the pills. He can't have the greens of OxyContin mixing with the blues of Viagra.

"Well," the guy says, looking at the bag.

"So what are we thinking here? Insomnia? Pain? Depression?" Alfredo looks from the inside of the bag to the guy in front of him,

going back and forth as if one will tell him about the other. As if Alfredo is a used car salesman, trying to size up this mark as a Vette guy or a Cadillac gent. Inside the bag, Alfredo's fingers pinch a Xanax. "Anxiety?" he says. "Is that what we're talking about?"

"Here I am. Complaining about hospitals. And you're a fucking pharmacist."

"Well, I left my prescription pad at home."

The guy turns off the faucet and the bathroom goes quiet. He smiles. Alfredo expected to catch him off-balance, to pressure him into a quick, one-pill sale. The way Alfredo imagined it, the guy gives him twenty bucks for a Xanax because Alfredo convinces him he actually needed it, or because the guy convinces himself twenty bucks ain't a bad deal to get away from an aggressive Puerto Rican pusher. Now, however, Alfredo's starting to think he imagined this all wrong.

"Stress," the guy says. He grins like a wolf sniffing at a rabbit hole. "What have you got for stress?"

Alfredo thinks one thing: *cop.* It'd explain the cynicism, the condescending grin, the nonchalant appraisal of drugs. And if he were a shield-chaser, late twenties would put him at just the right age for the NYPD's narcotics squad. Here's Alfredo about to get locked up over twenty measly dollars. With Isabel waiting for him on the other side of the hospital! He looks for bulges on the guy's hips, by his ankles. He looks for cheap shoes, skin puffy with alcohol, coffee-stained teeth, powdered sugar around the mouth, a wristband with the color of the day, a palpable and nauseating air of superiority. Alfredo goes back through their conversation—did the guy laugh at his own jokes? Is he here visiting his partner, winged in some Elmhurst shootout? Does he use fake tanner because he never sees the sun, because he walks a beat all night and sleeps all day? Alfredo zips up the bag. He says, "Sorry, but I don't have anything for stress."

"Sure you do. I saw some Zoloft in there. White oval pill? Looked like you had the hundred millis."

"No, no, no, no, no." Alfredo puts the bag in his pocket. "That was something else."

The guy smiles like he washes his hands: for way too long. "Don't worry about it," he says. "Stress can be a positive thing. Keep you sharp. Alert."

"Maybe I should join the army then," Alfredo says. "Go over to Iraq

like they're talking about. Take down Saddam. Plenty of stress there, I bet."

"Ha ha. Get that Medal of Honor, huh?" He rips a paper towel out of the dispenser. "You don't have any Zoloft? That's cool. What I really want—hey, stick around for a second. What I'm really looking for is some Ecstasy. You got any X, my friend?"

Holding a cup of her own warm pee, Isabel hurries into the examination room. She finds it empty. She walks back out, checks the room number above the door, looks both ways down the hall. Feeling embarrassed, exposed—her pee is shockingly yellow—she goes right back into the room and sits on the examination table. The strip of paper crinkles under her ass. Her feet dangle. Is it possible for a grown adult human being to sit with her feet kicking at air and not feel ridiculous? In the movie version of her life—Isabel knows this one's a stretch—her pee would not be so yellow. She'd be better hydrated. Inside that cup, Isabel imagines, it smells like the Port Authority bus terminal. She eases herself off the table and goes to the sink. She bends her head to the nozzle, drinks cold water straight from the tap.

"Just last week I look out my window and see my wife in the backyard. Gardening. She doesn't know I'm watching. And I catch her taking a long drink from the hose, and I'm thinking how lucky am I? How incredibly beautiful is this wife of mine?"

He is a big-bellied Indian man, with receding hair and one large eyebrow stretched out across his forehead. If his wife is beautiful, or even moderately attractive, then this is one lucky man indeed. Consider the eyebrow alone. Exceptionally bushy, it threatens to sprout tentacles, threatens to grab the stethoscope off his shoulders, to pass him scalpels whenever he needs them. More hair shoots out of his nostrils and from the cuffs of his lab coat. This is Isabel's sixth prenatal exam and her sixth doctor.

He takes her cup of pee. He looks down and away, clucking his tongue.

"But I didn't get *you* anything," he says.

Isabel stares at this Indian man, at his big belly and fleshy nose, and she wonders—briefly, insanely—if this is Alfredo in disguise. She used to have thoughts like these when she was a kid, when she imagined

her white, elderly third-grade teacher, Mrs. Rosenstock, was really her mother dressed up in a wig and rubber mask. At school, Isabel would whisper words in Spanish while looking into Mrs. Rosenstock's eyes for some glint of understanding. At home, she would raise her hand at the kitchen table, hoping to catch her mother unawares. Ridiculous? Of course. But never were Mrs. Rosenstock and Isabel's mother spotted in the same place at the same time!

"Have you seen my boyfriend?" she asks the doctor. "He was in here like a minute ago."

"Afraid not." With his thumb, he flips the cap off the cup of her urine. A white stick appears in his hand, and he jabs it into the cup. He stirs, as if mixing café con leche. This is normally the lab tech's job, but the doctor gives the impression that he must keep his expert hands occupied. Isabel imagines that when he goes home to India, if he goes home to India, he spends his vacation administering physicals to the entire population, checking every pulse, asking every man, woman, and child to open up and say *aaaaaaaaah*. "Please, my dear. Sit down."

She has questions about the health of her baby, but the doctor, breathless, runs her through tests as if trying to outpace her anxieties. He makes little eye contact. He takes her blood pressure, squeezes her hands and ankles, puts her on the scale, asks about varicose vein developments, pulls the stick out of her urine cup, draws blood from her arm—and all the while, Isabel feels like she's not even in the room. But when he lifts the bottom of her shirt, she goes stiff. She lies on the table, smelling the lemon tea on the doctor's breath. She closes her eyes. Because she is all alone, she summons Christian Louis. She hopes not to hear the names of new diseases, but rather his kind, soothing words: *Is okay, Mama. Relax.*

But Isabel's ears are stuffed. She hears nothing and the doctor's hands are cold. Checking for fetal size and position, he palpates the uterus, prods at the baby's head and shoulders. Isabel's fists are clenched, her body rigid. Despite his mama's summons, Christian Louis does not appear on the inside of her eyelids. All she sees is darkness. But Isabel keeps the hope. Her eyes stay shut, and in the middle of darkness blooms a crimson ring. It is only the imprint of the fluorescent light above her head, penetrating the thin skin of her eyelid. But to Isabel, whose eyes are still closed, it is a small red world, on fire.

She sat in Travers Park and watched the handball games. It was 1998. She was fifteen years old. She'd gone down to the park because at home her mother's new boyfriend was moving in, carrying his boxes into the apartment and plopping them down in the living room. Out on the handball court one man in particular caught her attention. Wearing a wife-beater, banging into the other players, he hammered the ball, swung through it as if it owed him money. After the game, while the other guys reclined against the fence or doused their heads in water, the man stood alone in the middle of the court. Isabel moved toward him. She was frightened but she sounded strong and calm when she told him he was very sweaty and if he wanted to cool off he ought to take her to the movies. His cheek twitched. *You smell good,* he said. With an almost snarl he told her his name, as if daring her to be unimpressed. Jose Batista Jr. looked down at the hand she extended toward him. He laughed.

He fingered her on the floor of the movie theater. This was before stadium seating. The two of them were lying down between rows of seats. Isabel kept her head off the floor, so she wouldn't get any spilled soda in her hair.

When he drove her home, she asked him to come upstairs and meet her mother's new boyfriend.

That night, trying to fall asleep, Isabel decided she won't go to any more movie theaters with Jose. Can't shit where you eat, as the expression goes. She established new rules. Kissing and hand-holding were fine. If necessary, he may feel her up and/or she may give him a hand-job. But there will be no bj's. There will be no more fingering. There will be absolutely no sex. Underline that one. Put it in bold.

Forget the subway. Forget about taking the R train from Roosevelt Avenue to Woodhaven Boulevard. Jose had a van. He drove her to the Queens Center Mall, where he bought her jewelry from Claire's. Junky bracelets, that kind of thing. They shared a plate of nachos from the food court, and afterward he asked her if he had any gunk in his teeth. On the drive home, he showed her the van's hiding spots. Behind interior panels and underneath seats, he kept bags of coke and weed, vials of crack, things Isabel had never seen before.

He said if they're not going to have sex, then there wasn't no point

to kissing. It was all signs of affection, right? He stopped holding her hand. He asked if she'd ever heard of blue balls. He told her his friends thought she was immature, that he could do a lot better.

Her first experience with consensual sex: the Costco parking lot, in the back of Jose's van, where silver duct tape covered the rips in the seat cushions. A cardboard lemon tree dangled from the rearview mirror.

She said she had her period. She said she had to go to work. She said she had to write an essay on John Adams for school. She said, cough cough, that she was sick. She said she got her period again. He told her he could do much better. He told her he had girls lined up. Once she found a used condom in the back of his van, and when she confronted him about it, he said, *Promise you won't laugh? I come back here sometimes and masturbate into rubbers.* She believed him.

Sometimes when they were having sex, she'd step outside of her body and sit in the front seat and do something real cool and casual-like. File her nails, for instance. Or flip through a magazine.

He never hit her. He told her he loved her. When he drove her home and her mother's boyfriend was smoking a cigarette on the stoop, Jose escorted her to the front door, let her hang off his powerful arm.

You're a bad fuck. You just lie there. You don't like trying new positions. You don't ever say anything. You're dry. You can't come and there's something wrong with you. What else did he tell her? Oh, yeah. He said he could do a lot better, but she knew that already.

To become initiated into the Latin Queens a woman needs to allow three Kings to fuck her at the same time. Or she can let them beat her for thirty seconds apiece. Forget it.

They swapped stories from childhood, and here's one of his: His father used to take him and his little brother onto subways to panhandle. The father told people on the train that his daughter had recently passed away. He showed a picture of the little girl and a photocopy of the obituary. He offered to give people the name and number of the funeral home, in case anyone wanted to check up on his story. He owed the home $1,700. Every dollar, quarter, dime, nickel, and prayer helped. He sent his sons down the car to collect money in their hats, and Jose's little brother always got more because he'd blubber like a baby. Even between the cars where no one could see him. Snot coming out of his nose. *Oh my God,* Isabel said. *I'm so sorry.* She asked how his

sister passed away, and Jose told her she didn't understand. There was no sister. The picture was of his cousin Angelique, who grew up and lives in Jersey and works in a dental office. When he saw Isabel's face, his eyes went wide and she could tell he regretted telling her this. *But my father's a cripple now,* he said. *That's a sad story that's true.*

She loved him. She talked about him all the time at the kitchen table. She talked about the gun he bought off a Chinese guy from Flushing.

After the Virgil's robbery, after the police arrested Jose, after he spent a couple days in lockup, the Batistas sprung him out on bail. So there was that at least. For a little while, until the trial, she would be able to hold on to him. They spent New Year's Eve together, driving around Queens and Manhattan, making coke deliveries. At midnight, while Jose was up in a Forest Hills apartment, selling an eightball, Isabel sat alone in the van, listening to the ball drop on the radio. This was 1999 becoming 2000. The tabloids anticipated a Y2K computer Armageddon of reset clocks and erased debts and falling airplanes and a whole world plunged into darkness. But when Isabel looked up she saw lights still burning in dozens of windows. She imagined champagne-flushed faces pressed to the glass. She checked to make sure the doors were locked. She turned down the volume on the radio. She switched seats, got behind the wheel, and wished she knew how to drive. This was it, she thought. For the next two to three years, maybe more, depending on the judge, this was going to be her life. Sitting alone. Waiting for Jose to come back.

The doctor tucks Isabel's shirt under her breasts. From what looks like a tube of toothpaste, he squeezes a clear sticky substance onto her stomach. Gelatinous lumps swim in the goo. Isabel's belly button—recently outied—glistens. She feels cold. When the doctor leans over her body, she pinches her thighs together.

"Have you been having any strange symptoms?" he asks, as if making small talk.

"Strange symptoms?" she says. Her nipples are darker, her back hurts, she passes gas through the night. All normal, pregnancy-related symptoms, apparently, but what about the white discharge that sometimes leaks from her vagina? What about the bleeding? She gets nose-

bleeds; she wipes her ass and there's blood on the toilet paper; she pulls her toothbrush out of her mouth and the bristles are tinged pink. What about absentmindedness? After making scrambled eggs the other day, she came back into the kitchen two hours later to find the stove still on, its blue flame tickling the bottom of the pan. In the last four months, she's lost her house keys twice. She sometimes forgets what day of the week it is. Normal, pregnancy-related absentmindedness? Or not-fit-to-raise-a-child absentmindedness? Isabel has difficulty sleeping, but she's always had difficulty sleeping. She feels faint, dizzy, itchy, and constipated. Her legs cramp up something terrible, her face swells, and sometimes she can't breathe. If she could get any information at all in this hospital—for instance, what vitamins she should be taking, how much weight she should have gained, how much anxiety is too much anxiety, where the fuck have they taken her boyfriend—then maybe she'd be better able to answer this doctor's question, better able to separate the strange symptoms from the normal ones. She says, "I feel like my head is underwater."

"Stuffy ears," the doctor says. "That happens. That's okay." He taps her nose. "And I bet a little nasal congestion, too?"

Alfredo opens the door. For a moment he hovers in the doorway, his hand on the knob. He squints, and when he decides he likes what he sees he bursts into the room with apologies. Got lost going to the bathroom, he explains. Got lost coming back. His voice booms. He takes the bottom of Isabel's shirt and is about to roll it down over her stomach, cover her up, when he sees the gunk spread all over her belly. He scoops some of it up, rubs it between thumb and index finger. When the doctor comes nears him, Alfredo starts pumping his hand. "Nice to meet you," Alfredo says. "A real pleasure." Still shaking the doctor's hand, Alfredo hooks a thumb toward Isabel's belly. "I'm the father. Hey, listen, sorry I'm late."

"Better late than never," the doctor says. "Lots of fathers don't come to these checkups at all."

"Lost going to the bathroom?" Isabel says. "What else happen? You fall in the bowl?"

Like a little boy, Alfredo shrugs. As if Isabel asked him if he ate all the cookies or finger-painted on the walls. She grabs his waistband and pulls him close. She wants to shove her nose in his chest. She

wants him up on this table next to her, so she can whisper in his ear, *Don't you ever leave me alone again.*

While Alfredo squeezes Isabel's hand, the doctor waves his magic wand over her slime-slicked belly. Presto zesto! The computer monitor's speaker vibrates with the *thump-thump* of Christian Louis's heart.

"My God," Isabel says. "Listen to that."

The doctor nods approvingly. "All the tests look great. Healthy baby, healthy mama."

"Good work," Alfredo says. He gives her a thumbs-up. Disaster averted for one more day. With a healthy baby and a healthy baby mama, Alfredo starts bopping his head. "That's a pretty ill beat, don't you think? Thump-thump. Yeah. That's what I'm talking about. Little man's gone be a *rapper.* Thump-thump." Alfredo taps his toe. "Thump-thump. *Mama carrying a strong-hearted baby / Gonna be pimping gold chains and Mercedes.* Thump-thump. Turn that joint up, Doctor!"

The doctor taps his lips, as if deciding how best to proceed. He puts the wand in Isabel's hand so that she can hold it over Christian Louis herself. Free now of all medical responsibilities, the doctor gets up off his stool. He snaps his fingers. Puts some wiggle in his hips and shoulders.

"My man!" Alfredo says. "That's some Calcutta shit, right there! Thump-thump. *Our baby's the ultimate MC / Gonna buy us a house with some cable TV.*"

Alfredo freestyles while the good doctor waves his arms. The men are grooving. Alfredo gets louder, more pumped. The doctor's belly jiggles. Sweat streams into his eyebrow. He's getting tired—the stethoscope doesn't bounce as high off his shoulders as it did just a few moments ago. Soon he'll wipe his brow, button his lab coat, and move on to the next patient. Maybe later tonight at dinner, while uncorking a bottle of wine, he'll tell his beautiful wife about the little jig he did with a Latino couple.

Alfredo stomps his feet, bends his knees, rolls his shoulders, dips his hips—tries, all by himself, to keep this dance party going.

Christian Louis Batista says, *Thump-thump!*

Isabel puts her hands in the air.

A Brief Interlude on the Art of Talking Shit

The streets started murmuring a couple of years ago, after the Virgil's robbery. Gio, Conrad, and Jose Jr. stole over twenty-five hundred dollars from the catering hall, and a mere two days later detectives showed up at their homes. Spiral-bound notebooks in their hands, cuffs in their pockets. *That's some awfully quick police work,* the neighborhood shit-talkers said. *And what a coincidence Alfredo happened to step out of that car.* Alfredo's defenders—principally Winston—argued that coincidences happen every day. That people were just trying to stir up trouble for the sake of stirring up trouble. That they were looking for conspiracy where none existed. That Alfredo caught a lucky break, that's all. No big deal. End of story.

This became a slightly harder position to maintain after Jose went to prison and Alfredo took over his business. Buying trees directly from Baka, Junior's old connect. Raising eyebrows all over the neighborhood. *Well, there you go,* the shit-talkers said. *There's your motive. Greed. Second oldest story there is.* Alfredo's dwindling supporters found this laughable. *Jose's in prison! His little brother can't make a few bucks? Maybe Jose put Baka and Alfredo in touch himself. Ever think of that?* (Voices rising, voices cracking.) *Jesus, man—that shit happens every day of the week.*

This became an almost impossible position to maintain after Alfredo was caught—in Manhattan, at South Street Seaport—sucking

face with Isabel Guerrero, as in Isabel Guerrero, Jose's girlfriend Isabel Guerrero.

Damn, said Alfredo's defenders.

Love, the shit-talkers said, rubbing their hands together. *Oldest story there is.*

And then—like a gift from the gossip gods—Izzy got pregnant, and the streets went buck wild. Some of the chattiest shit-talkers must've gone to bed with their gums bleeding, with ice packs pressed to their overworked jaws. Must've spent their days recuperating with herbal tea, straight from the pot. Thanks to their efforts, the gossip grew legs, left the neighborhood, spread out to the borders of Queens, and then, eventually, farther north, upstate. How could it not? People got arrested and some of them were sent out to Woodbourne and Sing Sing and Attica and Otisville and Bedford Hills, but a small number rode the bus up to Fishkill, and of that number, all of them—Alfredo was sure of this—all of them found his brother as soon as their feet hit the ground. Big grins on their stupid fucking faces.

You heard, man? You heard?

Alfredo wondered how often his brother found himself on the other end of that news. And man oh man, what fun the other inmates must have had. When Tariq walked through the mess hall with a brown-lettuced hamburger on his tray did the other tables grow suddenly quiet? Or did they burst into laughter? Did the guards find out? Did they use it to taunt him? When Alfredo couldn't sleep—which was every night—he asked himself these questions, and they always led him to the same place, the überworry, the mother of all questions: What's Tariq gonna do when he comes home?

Yeah, well, join the club, Dito. That's what everyone else wants to know, too. While chalking up cues at the pool hall, while bending slices at Gianni's, while getting haircuts at Headz Ain't Ready, while waiting on the platform for the 7 train, while tagging up streetlamps, while splitting open blunts, while sitting on bar stools and milk crates and beach chairs and apartment stoops, the shit-talkers speculated as to what the Batista brothers have planned for their upcoming reunion. They couldn't ask Tariq, for obvious reasons. But they could always find Alfredo outside the Alleyway and tap him on the shoulder, put the question to him directly. But they won't. It seemed somehow less rude—and definitely more fun—to talk about Alfredo behind his

back. Everyone wanted to know what he had planned, but no one was willing to come right out and ask him.

Except for Max Marshmallow. Rude questions? Please. He was seventy-two years old. Asking rude questions was one of his specialties.

Last Sunday, with street-corner business slow to nonexistent, Alfredo walked into a late-night bodega to rifle through its magazine rack. This was days before Alfredo had ever even heard of Vladimir Shifrin. Max Marshmallow, the bodega's owner, sat behind the counter, reading four different newspapers—his nightly research for a book he'd always been planning to write, *A Comprehensive History of New York Schemes.* In one hand he held a yellow highlighter, in the other, a red-handled pair of scissors. He put both away as soon as Alfredo walked in.

"How's that beautiful mother of yours?" Max asked.

"Come on," Alfredo said. He stood staring at the magazines, his back to the counter. "Why you wanna know?"

"It's called making conversation," Max said.

"She's fine."

"And your father?"

"He says hello, actually."

"Really?"

"No, not really. It's just something people say. It's called being polite."

"And the gorgeous Isabel?" Max said. "Who—I hope you don't mind me saying—puts blood in my penis. How is she? Seven months along now, if I'm not mistaken."

"Six," Alfredo lied.

"Great, great," Max said. He leaned forward on his stool, his elbows on the counter, and got to the good stuff. "So what you gonna do when your brother gets home?"

Alfredo groaned. "You're as bad as the rest of them."

"I'm worse," Max said. He grinned, his false teeth gleaming. They were bright white, these teeth, and while most fogies opt for at least some slight discoloration—chompers artificially stained by artificial packs of cigarettes and artificial cups of coffee—Max went with the ivories. A smile that dazzles. He said he couldn't figure out why anyone would choose—would pay!—to look old. The teeth shared tenancy

with a perpetually refreshed set of marshmallows, always two, one in each cheek. They started as a punishment, quickly became a trademark, and now, all these years later, they were one more boyish affectation. He claimed that his mother used to stuff his mouth full of marshmallows to keep him from talking, but, clearly, it never worked. "Humor me," he told Alfredo. "Soon as you see your brother—what do you do? What you got planned?"

"Noisemakers," Alfredo said. "Pointy hats. A piñata maybe, although I don't know if I wanna put a bat in his hands."

"Probably not."

"No," Alfredo said. "Probably not." He scanned the titles in the magazine rack, looking for the latest issue of *GamePro*, the video game monthly. He wasn't looking for himself—if he was going to read a magazine, it'd be *Baseball Weekly* or the *Source*—he was looking for Winston, across the street in the Alleyway, guarding the stash. "Tell you the truth," Alfredo said, "I don't really have a plan. Drugs. I'm trying to find a package of drugs for him. Winston thinks it's a nice gesture." He couldn't keep himself from shrugging, from keeping the self-pity out of his voice. "Beyond that, I don't know. I'm trying not to think about it too much."

"Maybe you should start," Max said.

"Maybe you should mind your own business."

"I would," Max said, sweeping his arm out, gesturing to the unplugged deli-meat slicer, the unsold roach hotels, the unsold squeeze bottles of Fox's U-bet Chocolate Syrup, the unsold naan next to the unsold hot dog buns, "but my business isn't as interesting as yours."

Separated by age and ethnicity, Max and Alfredo are unlikely friends, but both men love to talk, and gabbers will always find each other. The Batista family used to own this store, used to live in the little railroad apartment set up in back. (You couldn't beat the commute.) But after Jose Sr.'s accident, they sold the place to Max, who reversed a neighborhood trend and became the first non-Arab, non-Korean, non-Latino to purchase a bodega in over twenty years. Not that he called it a bodega. He insisted instead on the anachronistic "candy store," the term connoting for him a bygone borough of egg creams, pitched pennies, Koosman's Mets, and the '64 World's Fair. When Alfredo started peddling reefer on the sidewalk, it must have challenged Max's sepia vision of The Way Things Were—but as a

functioning New Yorker, he quickly adapted to The Way Things Is. It helped of course that they enjoyed each other's company. Max liked coming up with schemes, and Alfredo liked shooting them down.

"This is what you do," Max said.

"Great," Alfredo said. He found the issue of *GamePro* and plucked it out of the rack. "Let's hear it. Lay it on me. Tell me what to do."

"Poker," Max said. He folded his arms triumphantly across his chest.

"Poker," Alfredo said.

"You tell Jose—"

"Tariq," Alfredo corrected.

"You tell Tariq you're throwing him a welcome home party. These meshuggener types? They're easily flattered. Trust me, I know. You tell him you're throwing a party in his honor, but not the kind of party with noisemakers and pointy hats. A poker game, okay? We do it under the store, in the basement. Move some boxes around. Get a nice green felt table from Costco. Yeah? We'll invite over some of your friends, invite over some of his friends. Crack open some beers. It'll be beautiful."

"And then what?" Alfredo said. "We charge all the players fifty bucks a head? House keeps ten percent of all winnings?"

"Ten percent seems a little high, if you ask me."

Above their heads Max's idea spread its wings, and Alfredo took aim.

"I don't know about poker," Alfredo said. He thought his friends would actually love to participate in an underground poker game, but he wanted to punish Max for sticking that schnoz of his where it didn't belong. "Guys I know? If they play cards, they're doing it on the Internet."

"That's not the same," Max cried. A marshmallow quivered on the tip of his tongue. "Where's the camaraderie on the Internet? Where's the bullshitting?"

As Alfredo moved toward the door, he held up the *GamePro*. "I'm taking this," he said.

"It defeats the whole purpose, the Internet. There's no *stories*."

"Sorry, Max. The poker's a dud."

"It's a better idea than your piñata," he said with the fat, lower-lipped petulance of a child.

"The piñata was a maybe," Alfredo said. "It was always up in the air."

He laughed at his own joke, as he had a tendency to do.

"Where you going with that magazine?" Max asked him, but he'd already escaped. The door slammed shut behind him.

An hour later, Max walked out onto the sidewalk, the candy store's awning glowing yellow and red behind him, his seventy-two-year-old face pink and exhilarated. Alfredo, who handled the money transactions, stood on one side of the street, and Winston, who handled the drugs, stood on the other. When he looked up from his magazine, Winston smiled and waved, and Max, with equal vigor, waved back. It was three o'clock in the morning.

"My man, Fredo!" Max said. Arms swinging, pelvis out, he strutted over to where Alfredo was standing. If not for the marshmallows, he might've whistled. "What's poppin, homeboy? What's crack-a-lackin?"

"If you're here to buy prostate shrinkers," Alfredo said, "I don't have any."

They stood shoulder to shoulder, both men staring into the street as if waiting for a bus. "You know why you didn't like the poker idea?" Max said.

"Why didn't I like the poker idea?"

"Because it was boring," Max said. He grabbed hold of his crotch and gave it a squeeze. "It didn't have any balls."

"I'm thinking—I can't be sure about this—but I'm thinking you got a new plan, yeah?"

"I know you're real busy," Max whispered, looking both ways down the deserted sidewalk. "But I'd like to show you something."

He turned on his heel and strolled away toward the candy store, walking with the air of a man who fully expected to be followed. Winston, apparently, expected the same. He stuck a finger in his magazine, marking his place, and hollered out a request for a diet soda. Anyone else? Any other requests for the errand boy? Sure! Perched under an AC, a pigeon lifted its groggy wing and asked for a five a.m. wake-up call. The streetlamps wanted new bulbs. The tires of parked cars, more air. And if Alfredo wasn't too busy, would he mind emptying out the wastebaskets on the corner? It never ends. When he closed his eyes, he saw spots, little novas of light. In the last hour and a half, he had made exactly one drug sale, a dime bag sold to a teenager named

AIDS. Alfredo wanted to go home, pour himself into bed with Isabel, wrestle with the twin icebergs she called her feet. But instead, like a good boy, he followed Max Marshmallow into the candy store.

On the counter a newspaper sat primed for Alfredo's inspection.

"Check this out," Max said. He pointed to an AP-credited photo of a sweaty-faced black guy, his hands wrapped tight around a microphone. "You know who this is?" Max asked, and didn't wait for an answer. "DMX. That's what it says right here. Dark Man X. You listen to his music?"

"Not really," Alfredo said. "He's from Yonkers. I don't listen to rappers from Yonkers."

"I don't know anything about that," Max said. "But it says right here"—he looked down at his finger, as if to make sure it was still under the photo and hadn't wandered over to the lingerie ad on the other side of the page—"it says right here that there's some controversy over his lyrics. I don't give a shit about any of that, but it gave me an idea. Every great idea—I ever tell you this?—every great idea you're ever going to get is going to hit you while you're reading the paper. I read four papers a day. The *Post, Newsday,* the *Daily News,* and the *New York Times.* The *Times* is the best. If I spoke Spanish, I'd read your *El Diario.*"

"Max," Alfredo said.

"So I'm looking at this DMX guy, and I get to thinking, right? I have all that space under the store. I want to get some gambling going, there's big money in gambling, but you tell me we need something your friends can't find on the Internet. So Alfredo, let me ask you— what do you know about dogfighting?"

"Dogfighting?"

"Dogfighting," Max said.

"I don't know anything about dogfighting," Alfredo said. "I don't know anyone who's ever even *been* to a dogfight."

"Yeah, but think about it for a second. Imagine the effect it would have on Jose."

"Tariq," Alfredo corrected.

"Okay, imagine the effect it would have on Tariq."

Alfredo imagined it. He imagined Tariq walking down into the basement on Saturday night, the night he comes home, the dogs nipping at air, Alfredo standing between them, arms raised, a wad of cash

in his fist. Huh. A thing like that might actually impress Tariq, a man who respects only power and violence. He'd see that Alfredo ain't the greasy-faced seventeen-year-old he left behind. Little brother was all grown up. A neighborhood player. A dogfighting entrepreneur who will not be easily intimidated.

"I don't know," Alfredo said. "I think maybe it's not a bad idea."

A small current of panic jolted Max's face. "Really?"

"You're serious about this, right?" Alfredo said. "I don't want to make moves on this unless you're for real."

Max bit into a marshmallow, and for a brief moment Alfredo felt sorry for this old man, who spent his days and nights dreaming up credit card schemes and calling card schemes and bail bond schemes and sweetheart schemes and underground gambling schemes without ever intending to follow through on any of them. Just another shit-talker. A cash-register jockey trying to protect himself from the sharp teeth of boredom.

"Are *you* serious?" Max asked.

"I'm not sure," Alfredo said. "I think so."

"Then I think so too," Max said. "Why not, right?" He rolled back his shoulders. "Let's do it."

Things moved quickly after that.

Alfredo went out onto the sidewalk and phoned the Alphabet Brothers, the only guys he knew who owned a pit bull. He asked them if they might be interested in some dogfighting, preferably on this upcoming Saturday night. Violence and mayhem? Of course they were interested. One slight hang-up: they didn't own a pit bull, they owned a German shepherd. Was that gonna be a problem? Not at all! It was even better, matter of fact. A pit bull brawling a German shepherd would be a more unexpected matchup and therefore, to Alfredo's thinking, a more authentic dogfighting experience.

"What's the dog's name?" he asked, wanting to know for publicity purposes. When they told him, he said, "You're kidding."

The next day he went to the shit-talkers. It was like the Mets reaching out to the Yankees, like Piazza canoodling with Clemens. Alfredo visited the neighborhood gossips outside their bodegas and barber-shops, their pizzerias and pool halls, and he whispered in their ears, asking that they please not tell anyone, thereby ensuring they would. Within hours, the word was on the wire.

Now all Alfredo needed to do was find himself a dog. On Tuesday, he took the R train to the Animal Care and Control center in Rego Park, only to find out that they're not open on Tuesdays—not that it mattered since according to the sign in the window they don't even offer any animals up for adoption. They just take them in. Well great. On to Plan B. If he couldn't adopt a pit bull, he'd steal one. On Wednesday, Alfredo (taking shallow breaths) and Winston (smoking blunts) walked through what seemed like every last alleyway in the neighborhood, including the Alleyway, looking in people's backyards for a chained-up, left-alone pit bull. They found a thousand dandelions, nine deflated soccer balls, dozens of white plastic patio chairs with pockets of week-old rainwater in the seats, a little Filipino girl fiddling with matches (they told her to stop), a tireless car propped up on cement blocks, abandoned baby diapers, busted TVs, cigarette butts, countless planes above their heads roaring into LaGuardia Airport, a pair of sneakers tied together and hung from a telephone pole (the sight of which made Alfredo's blister-clad feet squirm in their Timberlands), nice old ladies, mean old ladies, basketball hoops, barbecue grills, and hundreds of American flags, draped over balconies and stuck in the ground, big flags and little flags, all of which had been purchased in the last nine months. What Alfredo and Winston did not find, however, was a pit bull. On Thursday, exhausted, they loitered outside 7-Eleven and waited for a Slurpee-craving dog walker to leave his pit tied to a parking meter. It didn't happen. By late evening, with only forty-eight hours to go, Winston and Alfredo started thinking beyond pit bulls: they would have settled for another German shepherd, a rottweiler, an obese rat, a rabid squirrel, a piranha in a fishbowl. Any animal, really, with a cantankerous disposition. On Friday, after coming back from Elmhurst Hospital with Isabel, Alfredo called Winston and told him all the prenatal tests came back strong. Healthy baby, healthy mama. Disaster averted for one more day. Alfredo had a good feeling. This is the night, he told Winston. This is the night, this is the night. We gonna get ourselves a dog.

The Heist, Part One

When Alfredo walks into Gianni's Pizzeria, he finds Winston exactly where he expects to find Winston: by the front door, hunched over the *Street Fighter II* machine. Surrounded by Asian onlookers, he hammers the keypad and throttles the joystick. When his on-screen avatar leaps, Winston goes up on his tiptoes. When the character moves left, Winston leans with her; when she moves right, Winston bangs into his opponent, a Chinese teenager with liberally gelled hair. Like most experienced gamers, the Chinese kid plays with his back straight and his fingers loose, an even-tempered maestro conducting an orchestra. Alfredo can see, however, that the kid's shoulders have started to slump.

In a video game there are a certain number of frames per second, layered sequentially so as to give the impression of continuous movement. Just like a movie. What Winston can do is see *between* those frames.

Whatever the hell that means. When he tries to explain it, Alfredo usually zones out and starts thinking about something else: the Mets, Isabel, a folder in the cabinet. As far as Alfredo can tell, Winston plays defensively. He waits for his opponent to make an aggressive move, reacts before the next frame pops up, and then beats the virtual shit out of him. For instance:

In one fluid motion, the Chinese kid taps his buttons and crooks his joystick, and his on-screen character, the ninja Ryu, shoots a pixilated fireball from his pixilated fingertips. But Winston sees between the frames. His character, the ninety-eight-pound Chun-Li, has already leapt over Ryu. She crouches behind him, her chest heaving. While the fireball moves into empty space, Chun-Li takes out Ryu's legs with a low roundhouse kick. As he falls, she catches him with an uppercut; while he's in the air, she finishes him off with a series of punches and kicks: low, medium, and high. An eight-hit combo. The fireball spirals off the screen, exits stage left and into the wings. Game over.

The boys in the crowd turn to look at one another. Almost all of them, Alfredo imagines, made the trip out here from Flushing, riding the 7 train from Main Street to Eighty-second for the opportunity to challenge Winston in a game that's almost as old as they are. Those who have never seen Winston play before allow their eyes to widen.

It is a cutthroat world, the world of high-level competitive gaming. The participants are almost universally the socially abused—the stutterers, the BO challenged, the acne pocked, the alopecia afflicted, the kids who collected Magic cards and lurked in the back of the gym during dodgeball. Whupping somebody's ass in *Street Fighter II* is their chance to stand tall, to get in an opponent's face and talk some shit. But that's not Winston's style. He gives the Chinese kid a slight bow, then turns to the crowd and quietly asks, "Who's next?"

No one jumps forward. Reluctant to embarrass themselves, the onlookers drift toward Gianni's counter for some slices and garlic knots; others, the ones with particularly delicate egos, leave the pizzeria entirely and head for Flushing, running away from Winston as if he were a fire-breathing Godzilla. *That's my best friend,* Alfredo wants to tell them. *How do you like that?*

Outside the pizzeria, Alfredo launches into his usual post-Gianni's spiel: how Winston's getting exploited like a circus bear, how he's bringing in like 90 percent of Gianni's business, how that fat dago probably wakes up on Saturday mornings to push a wheelbarrow full of quarters to the bank, how Alfredo knows Winston gets his free slices and his unlimited Mountain Dews but maybe he should be getting

paid like the business partner he is—which is to say, maybe Winston should be getting paid cash money.

"Get your hands in the wheelbarrow, if you know what I mean."

Winston looks straight ahead, stares out of an empty face. His eyes are dilated, his pupils eclipsed. "What's good with that X?" he says. Behind him, two white kids circle each other, slap boxing. Winston pays them no mind. "You wanna go halfsies on a pill?" he asks.

"That shit's for my brother," Alfredo says.

"No, definitely. I'm really just talking about half a pill though."

The older of the two white kids—he must be around twelve—catches the younger upside the head with an open-hand stinger. Alfredo wants to tell them to stop, but he hasn't had much luck talking to kids today, and besides, he ain't in the business of parenting other people's children.

Winston says, "You think one pill's gonna make a difference to your brother?"

Because in addition to being a video game prodigy, Winston is also a skilled and insistent needler, and because Alfredo owes him money, and because Winston might still be shaken up over the Vladimir incident, and because it's supposedly his last night of doing drugs (and even if Alfredo wants to roll his eyes every time he hears that bullshit, friendship requires that he act like he believes him), and because, really, what's one more pill, because fifty is a nice round number, because Tariq will never know, because a crashing Winston is a foot-dragging Winston, because even if it goes against everything Alfredo believes in, sometimes it's just easier to give in—Alfredo decides to hand over a pill. He brings Winston around the corner where no one can see them. And where it smells like some seriously stank-ass shit. Damn! The fruit and vegetable grocers must have illegally dumped their overripe produce down the gutter, and now the smell of rot wafts up from beneath the sidewalk. Alfredo would pinch his nostrils together but he needs both hands to pull the top off the E-beeper. Like any magic trick performed twice, it's lost much of its pizzazz. He grabs a pill out of the beeper, but before he drops it into Winston's cupped palms, he first takes a peek. He brings the X close to his face for inspection, and his forehead runs cold. He feels an urge—it both frightens and exhilarates—to bash in Winston's skull.

What Alfredo sees in the middle of the pill, etched into its chalky surface, is this:

∞

A logo. A brand. A tattoo shared by all the other pills in the beeper. Meaning Winston's intelligence report was faulty. The pills *do* hit the streets with logos, and, even worse, it's a logo Alfredo recognizes, an infinity sign, which emblazons not only all of Vladimir's E, but Baka's as well. Meaning either Boris gets in his lab coat, brews up some pills, and stamps them with a copyright-infringing logo, or there is no Boris the Chemist. If one thing is inaccurate in Winston's report, why can't all of it be inaccurate? Maybe Vladimir buys his pills from Baka, or from the pusherman *above* Baka. And maybe—the thought tightens like a knot—that superthug won't be too happy about his boy getting kicked in the throat.

Of the five boroughs, Queens has the most efficiently run drug industry. From Jamaica to Astoria, the crack, coke, and H game goes through a small number of corporations, each one tightly structured. Records are kept. Codes are scribbled into ledgers. There is a hierarchy with easily replaceable five-oh lookouts kicking it up to corner boys kicking it up to enforcers and treasurers and runners, who are all kicking it up to local gang leaders who themselves are kicking it up to a dozen boss hogs. With their drug money, these top-of-the-triangle gangsters open up travel agencies and antique shops and any other business with easily fudged books, and they smoke Cubans and dream of hip-hop stardom, and then, after three, four, or maybe even five years, the federal indictments come hammering down and these gangsters go straight to jail. The twenty-five-year-olds on the rung below move up and become the new boss hogs. And then in three, four, or maybe even five years . . .

Alfredo ain't interested. He sticks to weed, buying a little at a time off Baka and marketing it creatively. Selling it, for instance, not in miniature Ziploc baggies but in clear plastic vials, the kind hospitals use. The rubber stopper at the top of the plastic tube gives the impression the weed was stuffed in an airtight container; the curved shape magnifies the amount of product inside, allowing Alfredo to skim a bit

off the top; and the vials' glassy smoothness suggests to consumers that these tubes have recently been plucked from the unfortunate anuses of Colombian drug mules. Freshness, therefore, is guaranteed. If he were keeping this Ecstasy, as opposed to giving it to his brother tomorrow, Alfredo would market it in a couples package, selling two pills at a time—one for your pleasure, one for hers—with a discounted Viagra thrown in to counteract E's dick-softening effects.

Not that Alfredo's *all* about the marketing. He also looks for income outside the corporate pyramid. Buying scrips off the Internet. Running dogfights in Max's basement. It was always Alfredo's brother who wanted to climb up the triangle, to push the real shit—yak, crack, and China—at the real weight, but Alfredo is happy to stay a free agent. Less money equals less jail time and fewer bullets in the ass. But Alfredo's survival as a free agent requires that he stay quiet, that he not shatter the wrong guy's jaw.

Disgusted, Alfredo throws the infinity-branded pill to the ground. While he rattles the E-beeper and explains the situation, Winston gets down on his hands and knees. He slips his fingers into the cracks between sidewalk panels. He takes out his cell, hoping to make use of its green glow, but the phone is off or the battery's dead—Winston having probably neglected to charge it. Alfredo's harangue is smoke, and Winston crawls underneath it. He brings his face close to the sidewalk, close to the subterranean smells of rotten fruits and rotten vegetables, until he finally finds his pill. Only a couple of inches away this whole time. And within striking distance of Alfredo's boot.

If candy and the fat man have the five second rule, then drugs and the drug addict have five years. Winston brushes the pill against his shirt and throws it down the hatch.

"What's the problem?" he says. As he chews the pill, his face sours, comes alive. "So the X got logos? That's beautiful, far as I see it. Saves us the trouble of branding it ourselves."

"You told me—"

"I was wrong. I guess that's my bad. But maybe—just hold on—maybe there's no reason to get our panties in a bunch. Maybe these logos will turn out to be a positive factor in our overall plans. Because like I'm saying—"

"Please," Alfredo says. Blood hammers his temples. He raises his

hand—for what? to bunch Winston's shirt in his fist?—and ends up just patting him on the chest, as if Winston were the one who needs soothing. "Just . . . okay? Just not right now."

"All I'm saying—"

"You're pushing me."

"Jesus," Winston says. "I'm not pushing anybody. All I'm saying is—"

"All you're saying should be nothing right now. Right now you should be keeping your fucking mouth shut."

Winston takes off his Spider-Man cap and flexes the bill. He and Alfredo do not speak to each other this way. Sure, they bicker. They know each other's limits, and sometimes—as if that knowledge is too much to bear—they test those limits. But bickering ain't fighting. Alfredo and Winston aren't supposed to raise their voices or bark at each other or curse each other out. Pain shoots across Alfredo's forehead. A cabinet drawer slides open.

Winston stares into the empty shell of his hat, as if it concealed some secret message, a cryptic code, a sun-bleached map. He says, "I just thought of where we might be able to find a dog."

He'd been clueless all week, but he gets yelled at and cursed at, and all of a sudden—how convenient!—he has an idea regarding the whereabouts of a pit bull. Okay, Alfredo thinks. That's fine. Alfredo's pulled this shit himself. In sixth and seventh grade, he'd hide his decent report cards in his book bag, saving them for when he got into trouble. He never had to wait long. He'd break a vase playing Wiffle ball in the house with Jose Jr., or he'd get lippy with his mother at the kitchen table, and then it'd be all *hijo de Diablo,* you're grounded, no TV for a month. After about an hour, Alfredo would slink out of his room and say, "Sorry, Papi—but I need you to sign my report card." And Jose Sr. would see A− in Language Arts, B in Social Studies, B− in Science, A+ in Math, and how could he stay mad at him after that, particularly when he probably didn't want to be mad at him in the first place. So it goes with Winston. He'd kept this dog info under his Spider-Man cap as a kind of collateral. Divulge in Case of Emergency. Or maybe not. Maybe Winston thought of it right when he said he thought of it. Doesn't matter to Alfredo. He's just happy for the distraction, happy to think about something other than his anxiety marquee: *The Return of Tariq,* and below that, just now added to the signboard, *Infinity-Branded X.*

"I figure we just been waiting to get lucky this whole time," Winston says. "Going through people's backyards. Waiting outside Seven-Eleven. We're like sitting around, expecting a dog to drop out of the sky."

"Okay," Alfredo says. "I like where your head's at."

Winston closes his eyes, as if he just misplaced the thread of his argument. "But what if . . . okay, hold on . . . what if we went to a place we *know* has dogs. Yeah? What if we went looking for an intimidating dog where dog owners need to intimidate?" Winston spreads his arms out wide and suggests a place they've passed thousands of times before, a place where at this time of night there'd be some scary moth-erfucking dogs just waiting to get took: the Queens County Savings Bank.

"A bank?" Alfredo says. "There ain't any dogs in banks."

"Sure there is. At night and shit. To guard the money. I've seen them, I think."

"Like you thought Vladimir's pills didn't have logos?" When Winston looks away, Alfredo says, "Even if Queens County had pit bulls—so what? How we supposed to rob a bank of its dogs?"

"I guess it's a dumb idea."

Alfredo wonders if it's an intentionally dumb idea. Is Winston playing stupid to be annoying, as payback for Alfredo's outburst earlier? In the end, it seems irrelevant—Winston's dumb idea sparkplugs a better one.

"What about the used car lots?" Alfredo says.

Because car lots in Queens, like little old ladies, all seem to huddle together, Winston and Alfredo are able to limit their reconnaissance to a ten-block radius. At the first lot they visit, Alfredo rattles the fence while Winston mimics *woof-woofs*. A cat darts under a fender. At the second lot they think they see some kind of dog crouching in the shadows, but it turns out to be a tire. At the third lot, at the fourth lot, at the fifth lot, more of the same, and so—who can blame them?—they approach the sixth lot with diminished hopes.

Northern Boulevard's redundantly named Allouez Preowned Used Cars Supercenter is protected by a twenty-foot-high fence. Razor wire slithers across the top, each coil evenly spaced as if a giant snake had

come here to molt. Behind the fence glint Caravans and Cherokees and Honda Odysseys, their respective prices scribbled onto their respective windshields in bright white soap.

$3800. $5295.
120,000 miles.   94,000 miles.
One owner.   Runs like new.

"What's that?" Winston says, pointing toward the back of the lot.

Alfredo squints. "What's what?"

"You don't see that? Between the cars? Way back there? What *is* that?"

Alfredo cleans his glasses against the hem of his shirt. Once he's respectacled, he thinks he sees something, a blur maybe—yes, yes, he *definitely* sees it, a black blurry creature dancing between cars, spinning and leaping.

"I think it's a cat," Winston says. Disappointment floods his voice. "Yeah, that's a cat for sure."

Alfredo kicks the bottom of the fence. The chain links' quivering shoots reverberations through the asphalt toward the back of the lot and tickles the bottoms of paws. The blurry black creature lifts its blurry black head. Slowly, as if annoyed, it squares its shoulders and begins to gallop toward them, revealing itself in long-legged strides.

"Doberman," Alfredo says, as the dog gets closer.

"Is that a fighting dog?"

"I wouldn't want to fight one."

It is possible—no, rather it is likely—that somewhere along the trip out west Lewis turned to Clark and told him to shut his fucking mouth. Perhaps they walked on for hours or even days in awkward silence, but all was surely forgiven when at last they passed Mount Hood and saw for the first time the shimmering Pacific. *Mission accomplished!* Grinning, Winston and Alfredo slap palms. For here, finally, is their own prize: a dog, and a mean-looking one too. Just inches away, close enough to tap on the nose. Close enough for Alfredo to feel its hot breath on his knuckles. The Doberman steps forward, darkly displeased.

In a threatening situation, a dog will often look toward its owner for cues on how to behave. Rounded eyes, open mouth, tense arms, shal-

low breaths: if a dog sees these in its guardian, it knows to attack. But the Doberman's owner is not here. The Doberman's owner—Mr. Allouez of Allouez Preowned Used Cars Supercenter—is probably at home on Long Island, watching Letterman throw pencils at the camera. Without Mr. Allouez's nonverbal input, the Doberman must make decisions on its own.

"Do not," Alfredo whispers, "look into its eyes."

The dog lunges. Up on its hind legs, it gnashes its jaws and claws at metal. Saliva, thick and heavy, spills across the fence. The blessed fence. The Doberman turns its head sideways and insinuates its long snout into a diamond-shaped chain link. Lips curl upward, expose sharp yellow teeth.

"Jesus Christ," Alfredo says, and immediately—to atone for the blasphemy—makes the sign of the cross. Both he and Winston take generous steps away from the fence. Their heels hang over the lip of the curb. "You looked in its eyes," Alfredo says.

"I looked in its eyes," Winston says. His hand covers his heart. "And while I'm admitting things let me admit something else. I ain't going *near* that dog."

Well that's too bad, Alfredo thinks. Because I ain't going near that fucking dog either. And that's just the start of their trouble. Not only is this Doberman snarling, but it is snarling within a well-lit compound, circumscribed by a twenty-foot-high fence. Alfredo closes his eyes. Think of it as a math equation with a complex string of integers, plus and minus signs, parenthetical asides. You need to break the problem down into smaller problems and isolate its component difficulties. Solving part one, Alfredo hopes, will help unlock part two.

He reaches into his baggie of prescription pills and pulls out a Valium. The pill—ten milligrams, the smallest dose he sells—costs about fifteen dollars on the street. It hurts to be throwing money away, but that's the cost of doing business. Gotta spend cash to make cash. Pill in hand, Alfredo rears back and goes into his windup.

One of the great frustrations of Alfredo's childhood was his excommunication from the green-grassed world of Little League baseball. The Elmjack baseball fields were four miles away from Alfredo's house, and after Jose Sr.'s accident, and after the cars were sold, and after Lizette went to work at Remmelts Oculists, there wasn't anyone around who could escort the eleven-year-old Alfredo to games. Those

four miles loomed large, and Alfredo, like Pete Rose before him, found himself banned from organized baseball. The prohibition may have elicited less door slamming in the Batista household if Alfredo's brother had not gotten his full Little League allotment. Or if people weren't always talking about how good Alfredo's brother was. *The line drives he smashed! The backpedaling catches he made!* Had Alfredo been allowed to stay in Little League all the way up to the Babe Ruth division, who's to say he wouldn't have matched, or maybe even surpassed, Jose Jr.'s talents? Given the extra Elmjack years, the extra games and practices, the tutelage of coaches and assistant coaches, the yearslong encouragement of his mother in the bleachers, doing her crossword puzzles between innings—given all that, Alfredo's arm might have finally bloomed and it could be him they talk about now when they talk about baseball. They'd say, *Remember that time Alfredito threw out that kid at home plate? Ball didn't even bounce.* But that never happened. Alfredo never threw anyone out at home plate, and so, understandably, nobody talks about it. All because Alfredo was born too late. When he came into adolescence, the party was already over. The plastic cups had been stacked high, the radio unplugged, the ashtrays all dumped out.

Alfredo's arm comes forward. Teeth gritted, he throws the Valium. A strike is the back of the dog's gullet, but, of course, the story of Alfredo's baseball-tossing career: impressive velocity, unfortunate aim. The pill bounces off a link in the fence and lands on the sidewalk outside the car lot. In the worst possible place. The fence prevents the Doberman from getting at the Valium, which lies on the sidewalk so close to the dog's snapping jaws that Alfredo feels reluctant to go pick it up. Unreasonable? Alfredo admits the fence looks perfectly adequate, but stranger things have happened than a dog chewing through metal to chase a young Puerto Rican down the street.

"Do me a favor," Alfredo says, pointing at the pill. "Go get that for me?"

Without taking a step forward, Winston says, "Sure. No problem. I'll do that right away."

Alfredo pulls out another Valium. He adjusts his trajectory, aims far and high. This time when he throws, he feels an icy tingling shoot down his shoulder all the way to his fingertips. The pill soars over the dog's head. Impressive velocity—if it were a Frisbee and not a Valium,

the dog might give pursuit. Instead, he gets low to the ground and growls.

"My turn," Winston says.

"One more."

"One more is going to turn into ten more. I want a throw while there's still some pills left. And to be honest I feel like maybe you owe me."

Alfredo wonders if in fifty years he and Winston will be sitting on a bench in Travers Park, fighting with liver-spotted hands over which one of them gets to toss Wonder bread to the pigeons. "If there's an aspirin in there," he says, handing Winston the bag, "save it for me."

Winston's fingers close around a Valium of his own. In an uncharacteristic display of self-confidence—as if to say *I will need only one pill to perform this feat*—he seals the plastic baggie and sticks it in his pocket. He tugs down on the bill of his Spider-Man cap. He adjusts his crotch. He'd probably spit too, if the Ecstasy hadn't dried out his mouth. Winston takes a deep breath and a step forward and—apparently unconcerned with the pretenses of machismo—pitches the pill underhand. The Valium arcs. It spins. It squirts through an opening in the fence and hits the dog square on the snout.

On the people side of the fence, there is much cheering. Alfredo goes for a high five and Winston comes in for a hug and any potential awkwardness is bulldozed by the glory of the moment, like when Gary Carter leapt into Jesse Orosco's arms. Somehow Winston and Alfredo do all things at once: hug, bump fists, high-five, slap each other's backs.

On the dog side of the fence, the Doberman bends to the pill, which is rattling on the ground like a dropped dime. A tentative paw clamps down on top of the Valium. Everything is quiet. The dog lifts its paw and gives the pill a deep and solicitous sniff. *Blecch.* Disgusted by the pill, bored with Winston and Alfredo and everything else, the dog saunters toward the back of the lot, disappointed perhaps that it didn't get to chew on somebody's jugular, but eager, surely, to resume dancing.

"This shit ain't meant to be," Winston says sadly. "We're gonna have to call people soon. I mean if this dogfight ain't gonna happen, we're gonna have to let everybody know. We've got heads coming out here from *Staten Island*."

"Nobody's canceling anything," Alfredo says.

"Whatever happened to simple parties?" Winston says. "Whatever happened to getting somebody an ice cream cake?"

If only it were that easy. Go down to Carvel, cop a Cookie Puss cake or a Fudgie the Whale, and let Tariq blow out the candles. Punch him lightly on the shoulder and say, "Hey big bro, sorry I knocked up your girl." *Fuck that.* Alfredo ain't sorry. Alfredo, who feels guilty about everything, refuses to apologize for falling in love with Isabel. In the intracranial filing cabinet, the Winston folder from this night alone is thicker than the Tariq folder. Fuck that maniac. And even if Alfredo were sorry—which he ain't, but even if he were—apologizing would make as big a difference as handshakes and ice cream. Power and violence. That's the way it's gonna have to be. Alfredo needs this dogfight, needs it to advertise his gangsterism. *I have gotten too big to be slapped around without repercussions.* It's the LoJack sticker in the window of a sports car, the horns protruding from a bull's head, the logo branded onto the surface of Ecstasy.

"Unless we going to all this trouble," Winston says, "so you and Izzy can have a guard dog. That's some shit I'd understand."

With the Doberman dancing at the back of the lot, Winston apparently feels brave enough to approach the fence. He scoops up a pill of Valium, the only one he can reach, and slips it into his back pocket. He's rolling on a double dose of X and God knows what else—a sleeping pill should come in handy at around six a.m., when he's under the covers, grinding his teeth and staring up at the ceiling. Unlike the Doberman, Winston won't hesitate to swallow the pill.

It occurs to Alfredo that the Doberman might not have been so eager to walk from the Valium if it had smelled like bacon. Or better yet, if it had tasted like bacon. "I've got an idea," he says.

"I'm sure you do."

"You wanna go for a ride?"

Winston laughs. "The ghetto car?"

The ghetto car is not an automobile of shabby or suspect value, a lemon with a busted window or broken carburetor. It has never coughed out foul smoke or dragged its muffler through the streets of

Queens, because, strictly speaking, it doesn't exist. It is, from bumper to bumper, an imaginary car.

Because of the hours Winston and Alfredo keep, their bellies rumble at inopportune times, when the only economical dining option is McDonald's. But McDonald's, late at night, locks all its doors for security reasons, keeping open only its drive-thru window. And to get food from this drive-thru window you absolutely, no exceptions, had to be in a car.

"No car. No food."

Because Alfredo can't afford a real automobile, used or otherwise, and because he doesn't even know how to drive, all he's got is the ghetto car.

Speaking into the McDonald's intercom and disguising his voice, Alfredo orders a couple of McChickens for himself, a bottle of water for Winston, a Happy Meal for Christian Louis (Alfredo is collecting the toys), and a bacon cheeseburger for the Doberman pinscher at Allouez Preowned Used Cars Supercenter. A garbled intercom voice instructs him to drive forward. And so, as he did last night, and the night before that, and all the nights before that, Alfredo pulls up to the pickup window in a squatting position, arms extended and firmly locked in front of him, hands clutching an imaginary steering wheel. He rolls down the imaginary window. He asks Winston, sitting shotgun, to scavenge under the imaginary seats and look for imaginary change.

The acne-scarred attendant closes her eyes.

"You guys need to get a life," she says.

"I'm sorry," Alfredo says. He turns down the knob on the ghetto car's radio. "I didn't catch that. What'd you say?"

"No car," she says. "No food."

"I ask you for a one-time exception," Alfredo says. "Give us this food tonight and we will never bother you again."

"Rules," the girl says.

"Rules?" Alfredo asks Winston. Winston shrugs. Alfredo turns to the girl and shakes his head: never heard of 'em, not familiar. But the girl doesn't smirk or roll her eyes or even frown. She stands in her balcony and stares. "Please," Alfredo says. "If nothing else, then just the bacon cheeseburger. I can see it back there. It's already been made. You're just going to throw it out."

"No car. No food."

It was perhaps foolish of Alfredo to think this night would be different from any other night. Foolish to think he could somehow charm a sack of greasy food from this acne-scarred gorgon. Behind Alfredo and Winston, a car, a real one, honks its horn. Alfredo wishes he could drive this ghetto car down the streets of Jackson Heights, drop Winston off on Northern Boulevard near the Doberman—here, you figure it out—and then keep going, all the way home. He's tired. It's been a night full of setbacks, and Alfredo wants to go home, wash his face, smear on his anti-zit creams, rub Isabel's belly, and, if he wakes her up, play their I Wish game. Like everyone else, she'll probably want to talk about Tariq. She'll want to know Alfredo's plan of attack, but he will insist they play the game. *I wish the baby gets your chin,* he'll say. *I wish he has your elbows,* she'll say, and Alfredo will contest that one. Whispering, they will argue under their sheet on the sofa bed, debating which one of them has the superior elbows.

The car hits its horn again. It isn't a polite *beep-beep* as before; this honk's got teeth. Normally Alfredo would maintain the charade. Still squatting, feeling the burn in his quads, Alfredo would hook an arm behind the passenger seat's imaginary headrest and back the ghetto car out of the drive-thru and into the parking lot. Tonight, however, he stands up—his knees popping—and walks away.

"Wait up!" Winston says. With his height advantage and longer legs, he catches up to Alfredo easily. "What a bitch, huh? That McDonald's girl?"

"I'm sorry about earlier," Alfredo says.

"About what?" Winston says. They match each other step for step, the two of them moving quickly down Northern Boulevard, their boots slapping the pavement.

"About saying what I said. I'm sorry."

"Thank you," Winston says. His hand flutters at his side, as if he was about to clap Alfredo's shoulder, but he apparently thinks better of it. "I'm sorry too."

They stop at the intersection so that traffic may pass. It is Friday night and there are plenty of cars, Camrys and Civics and Corollas, yellow cabs and gypsy cabs, drunks returning home from the bars and clubs in Manhattan, drivers escorting escorts to johns, janitors and doormen and security guards coming off their shifts—all of them

stream by while the light says go. Impatient, eager to get moving again, Alfredo hits the green button on the corner. He knows it won't do anything. These buttons—To Cross Street, Push Button, Wait for Walk Signal—were all disconnected years ago when the Department of Transportation switched to computer-controlled traffic signals. The only reason they remain scattered on street corners throughout the outer boroughs is because it'd be too expensive to remove them all. Mayor Bloomberg and Giuliani before him and Dinkins before him and Koch before him, they all figured, *Fuck it. So we've got some buttons in Queens that don't work. They'll act as placebos, as decoration. At the very least, they'll fool the tourists.* But Alfredo isn't fooled. This is his home. He knows this push button doesn't work, and yet . . . he pushes it anyway.

The light changes from Don't Walk to Walk.

Nothing to get all excited about. Alfredo pushed a nonfunctioning button and the cars stopped and a traffic light switched in his favor. Someone like Isabel might consider this an omen. She would take this blinking Walk sign as an indication that the universe is going to start tilting in his direction, that the infinity logos will turn out to be no big deal, that the bacon cheeseburger will prove unnecessary, that the Doberman is going to happily lick the Valium straight out of Alfredo's palm and a few minutes later the dog will yawn and his thin legs will tremble and he'll eventually pass out and then Alfredo will—will do what? Go get wire cutters from some twenty-four-hour hardware store. Open up a hole in the fence like the one near the handball courts at Travers Park. Breathing naturally, Alfredo will lift up the dog and take it to Max's basement and—because the push button worked—the next day the cops and Mr. Allouez will find a hole in the fence and the cars untouched and the dog gone and they'll perfectly misunderstand it. The headline in the *Post* will read "World's Smartest Doberman Escapes Confinement! Lock Up Your T-Bones!" And then Winston will quit drugs for real and the Mets will beat the Yankees in tomorrow's game and the dogfight will go off beautifully and Alfredo will make lots of money and an impressed and intimidated Tariq will leave Isabel alone and—a little further along in this favorable future—Isabel and Alfredo and their healthy-hearted baby boy will move out of his parents' apartment and into a place of their own, where Isabel will take bubble baths surrounded by candles. Someone else might think all

that, but Alfredo doesn't. He doesn't believe in omens. He doesn't think that in Queens white doves settle down onto the prows of arks. And even if for a tantalizing moment Alfredo allowed himself to believe in all that good-times-are-a-gonna-be-rolling bullshit, there is, five blocks away, a navy blue 1997 Chevy Impala that says otherwise.

"DT," Alfredo says.

"You sure?" Winston says.

Alfredo's authority in these matters should not be challenged. He has difficulty seeing something twenty feet in front of his face, but for whatever reason—call it experience, vigilance, paranoia—Alfredo can stand on the corner of Fifty-ninth Street and Northern Boulevard and spot a DT cruising down Arthur Avenue in the Bronx. A DT coming right at him, four, no wait, three blocks away? Forget about it.

Because he and Winston elicit more suspicion as a twosome than they do individually, Alfredo says, "I'll see you in a couple of minutes. Get in touch with you on your cell."

They don't slap palms or shake hands, because they don't want to give the impression they're completing some kind of transaction. Instead, they bump fists. Just a couple of law-abiding buddies saying good-bye. Winston walks up Fifty-ninth Street; Alfredo goes down Northern Boulevard to where the Impala waits. Best to walk toward it, to not look suspicious. The Impala has pulled up in front of a fire hydrant and sits there patiently, its engine humming, its hazards off. Rising up out of the trunk, a cluster of antennae stand at attention. Alfredo looks at the car for a full second, just as he would if a gorilla was eyeballing him on the sidewalk. A one-Mississippi beat. Not long enough to issue a challenge, not short enough to invite one. After the second passes, he looks forward again. Like his big brother taught him, he walks at a relaxed, regular pace. He keeps his head up, his shoulders straight. But, of course, it doesn't matter.

A tinted window rolls down. The driver, a fat-faced white guy, sticks his head out and says, "Help you with something?"

"Nope," Alfredo says. The driver waits for more answers as if more questions were asked. He wears a Jets jersey, the kind with the numbers ironed on instead of sewed, a cheap and flimsy thing. Alfredo can't see the name on the back, but he's sure it reads "Chrebet," the Jets' second-string wide receiver, a white guy playing a black position. Below the jersey's sleeve, the driver sports a green armband. Even

though Alfredo can't see anyone else, he knows there are three more guys in the car, one sitting shotgun, two more in back. Like the driver, all three of these guys will have green sweatbands wrapped around their biceps. Alfredo's sure of it. At roll call—which started almost seven hours ago—sleep-deprived sergeants across the city must've announced green as the color of the day, helping the uniformed cops identify their plainclothes brothers. Chevy Impalas, tinted windows, extra antennae, phosphorescent clothing accessories: Alfredo wonders why they just don't wear nametags that say NYPD Undercover.

"Thank you, sir," Alfredo tells the driver. "But I don't need any help at all."

"Who's the big black guy you said good-bye to? That your boyfriend?"

The cop sitting shotgun leans forward. "Hey, drug dealer," he says. He wears a green armband and an Islanders jersey. Even undercover, these guys can't stop wearing uniforms. "Let's see some of those drugs you got on you."

This is how they talk. They assume you're breaking the law and try to trick you into agreeing. "No drugs," Alfredo says.

"That don't make no sense. You're a neighborhood drug dealer. What about a dime bag? You gotta have a dime bag."

"How about your gun?" the driver says. "Maybe we can get a lookit at the gun in the waistband of your jeans."

If he were standing outside Max's candy store, Alfredo might have given these guys some mouth. What's a dime bag, Officer? Selling drugs is against the law, Officer. Out in front of Max's store, Alfredo could get lippy because he wouldn't have too much to sweat over. His stash would be off his person, across the street, behind a loose brick. Outside Max's candy store, Alfredo could give these four DTs his Alfred E. Neuman what-me-worry. Because outside Max's candy store, Alfredo wasn't a fucking idiot. He didn't have a bag of prescription pills in one pocket, fifty hits of Ecstasy in the other.

He shows the cops his open palms. "No drugs, sir. No guns."

"Your legs are shaking," the driver says.

"No they're not."

"Okay." The driver sticks his finger in his mouth and picks at something between his teeth. His face is contorted in concentration. "You don't have any drugs. You don't have a gun. Your legs aren't shaking. Lookit. Your palms are empty." Whatever was between his teeth

now rests in a wet clump on the tip of his finger. He flicks it into the street. "You're clean," the driver tells Alfredo. "You're a credit to the community."

"I should be getting home," Alfredo says. Stupid idiot that he is, he starts to walk away.

All four doors open at once, a navy blue insect spreading its wings. Alfredo can't run. His feet burst raw with blisters. And besides, these cops would love to stretch their legs and chase Alfredo just for the pleasure of beating the shit out of him. *And he resisted arrest, Your Honor.* They come toward him, wearing a Jets jersey, an Islanders jersey, a Mets jersey, and a Hawaiian shirt. They are white, white, Dominican, and Guyanese. Badges swing from chains around their necks. They push Alfredo against a wall. All day the bricks of this wall have been baking in the June sun, and they feel warm now against Alfredo's cheek. His glasses slip off his nose. There are fingers in his hair. Hands grab his ankles, pat down his legs, run up the bars of his rib cage. His feet are kicked apart. A cop bends Alfredo forward at the waist and credit-cards him, swipes the side of his hand up through Alfredo's ass crack. They are looking for intent to sell. For a weapon, a felony charge, some overtime. Fingers pinch the wetness under Alfredo's armpits.

"You nervous about something?" The cop's breath is warm and moist and smells like peppermint, like red and white candies in cellophane wrappers. "What you nervous about? You got drugs in your pocket?"

"Lookit those legs shaking!"

"They are not," Alfredo says, but the words snag on something as they leave his mouth.

"They are not," a cop says in a high, girlish voice.

Pressed up against the wall, Alfredo feels hands plumbing his pockets. The right and the left. His eyes burn. Alfredo has never spent a single night in lockup. Imagine the irony. Going to jail the day before Tariq comes home. Through the thin cloth of his pocket, a stranger's fingertips press into Alfredo's thigh. They brush up against his balls and his body tightens. He goes up onto his toes, and then suddenly— with these desperate hands clutching his body—Alfredo remembers he doesn't have the baggie of prescription pills because Winston took it away from him, nearly half an hour ago. He's going to be okay. The

Holy Ghost swirls around his feet, swells him with buoyancy. When Alfredo gets home, he will recite the Our Father. On Sunday, he will go to Mass and kneel down, eyes closed, head dipped to his chest, palms pressed together.

"What's this?" says the Dominican cop, the one who struggles to grow a mustache. He holds up Alfredo's beeper. "What have we got here?"

"Let me see," says the Islanders jersey. "Looks like a drug dealer's pager. Pager? Beeper? Is there a difference?"

"Ask the drug dealer," the driver says.

"Is there a difference, drug dealer, between a pager and a beeper?"

"It's just a beeper," Alfredo says.

"You get your drug pages on this it's-just-a-beeper?" the cop asks. "Call them back and say, 'What you need?' We're talking big weight, right? Selling over in Corona. I know all about it. Selling the good shit in Corona." He tosses the beeper at Alfredo.

In his shortened Little League career, Alfredo tended to overthink things in the field—the ball is rolling toward me, I should charge it, throw it to first—and was prone, therefore, to the occasional error. The beeper bounces off his chest, scuttles through his fingers, and hits the ground hard. But it does not split open. The top does not pop off. The Holy Ghost has Its fingers wrapped around the beeper, squeezing it tight.

The Guyanese cop picks it up off the sidewalk. He rubs his thumb over a corner of the beeper, where the plastic has been smoothed and flattened, scuffed by the fall. He is the cop with the Hawaiian shirt, the cop who apparently does not care for sports. Frowning, he presses buttons on the top of the beeper. "I think it's broke," he says. "It's not turning back on."

"Oh, I'm sorry," says the cop in the Islanders jersey. "How you gonna get your drug pages now?"

The Guyanese cop turns over the beeper. Alfredo stares at it, thinking of all the other things these guys could be doing. On Roosevelt Avenue, underneath the elevated 7 train, there are drag queens selling blowjobs. There are Wall Street CEOs whose doors could be getting kicked in. Without a doubt, a block away in any direction, some drunk guy is whaling on his wife or molesting his stepdaughter. Why don't the cops go do something about that? Why don't they keep their hands

out of my pockets and go find Osama fucking bin Laden? The Guyanese cop brings the beeper to Alfredo and clips it to the collar of his T-shirt. The beeper weighs heavy. It causes the shirt to droop downward, exposing the root of Alfredo's throat.

"Tell us about your boy Curtis Hughes," the cop says.

"You knew him," the driver says. "You both being drug dealers and all."

"No," Alfredo says.

"No, what?"

"No, I don't know him," Alfredo says. He isn't worried. These cops aren't investigators. Ninety percent of them aren't even detectives. DT is just something they're called on the street. These cops—to the left of Alfredo, to the right, sitting on the hood of the car, clipping beepers to his chest—are from the NYPD's Anti-Crime Unit. They are patrolmen who get to wear sports jerseys. They are bloodhounds, good for sniffing out drugs and guns, and that's about all. They don't know who Alfredo is. Anti-Crime comes heavy, assumes everything, knows nothing. If they were genuinely suspicious of Alfredo, they'd be acting like his best friend. There'd be polite questions in soft voices. So they mentioned Curtis Hughes? So what? Alfredo's curious, but unworried. Curtis Hughes is a name that falls out of policemen's mouths often. "He's a drug dealer?" Alfredo asks. "Does he live around here?"

"Stop jerking us off," the Dominican says, unsure of himself. "We know you know about him getting merked. Come on, hombre. We know you know about your boy Curtis getting beat to death."

"That's not right," Alfredo says.

"What's not right?"

"That's not right," Alfredo says again.

"I thought you didn't know him."

"Beat to death?" Alfredo leans against the wall. "I went out to get a cheeseburger and I couldn't because I don't have a car and I'm just walking along and you guys stop me and accuse me of having drugs and guns and you get out of the car and you push me around and . . ." Alfredo continues to detail the events of the last few minutes. Speaking in a monotone—it is the only voice available to him—he lists his grievances, the things that have happened to him, the things for which he is not responsible. There is a scratch in the lens of his glasses, he tells them. Caused by their hands pushing him against the wall. There

is a scrape on his cheek from the bricks. Alfredo talks because it keeps him from confronting the death of Curtis Hughes and he talks because he knows it bores the police officers. Look at them. The Dominican dips his head to his armband and wipes the sweat from his eyes. This was a mistake, they think. If this little Puerto Rican knew anything worth knowing, he wouldn't talk so fucking much. They stopped him looking for overtime, for drugs and guns at the bottom of his pockets, and when they didn't find anything they took a shot on this Curtis Hughes kid, the latest African American male DOA. Best-case scenario, they break open a homicide case. Worst-case scenario, they make a kid piss his pants a bit and they've got a funny story for later tonight. Something to talk about over vodka tonics at Legends Bar. But instead, four plainclothes officers near the end of their shift are listening to some spic drone on about—what's he blabbing about now?—some dog who dances to songs no one else can hear.

"Go home," the driver snaps. He looks like a man who's found mold on a peach he'd already bit into. "I don't want to see your face on these streets ever again," he says. It is the standard DT good-bye. "You understand? Comprende? Go home to your boyfriend. It isn't safe for you out here." The cops get into their 1997 Chevy Impala and speed away, leaving Alfredo behind, alone, slumped against a brick wall.

5

Ricochet

Late at night, Jose Sr. rolls his wheelchair across the Batistas' parrot-infested living room. The TV plays what sounds like an infomercial—the standard get-rich-quick scheme, how to make thousands before breakfast—but Isabel can't see the television, nor can she see Jose Sr.'s sweaty face hovering above hers, because she has her eyes screwed shut. She's a real pro. The Meryl Streep of simulated sleep. The sofa bed's metal bar burrows into her hip, but she gives no indication it bothers her. When Jose Sr. asks her if she's awake, she answers with a little snore action: breathes deeply through the nose, lets the air whistle through a nostril. She drools and twitches. Her eyeballs ricochet behind their lids, mimicking REM palpitations.

Wow, this is heavier than it looks. I'd like to thank the Academy, my agent, my fellow nominees, my boyfriend Alfredo, my baby Christian Louis . . .

"Hey, Isabel," Jose whispers. She can smell his aftershave. She can hear him chewing his nightly cherries, spitting the pits into a bowl. "Izzy?"

While he watches her, the room's parrots watch him. They are Lizette's bewitchment: wooden parrots, plush parrots, porcelain parrots, suspended from the ceiling by thin wires, perched menacingly on end tables. Alfredo's mother gives them a weekly dusting; no strange

thing, Isabel reasons, since everything around here is dusted weekly, or vacuumed weekly, or scrubbed or laundered or Windexed weekly. This is a fastidiously maintained apartment with as many rules as church—*thou shalt not eat in the living room*—and Jose bucks these rules as soon as his wife shuffles off to bed. Each cherry is a protest, each protest cataloged by the room's ever-watchful birds.

"Can you hear me? You awake, girl?"

Of course she can hear him! Of course she is awake! To fall asleep tonight would be conceding defeat to tomorrow, and Isabel needs to delay Saturday's arrival for as long as she can. The parrot with the clock in its belly argues that since it's way past midnight, Saturday's already here, but Isabel refuses to acknowledge such narrow-minded nitpickery. As far as she's concerned, if she never goes to sleep, Saturday never dawns, and if Saturday never dawns, then Tariq never shows up, and if Tariq never shows up, then everything gets to stay the same. Simple as that. In the movie version of Isabel's life, today is her Groundhog Day. With some obvious differences: the Hollywood version of Jose Sr. would've conked out by now, so that she could spend these precious hours in the kitchen, left alone, standing over the stove and preparing the Big Surprise for Alfredo.

"You fall asleep already?" Jose whispers. "You can't hear me at all?"

When she doesn't answer, he turns up the volume on his infomercial. Some extra decibels on the TV—that's all he was after. He wasn't looking to climb into bed with her, rub his feet against hers. How could he? His legs don't work. For something like eight years now, he's been paralyzed below the waist.

If Jose Sr. looked it up in the dictionary, he'd find the following bullshit:

ric•o•chet (rik´e-sha´, -shet´)—*n.* A method of firing by which the projectile is made to glance or skip along a surface with a rebound or series of rebounds.

A *method* of firing? You serious? A definition like that doesn't acknowledge just how random, just how accidental firearm violence can be—it's as if the OED were sponsored by the NRA. Because you

can ask anyone in western Queens, or in Brownsville or Shaolin or even the Boogie Down Bronx, and they will tell you a ricochet is a mistake. Scan an article in your local newspaper and you'll find "ricochet" coupled with "innocent bystander." Whoops! Ricochets are why the NYPD is instructed to aim always for center mass, for the solar plexus, to shoot to kill. Because when you try to wing the bad guy and shoot him in the leg, you either miss or the bullet enters the thigh muscle and exits clean out the other side, and then—whiz, bang—you've got yourself a ricochet. The word in Spanish is *rebote*.

Jose Sr. had been working behind the counter. It was late at night. While his family slept in the apartment behind the store, Jose listened to sports talk radio at a very low volume. Bored, he grabbed a porno from the magazine rack (*Club International*) and took it out of its plastic wrapping. Who's gonna tell? It was his store, his inventory. He spread the magazine open on the counter. Yawning into his fist, he flipped through the pages, stopping every now and again to bring his face close to the magazine and scrutinize a nipple.

A young kid walked into the store. The first customer in over an hour, he carried a brown paper bag, the crinkly kind one slips around a sweaty can of Modelo Especial. The boy—a Latino, maybe even a Puerto Rican, a boy who could've been Jose's own son—stuck that crinkly bag in Jose's face and told him, in a man's voice, to hand over the fucking money.

You can hear this story from anybody. Lizette knows it. Alfredo and Tariq know it. Even Isabel knows it well enough to tell it. But nobody talks about it with as much eagerness, with as much hand-waving flair, as Jose himself.

He didn't beg for his life. He'd had a gun shoved in his face before, and while that's not something one could ever get used to, he was at least able to maintain some composure. No tears. No quivering lips. With his words jamming together, he talked about his family, his wife and their two sons. He didn't tell the boy that they were all asleep behind an employees-only door. Of course not. Instead he talked about random things, silly things, hoping to appear calm so that the boy might be calm. *My youngest son is right around your age,* he said, even though it wasn't true. *Hey, maybe you two even go to school together.* For reasons he doesn't understand, he told the boy about how

Alfredo can multiply giant numbers in his head, how he can memorize all sorts of license plates. He didn't know what else to say.

The bag caught fire. People have told him that's impossible. A bullet punches right through a paper bag, no problemo. But Jose swears he saw a little curl of flame, there and then not there. The light on the ceiling above his head flickered, and he remembers thinking, That's something I need to do. Change that bulb.

Later, in the hospital, Lizette told Jose it was a miracle. Shot point-blank in the face and the bullet misses him? Doesn't happen. He should be dead. According to the cops, the bullet ricocheted off the wall behind him. According to the doctors, it entered the T12 region of his spinal cord. *It's a miracle you're not dead,* she told Jose. She talked about a higher power. *Higher power?* Jose asked. He wanted to know who caused the ricochet. Who put the bullet in his back? God do that, too? *That's right,* Lizette said, and blew cool air into her coffee cup.

Jose smelled the firecrackers smell, but he never heard the pistol's report. Not when it happened, not afterward. He saw a tongue of flame lick away the edges of the paper bag (maybe), and then he was on his back behind the counter, and then he was in a hospital room with a ponytailed nurse squeezing his shoulder, and then they were moving into this new apartment, Jose no help at all, unable to lift even a box.

He wonders why the boy pulled the trigger. Because Jose didn't move fast enough, or because he moved too fast, or because it was simply too hot in the store, or because the wrong commercial came on over the radio? Or maybe there isn't always a causal relationship with these kinds of things. Jose doesn't know. He thinks he never heard the gunshot because his eardrums ruptured. To this day he has trouble hearing, although Lizette thinks it's a ruse, her husband faking deafness so he doesn't have to wheel himself toward her when she calls for him.

But Isabel believes him. She figures he's gotta be deaf. Why else would he be turning up the volume on his infomercial? He doesn't know she's secretly awake. He thinks he's got no audience in this room, and without an audience there's no reason to fake it. Where's the angle? If Jose weren't sitting in that chair, she certainly wouldn't be pretending to sleep. She'd be up, boiling water for the Big Surprise. But

as it is—with Isabel under observation—there's nothing she can do but wait. She hopes Christian Louis will float by on the inside of her eyelids. She hopes he'll be riding a series of numbered, hurdle-jumping sheep. Maybe he'll be bent forward at the waist like a jockey, making *yip yip* noises, with his fierce infant fists buried knuckle-deep in wool. She tries to will the image onto the back of her eyelids, but all she sees is darkness. She's faking sleep, and Christian Louis doesn't stop by when Mama's being duplicitous. Fair enough, Isabel thinks. She waits. She schemes.

Alfredo turns over each deadbolt with a whisper. He cracks open the front door a couple of inches—push it any farther, it starts creaking— and he tiptoes into the living room. These late-night stratagems aren't for the benefit of his mother, who passes out shortly after sundown like a hummingbird, exhausted from the all-day effort of flapping her wings. Impossible to wake up, she sleeps at the back of the apartment with the extraneous aid of a slumber mask, a box fan, earplugs, and two Tylenol PMs. Forget about her. Forget about Papi too, who is snoring loudly only a few feet away, a lumber mill crammed into a wheelchair. Jose's a lighter sleeper than his wife, but Alfredo's gonna have to wake him up soon anyway. No, all these stealth moves— Alfredo feels like he's been walking on his toes ever since he slipped into the apartment—are for Isabel's benefit alone.

Then it's all for nothing, because she ain't even here. The sofa bed's thin mattress bears only the imprint of her body. He assumes she's either stuck on the bowl, battling pregnancy-related constipation, or she's in the kitchen, asleep on her feet and snacking on cookies. Lately, in the middle of the night, she's been staggering into the kitchen to pour herself a glass of milk and twist off some Oreos. The next day she claims no recollection. With chocolate mashed in her teeth, she denies all accusations. Sometimes Alfredo will open the freezer and find a pint of ice cream with the lid off and a spoon sticking straight out of the top. Isabel will say, *Nah, wasn't me, I don't even like pistachio.* Alfredo will say, *Okay.* He thinks those Kansas farmers who wake up with crop circles in their backyard should stop squinting up past the sky and look instead across the breakfast table, check the wife's house-coat for tractor keys.

Of course it's always possible Isabel's being framed. Stranger things have happened around here. But Alfredo knows he isn't doing the framing, and his father couldn't plant a spoon in a freezer he isn't able to reach, and Alfredo's mother—admittedly the most likely suspect— would never sully her own kitchen. One morning he caught her dragging a finger over the countertop, scooping up Oreo crumbs. Her lips were drawn back in panic, as if the chocolate were anthrax.

"Parrot droppings?" Alfredo had said.

"Your girlfriend, she's going to give us mice."

"Actually it was me. I had the midnight munchies." Not that she believed him. Lizette had been lied to so often in her life that she'd built up an immunity. Bullshit clanged off her. She wiped down the countertop and stuck the milk-coated glass into the dishwasher.

"We'll be infested," she said. "More so than we already are."

"I won't do it again." Lying to his mother, Alfredo felt like a boy playing chopsticks for a woman used to the symphony, and yet it pleased him to have covered for Isabel, even ineffectively. He felt taller somehow, taking responsibility for a thing he did not do.

Meanwhile, outside this apartment, Curtis Hughes is dead. Alfredo double-checks the deadbolts, makes sure to fasten all the door chains. He imagines Curtis lying in the back of an ambulance with the lights flashing and the sirens turned off. Something cold and dark like seawater takes hold of Alfredo's throat. It drops whispers into his ear. If Curtis's beating is linked to this Vladimir/infinity-logo disaster, then "C. Hughes" is merely one name at the top of a list that includes "A. Batista," and "Winston," too.

Winston. After the police left Alfredo, he called Winston six times, and six times the phone went straight to voice mail. *Hey, uh, leave a message?* Alfredo pictured Winston holding the phone to his ear as an aluminum bat caught him from behind, smashing the bones in his hand, breaking the phone into bits. Alfredo searched the streets for the Spider-Man hat, looking near gutters and under parked cars, before he spooked himself and ran all the way home.

For the seventh time in the last twenty minutes, he dials Winston's number. He knocks his knuckles against the beak of a wooden parrot, hoping—praying really—that this time the call will be answered. Just give me a ring. Tell me the phone is *on*, at least.

Hey, uh, leave a message?

The TV flickers light onto Papi's sleeping face. Jose watches, or rather he was watching, at an unreasonable volume, the Home Shopping Network. He doesn't buy anything, not anymore at least, not since Lizette canceled his credit card. About a year after the accident, an HSN package arrived every other day: candleholders, digital cameras, vacuum cleaners, cologne, a sauna belt, dual drills, lint rollers, magic blenders, suction cup hooks, Space Bags, a knife sharpener called the Samurai Shark, Dr. Ho's neck massager, the Lauren Hutton Face Disc. These brown-boxed parcels became for Jose one of the few ways he communicated with a world outside this two-bedroom apartment. The collapsible ladders and magical mops were his street gossip, his walk to the mall.

Alfredo turns off the television. In the sudden silence Jose's head tilts back and he snores more deeply than before. His face shines with sweat. It's hot in this room—hotter even than it is outside—and every degree seems to glaze Jose's cheeks and neck. Even his glasses look damp. Alfredo knows that tomorrow morning Tariq will come home from prison and he will see this face—the liver spots, the mustache dappled gray—and he will think their father has aged decades. But that's all wrong, Alfredo thinks. Couldn't be wronger! Look at the button-down shirt Jose wears. Look at his hair slicked back with gel. These aren't the signs of a shriveled enfeeblement, but rather the bulwarks erected against it. Granted, one sideburn extends lower than the other, but you try shaving in a wheelchair, your eye line below the mirror. Isn't it enough, big brother, that Papi shaves at all? How could a man be old if his cheeks still smell of Aqua Velva? If his lips are stained with cherry juice?

Of course, unlike Tariq, Alfredo never went away for two and a half years. He knows what it's like to see his father transformed—from walker to sitter, from upright to broken—but he doesn't know, and he can't appreciate, what it's like to see the man suddenly grow old. Their only significant separation dates back to when Alfredo was in the third grade and Jose lived with a white woman for four days in Rego Park. Four days—that's it, the longest amount of time father and son have spent away from each other. Alfredo never enrolled in college or joined the merchant marines. He never even went to summer camp. In the living room, in the dark, Alfredo approaches his father's wheelchair, stepping around the empty sofa bed, head brushing against a low-

hanging parrot, and he wonders if now is not the time to get the hell out. Leave this room, this apartment, this neighborhood, this borough, this city of New York. His brother comes home in a few hours. A guy is out on the street murdering drug dealers, avenging Vladimir. Maybe. So maybe what Alfredo needs to do is pack a bag, buy a bus ticket for him and his pregnant girlfriend, and head . . . like west or something. Alfredo catches his lips moving. It's a stupid idea. What would you tell Isabel? *We need to get out of Jackson Heights for a little while. Nothing to worry about. Plenty of women go into labor at the back of a Greyhound.* Moving through the dark, he accidentally kicks over a bowl. Cherry pits and cherry stems skip across the floor. The bowl goes *clatter clatter.*

"Nice going," Jose says. Behind the lens of his glasses, his eyes stare down at the ground. Bright red cherry flesh clings to some of the pits; the juice bleeds onto Lizette's carpet.

"You're not supposed to eat in here," Alfredo says.

"You're not supposed to kick my bowl."

Too tired to argue, Alfredo moves behind the wheelchair. His feet hurt. Since Thursday morning he's gotten four hours of sleep. Alfredo hopes that this—getting wheels to roll forward in a room with wall-to-wall carpeting—will be the last difficult job in a day full of difficult jobs. He lifts the handlebars, digs in, and pushes hard. The wheels tangle with the carpet, but after a little time and with a little effort, the Batista boys get rolling. They cruise toward the bedrooms at the back of the apartment.

"You pick up our investment?" Jose asks. By which he means, *Did you get me my Lotto tickets?* He's an every-day player, a purist who never lets the machine Quick Pick his numbers, but instead chooses himself, playing his sons' birthdays or his Social Security number or particular license plates or—if a bad streak gets bad enough—the date he got shot, Jose hoping the Lotto gods appreciate irony. The morning after a drawing, he spreads his pink tickets across the table and opens up his *Newsday* and checks his numbers against the winning numbers, Jose circling matches, crossing out misses. Lotto, Take 5, Mega, Win 4, the Numbers—he'll play them all. But he won't do scratch-offs. They're low class, he explains. A sucker's game. But the real reason, Alfredo knows, is that the scratch-offs provide too instant a gratification, too immediate a disappointment. Where's the suspense? After

closing his *Newsday* and after finishing his buttered bialy and café con leche, Jose methodically balls up the loser Lotto tickets and tosses them in the trash. Then he re-ups. He'll give Alfredo five or ten or fifteen dollars and tell him to go buy more—*and make sure you play these exact numbers.* He sends Alfredo out into the world on his behalf so that the father can be, once again, for the next twenty-four hours, a possible millionaire. Their agreement is Jose keeps 90 percent of all winnings and Alfredo pockets the rest. A little scratch for doing the legwork, so to speak. For picking up the tickets. Except tonight— understandably—Alfredo forgot. "I saw this set of knives on HSN I'd like to buy with our earnings," Jose says. "These knives, I swear to God, they'd cut off a finger."

"Well," Alfredo says. He speaks into the heartbreakingly boyish swirl of hair at the back of his father's head. "The thing is . . ."

Jose's hands flare out as if he's going to clutch the wheels and arrest their progress. These hands hover in the air for a moment before drifting back into his lap. He crosses one muscular arm over the other. "That's not like you," he says. "To forget like that. What if those numbers hit, Dito?"

"Then I owe you a million dollars."

"Am I gonna have to partner up with your brother when he comes home? Hire him to pick up my tickets?"

"He can't," Alfredo says. "He can't gamble. He'd violate his parole."

"Oh please. What, are they staking out bodegas now? Junior can just go straight downstairs—"

"Tariq," Alfredo says. "Not Junior. *Tariq.*" With his fists choking the handlebars, he shoves Jose out of the living room. The chair's wheels jump the lip of the carpet and hit the smooth linoleum of the kitchen floor. Ordinarily, this tactile transition is Alfredo's favorite part of the journey. He doesn't know how to drive, but when he hits the linoleum Alfredo usually imagines that this is what it must be like to catch a string of green lights, or to punch the gas on a blacktopped highway. Tonight, however, Alfredo finds no satisfaction in the creamy smoothness of rubber wheels on a kitchen floor. "Even if Tariq could pick up your tickets, he wouldn't. It's against his new *religion.*"

Isabel stands at the range, her face hovering above a giant pot. The kitchen is as dark as pitch, save for a few purple fingers of fire. Alfredo doesn't know if the fire comes from the stove or from Isabel her-

self, doesn't know which one of them is illuminating and which one is the illuminated. She wears his old Our Lady of Fatima gym shorts. With her third-trimester belly swelling her tank top, she looks beautiful and monstrous and strange.

She turns to them but doesn't say anything. Water sizzles, the refrigerator hums. Is she sleepwalking? Has she graduated from late-night Oreos and ice cream to some serious stovetop cooking? Alfredo doesn't know what's in the pot but he imagines it can be anything—a box of linguine, the head of a pig—and just as he's about to ask, she brings her finger to her lips as if to say *Shhhhhhhh.* Fire crawls up the side of the pot. It occurs to Alfredo that he has possibly steered his father's wheelchair into some kind of dream.

Someone—in the apartment above or below or around them—turns on a faucet, and the pipes in the Batistas' walls begin to moan. A neighbor getting a late-night drink of water perhaps. Someone who has been asleep all night and will be able to go right back to bed. Alfredo wonders what the hell they've got to be so thirsty about.

"I just hope those numbers don't hit," Jose whispers. "That'd be just the thing."

Alfredo pushes the wheelchair down the hall to an open door, his father's bedroom. A queen-sized mattress dominates the room. Scattered across the bed lie a dozen pillows, each one autographed by Jose's signature hair grease. Lizette visits the Laundromat as frequently as she visits church—the entire bedroom smells freshly laundered—but Jose's grease stains are just that, stains, impossible to get out. Lizette keeps trying, however. She hasn't lost faith in the redemptive powers of a good scrubbing. Her dresser and Jose's dresser face each other on opposite walls, as if locked in an interminable staring contest. Alfredo parks his father at the foot of the bed and turns on the light.

Lizette doesn't yank the sheets over her head or roll over or throw an arm across her eyes because Lizette sleeps next door in the boys' old room. She made the move a few months ago, on the same night Isabel showed up at the front door with a duffel bag and a DVD player and with bruises on her neck. Lizette went into Alfredo's room; Alfredo and his guest were deported to the living room sofa bed. *It's your father's late hours,* Lizette said. *He's always waking me up.* Now where Tariq will sleep—with both bedrooms and the sofa bed occupied—is yet to be determined. Alfredo considers asking his father but it's

unlikely he's got any idea. Papi's not on the wire, not in this house, not anymore.

Alfredo depresses the wheel brakes and locks the chair in place. Both men share the same warped, nervous smile. Alfredo hooks his arms under his father's damp armpits. With a grunt, he scoops him clean out of the chair. They stagger backward. He and his father are chest to chest, one body, and while Jose isn't particularly heavy, it is all dead, helpless weight. His legs dangle. His hands scramble to touch each other behind Alfredo's back. When his father starts slipping, Alfredo shoves his face into his neck, which feels smooth and smells of Aqua Velva. Together, father and son spin around, dancing dangerously, until the backs of Jose's knees kiss the edge of the bed. Alfredo eases him onto the mattress. Both men breathe with their mouths open. They gorge themselves on great big gulps of air.

"Tomorrow night," Jose says, "we'll get Junior to help." He unbuttons his pants slowly, his hands shaking. "Unless it's against his religion."

Alfredo pulls at the cuffs, wiggles the pants off his father. His legs are spidery, thin and awkward, and in the move from chair to bed, fresh capillaries have burst. Purple splotches speckle his thighs. Hugging his waist is a pair of underwear that's as old as Alfredo. They are white cotton and damp in the middle.

"I guess I had an accident," Jose says. He sits up on his elbows, to stare into Alfredo's face. "Can you take them with you? The underwear? Can you hide them or throw them out or something? I don't want your mother to know."

With his head turned to the side, Alfredo pulls off the underwear. The smell of urine is released into the room. As is Jose's penis, which is sizably serpentine, thick and substantial. Impressed, as he always is whenever he sees this penis, Alfredo is careful not to smile. He is also careful not to hold the underwear at arm's length or daintily pinch the elastic waistband; instead, he lets the damp undies hang from his fingertips casually, so as to show Jose how little this bothers him, how pleased and honored he feels to be able to do this thing for his father.

"You gonna change the diapers for your son?" Jose asks.

Alfredo props pillows around his father's legs. "You want the covers on you?"

"No," Jose says. "I want your mother to come in here in the morning and catch me with a raging hard-on."

"Good night, Papi."

"We'll play those same numbers tomorrow? In the Lotto? Or we can run with some new numbers. If you want. Maybe Isabel's birthday?"

"Yeah," Alfredo says. "I better get out there before she sets the kitchen on fire."

"You see any license plates tonight?"

"A few." Alfredo knows his father doesn't want him to leave. "I saw an unmarked police car."

"They stop you?"

"Plate number 3AT649."

Jose asks him what's all that multiplied together, three times six times four times nine, and Alfredo tells him instantly. Jose asks him what's that number times four (Jose's lucky number), and the answer takes Alfredo as long as it takes him to close his eyes and see the digits—green-and-purple-hued—fall against a black backdrop and lock into place: 2,592.

Jose lets loose a low whistle. "Good man, Dito. Good man."

Now it's Alfredo who doesn't want to leave. He leans into the doorframe, lingers inside his father's benediction. Above the bed's headboard floats the ghost outline of a giant crucifix. When Lizette switched rooms she took only the alarm clock off her dresser and the cross off the wall. But it's still there, sort of. Alfredo can see a T where the cross used to hang; the paint on that part of the wall seems fresher. He wants to know if this pseudocrucifix might still work, if it might still impart a sliver of divine protection for his father's unbelieving soul. And if so, Alfredo wonders, might there be any juice left for a good man like me?

Isabel and Alfredo lie in bed, careful not to touch each other. Out on the street, below their open window, rubber-gloved men from Staten Island toss bags of garbage into the jagged maw of a sanitation truck. Pizza boxes, expired milk, cleaned-out cans, discarded magazines, uneaten rice, shredded bills—it all gets gnashed up and digested. With a release of hydraulic pressure, a noise somewhere between a belch

and a sigh, the truck moves on to the next apartment building. Isabel and Alfredo listen to it *beep-beep-beep* away.

Alfredo laces his hands behind his head, so that his elbows jut out, twin antennae trying to pick up a signal. His armpits reek. *Talk about garbage!* He must feel guilty—he *should* feel guilty, Isabel thinks—otherwise his BO wouldn't be so brolic. It's as if something inside of him has curdled. She can smell his pits even with her back to him. She lies on her side, faces the parrot with the clock embedded in its belly. It is 3:47 a.m. It is 3:48 a.m., and Isabel is a kiddie pool. Because he knows something is wrong, Christian Louis swims laps. He crashes into his mama's uterine wall, turns, crashes into her bladder. He swims freestyle. He swims the butterfly and backstroke. He churns his fetal arms, kicks his fetal legs. Isabel wants to roll over and lie on her other side, but she can't, because if she rolls over, she will have to face Alfredo, and if she faces Alfredo, she will have to claw out his eyeballs.

The Big Surprise did not go as well as she'd hoped.

Things *had* been going just fine. Just as they were supposed to go. When the water began to simmer, Isabel turned off the gas. Step two: she put on some oven mitts. She experienced a minor hiccup when she had to carry the pot into the bathroom. Not only was the pot heavy, but the floor felt tilted at an angle. And not only did the floor feel tilted, but her foot had fallen asleep. (Increased clumsiness, pins and needles in her extremities—add it to the list of things she forgot to ask the doctor.) On her way to the bathroom, Isabel banged into the kitchen table. Inside the pot, hot water swished.

Don't spill that shit on your belly, Christian Louis said. When Isabel told him not to curse, he said, *I've got Tourette's! I'm autistic! I've got a rotten case of thalassemia!*

Isabel set the pot down on a bath mat. She can't be sure if she heard a sizzle. She was too busy running back into the kitchen, tossing off oven mitts. She was too busy reaching under the sofa bed, grabbing the box of Epsom salts she'd bought earlier in the day. The box rattled—maraca-like—as she ran with it into the bathroom. She dumped columns of salt into the pot. The water swirled gray with clouds.

"What are you doing?" Alfredo said. In his hand he held what looked like a pair of droopy tighty-whities, definitely not the pair of silk boxers she'd given him for Christmas. "Are you sleepwalking?" he said. "Is it dangerous to wake you?"

Isabel stood up, her back screaming. With a majestic sweep of her arm, she beckoned her boyfriend to the toilet seat. "Welcome," she said, feeling suddenly silly, "to Spa de Batista."

Because Alfredo walks all night from one end of Queens to the other, and because—for God knows what reason—he insists on wearing those heavy Timberland boots, his feet break out in calluses. His heels coarsen, his soles blister, his dogs get to barking. So Isabel—stunning girlfriend that she is—set up this foot massage with the idea that Alfredo would sit on his throne, kick off his boots, and plunge his maltreated feet into the salty water. He would feel like a sultan, fanned by the giant feathers of a mystical bird. Isabel put all this together so that later tonight in bed she could look for some indication in the outward signs of his sleep—some hint in his fluttering eyelids or twitching fingertips—that he was dreaming about her, a woman who loves him, who knows when his feet ache and who does something about it. A woman, in other words, worth fighting for.

"Baby," Alfredo said. He pressed his palms to his forehead. "I'm tired."

"Exactly," she said.

"I'm not really in the mood."

"I set this all up," Isabel said.

"Okay, but I'm just trying to go to sleep. You know what I'm saying? I'm just trying to get to *bed.*"

"Exactly," Isabel said. "This will relax you. Get rid of your aches and pains. See? It's a foot massager."

"You want me to stick my fucking foot in there?" Needless to say, in the movie version of her life Alfredo does not say this. "Don't be stupid, baby. That's a pot. That's a pot my mama uses to cook rice."

Isabel let him know that if they had more money then maybe she could afford a *real* foot massager, and maybe she could get some other things too, like a crib or an OB-GYN or a crisscross support sling for her back, or maybe even their very own apartment (!), where Isabel could take baths surrounded by candles. But you know, that's if they *had* money, which is a ridiculous idea—like all her ideas, of course, since she's so stupid, right?—because as we all know there ain't no foot massager money and there ain't no moving out money coming around here either.

Alfredo sat down on the toilet. He tossed the underwear into the

tub. He untied his boots and neatly placed them to the side. From his pockets he removed a beeper Isabel had never seen before, and holding it with both hands he slid it into the open mouth of his boot. He took out his cell phone, dialed a number with his eyes closed, and when what sounded like a message clicked on, he hung up the phone. She didn't ask. She watched him peel off his socks. From the bottom of one of those socks he pulled out a small wad of cash, no more than three or four bills, and threw it at Isabel's bare feet. They stared at each other, Isabel and Alfredo did, with this pathetic sum of crumpled money on the floor between them—it was maybe thirty-five dollars, maybe less—and then Alfredo thrust his foot into the water.

His head snapped back, banged against the wall behind him. His foot came out of the water looking pinkish-white and soft.

"Is it too hot? Are you okay?"

"Are you kidding me, Isabel?"

"Please don't yell."

"Who's yelling?"

She clamped her hands onto the sides of her belly, as if to cover Christian Louis's underdeveloped ears. "What if you wake up your mother?" They both knew that'd be impossible. "Please," Isabel said. "Please don't yell."

"Who, Isabel, is yelling?"

"I was just trying to do something nice. I was just trying to take care of you."

"Everyone needs to stop trying to help me. Please." Alfredo wrapped a towel around his foot. He lifted the pot and peeked underneath it. "You know the rug is completely burnt. Because you are *retarded*. Because you are a *child*. My mother's bath mat now has a big black circle right in the middle of it."

The water got dumped down the drain. Lizette's scorched bath mat got balled up and stashed under the sofa bed, along with the Epsom salts and damp underwear. And now Isabel stares at the parrot clock. She's halfway convinced it will take off and fly shrieking into her face.

The garbage truck turns the corner. It is 3:49 a.m. With the truck gone, Isabel and Alfredo listen to nothing. Soon the paper guys will come. The *New York Times,* the *Daily News,* the *Post, Newsday, El Diario.* No prepubescent boys in this neighborhood, pedaling down maple-shaded streets, tossing the morning edition over rose bushes

and onto welcome mats. Here the papers get delivered by men, immigrants from Ecuador, Colombia, Pakistan, Korea. They drive cars through all of Queens, stopping at the buildings on their list and leaving the engine running while they run out and drop thick stacks of plastic-bagged newspapers onto stoops. They will be here soon, these men. And when they arrive, there will be no denying a new day has begun. The midnight transition from p.m. to a.m., the sunrise, the beeping garbage trucks, the morning papers—Isabel can fool herself no longer. Extra, extra! Saturday's coming, whether she likes it or not. She and Alfredo lie in bed, waiting. The silence sits on their chests.

"You got any new songs?" he says.

She scoots closer to the edge of the bed.

"Not for me, of course," he says. "Don't sing for me. I don't deserve to hear a new song. But the baby. It's not fair the baby doesn't get—"

"You were mean. I was just trying to do something nice. I made a mistake. I'm sorry. But you were *mean*."

"I'm a bad person," Alfredo says. He reaches toward her. He taps her recently outied belly button. "This is your microphone. This belly button right here. Sing into that. You want, I'll close my ears. I'll stick a pillow over my head."

Isabel is a wealth of lullabies. Alfredo assumes she's carried them with her from childhood. He assumes they were passed down from Isabel's mother to her. But that's not the case at all. Isabel grew up in a tuneless home and she's had to work hard for her lullabies. Secretly, without anyone knowing but Christian Louis, she goes down to the public library, logs on to their computers, and searches the Web for cradlesongs. She writes down the lyrics, commits them to memory. Never having heard any of these songs, she needs to work out the proper beats and cadences—and so at night she practices. She rehearses.

Alfredo rests a hand on her stomach. "Little man's had a rough day," he says. "The hospital and shit. Listening to us fight. He only wants a little lullaby. Half a lullaby, even."

She just learned a new one, too. It's about three little bears who roll over in bed and fall crashing to the ground. Alfredo's right—a song would be just the thing to get Christian Louis to chill out, to balm his thrashing legs—but there ain't no way she's singing. She'd rather suffer.

"Don't make me break out some Nas," Alfredo says.

"You think if you ignore something long enough it'll just go away."

"She speaks!"

"Where's he gonna sleep? What happens the first time you leave me alone with him?" When he doesn't answer, she says, "He's going to try to kill you."

"He'll have to get in line. Right behind you, yeah?" Alfredo laughs and rattles her elbow. He tries to keep his voice bright, but she knows better. "I'll tell you what we're gonna do," he says. "This'll pick you up. You listening? It's about tomorrow. Hey, you listening? First things first, we tell my mother I was smoking a giant cigar and I put it out on her bath mat. I'll take the blame. No? Okay, then we'll tell her I was taking a shit, drinking the world's largest cup of coffee and I couldn't find a big enough coaster. Or how about this? Hey, listen up. We run away. From the road we send her a check for a new bath mat."

Isabel rolls over. With the living room dark, she sees only the outline of Alfredo's face. "We run away?" she asks.

"You'd be cool with that? Packing up? Leaving here?" Alfredo kicks the sheets off of him, plants his feet on the ground. "Ask the baby. Find out what the baby says about leaving on up out of here."

She doesn't need to ask. Christian Louis is curled up inside her ear, a megaphone pressed to his tiny lips. "The baby wants us to run," she says. "The baby says, 'Go. Right now. Run away.' "

Above Isabel and Alfredo's heads the parrots eye one another nervously. Their beaks are closed, their wings tucked tight to their chests. Outside a car passes and the room fills with light.

Part Two

6

From the New York State Department of Correctional Services

STATE OF NEW YORK—EXECUTIVE DEPARTMENT—DIVISION OF PAROLE
INMATE STATUS REPORT FOR PAROLE BOARD APPEARANCE

PAROLE SUMMARY—RELEASE APPLICANT
(May, 2002)

PART 1

Name: BATISTA JR, Jose	CR: 2-0 ME: 4-0	PE: 1/12/04
NYSID: 7153902J	DIN: 92G0192	DOB: 7/12/81
Rec'd Date: 1/12/00	PVNT: NO	Time on Parole: —

Crime, (felony class), sentence & date p(lea) or v(erdict);

1) BURGLARY 3rd (D)   2-0/4-0 12/5/99   PLEA

Guideline Range: 12–48 Months;
                28 Mos. Total Time Served at Time of Review

EEC—   Granted   Denied   Non-Certified
            If Denied or Non-Certified, are reasons in file:

Special Programs: WR/   from   to
        Furloughs: ;   Day Reporting from   to
        Program Violations:

Mand. SPP: Y ; Citizen: Y ; INS Warrant: N ; Other Warrants: N
Comments:

Official Statements: Judge N   ; DA N   ; Def. Atty N   ;

Certificate of Relief: _____ Eligible

Co-Defendant:	Name & NYSID	Status
HALL, Conrad	2465190Z 92A1088	BURGLARY 3rd (D) 2-0/4-0 Altona CF 1/03 I
DUPRE, Giovanni	3599201R 92H4537	BURGLARY 3rd (D) 2-0/4-0 Otisville CF 1/03 I

INMATE STATUS REPORT FOR PAROLE BOARD APPEARANCE
Page 2

NAME: BATISTA JR, Jose   NYSID: 7153902J   DIN: 92G0192

Present Offense:

The description of the Instant Offense was derived from the Presentence
Investigation. On December 5, 1999, the subject, Jose Batista Jr., along
with his co-defendants, Conrad Hall and Giovanni Dupre, did unlawfully
enter the commercial premise, Virgil Caterers at 75-01 31st Avenue,
East Elmhurst, NY, and did unlawfully remove from the above premises
$5000 cash US currency belonging to the victim/complainant, Virgil
Barbaretto.

The subject was identified via surveillance tapes delivered to the NYPD by
Barbaretto, and via the affidavits of co-defendants Hall and Dupre. The
subject was summarily arrested at his place of residence, 79-09 34th Ave,
Jackson Heights, NY, on 12/7/99.

CRIMINAL RECORD

Arrest Date	Arrest Charges	Place	Disposition

INSTANT OFFENSE :

12/7/99	BURGLARY 3rd (D)	Queens Cty. Crt. 1/10/2000	Conv. upon plea BURGLARY 2-0/4-0

PAROLE INTERVIEW

INMATE'S STATEMENT:

The subject was interviewed on 5/22/02 at Fishkill C.F. Regarding the I.O., subject admits participation. He continues to state the I.O. was his first offense, and, indeed, he has no prior criminal record.

Subject states his motivation for this act was for quick monetary gain. Subject states at the time of the I.O. he was unemployed and living in his parents' residence. In contradiction to the testimonies of his co-defendants, subject states he never received any of the money that was removed from Virgil Caterers; and, indeed, at the occasion of his arrest he only had $7.00 in his possession.

INMATE STATUS REPORT FOR PAROLE BOARD APPEARANCE
Page 3

NAME: BATISTA JR, Jose   NYSID: 7153902J   DIN: 92G0192

Subject states he is guilty for the I.O. Subject states he "has learned his lesson."

INSTITUTIONAL ADJUSTMENT:

Subject has had difficulty making custodial adjustment. During the first nine months of his institutional incarceration, subject incurred numerous

disciplinary infractions. Disciplinary infractions include failures to report, failure to maintain acceptable living area, and, most frequently, violently aggressive behavior toward both C.O.s and other inmates.

Subject's custodial adjustment has improved. He has not incurred any disciplinary actions since September 2000. Subject credits improvement to a "spiritual awakening."

Subject continues his educational pursuits, obtaining his G.E.D. in February 2002. He is currently enrolled in the College Bound program working toward his Associate's Degree.

PROPOSED RESIDENCE:

The subject proposed to reside with his parents, Jose Batista Sr. and Lizette Batista, at the following address:

> 79-09 34th Ave
> Apt. 52
> Jackson Heights, NY 11372
> (718) 424-9131

PROPOSED EMPLOYMENT:
  To be developed.

INMATE STATUS REPORT FOR PAROLE BOARD APPEARANCE
Page 4

NAME: BATISTA JR, Jose   NYSID: 7153902J   DIN: 92G0192

INMATE'S PLANS:

The subject proposes to go back to school to finish his education and to be reunited with his family. He is seeking assistance through the Prisoner Reentry Institute.

SUPERVISION NEEDS:
 1. Vocational training.

SPECIAL CONDITIONS RECOMMENDED:
 1. Anger management therapy.
 2. Substance abuse counseling with periodic drug testing.
 3. Curfew.

Prepared by: Approved by:
FPO I, D.N. Landry   FPO II, L.R. Flory
Date: 5/22/02   Date: 5/22/02

Facility: Fishkill C.F.
DBT:rw

Ticket:: ticket

STATE OF NEW YORK
EXECUTIVE DEPARTMENT—DIVISION OF PAROLE
CERTIFICATE OF RELEASE TO PAROLE SUPERVISION
DETERMINATE—POST-RELEASE SUPERVISION

SENTENCE: 2-0/4-0   NYSID NO. 7153902J

BATISTA JR., JOSE , now confined in Fishkill CF who was convicted of
BURGLARY 3rd (D) and sentenced in the county of Queens at a term of the
County Court, Judge Richard J. Oh presiding on the 10th day of January
2000, for the term of 2-0/4-0 the maximum term of such sentence expires
on the 10th day of January 2004, has agreed to abide by the conditions to
which he has signed his name below, and is hereby released by virtue of the
authority conferred by New York State Law.

Jose Batista Jr. is additionally subject to a period of 2 (two) years Post-
Release Supervision, which will commence on the release date of June 15,

<u>2002</u> and he will be under the legal jurisdiction of the Division of Parole until the Post-Release Supervision maximum expiration date of <u>June 15,</u> <u>2004</u>.

Date of Release: <u>6/15/2002</u>
Post-Release Supervision Period: <u>2 (two) years</u>
Post-Release Supervision Maximum Expiration Date: <u>6/15/2004</u>
Residence: 79-09 34th Ave
Apt. 52
Jackson Hts, NY, 11372
718-424-9131

I, Jose Batista Jr. 92G0192, voluntarily accept Parole Post-Release Supervision. I fully understand that my person, residence and property are subject to search and inspection. I understand that Parole Post-Release Supervision is defined by these Conditions of Release and all other conditions that may be imposed upon me by the Board of Parole or its representatives. I understand that my violation of these conditions may result in the revocation of my release.

CONDITIONS OF RELEASE

1. I will proceed directly to the area to which I have been released, and, within twenty-four hours of my release, make my arrival report to the Office of the Division of Parole unless other instructions are designated on my release agreement. Report to: **P.O. Dimmick, SPO Hebert, Queens I Area Office 1010 Hazen St., East Elmhurst, NY 11370 718-546-5891**

2. I will make office and/or written reports as directed.

3. I will not leave the State of New York or any other State to which I am released or transferred, or any area defined in writing by my Parole Officer without permission.

4. I will permit my Parole Officer to visit me at my residence and/or place of employment and I will permit the search and inspection of my person, residence and property. I will discuss any proposed changes in my residence, employment or program status with my Parole Officer. I understand that I have an immediate and continuing duty to notify my Parole Officer of any changes in my residence, employment or program status when circumstances beyond my control make prior discussion impossible.

5. I will reply promptly, fully, and truthfully to any inquiry of, or communication by, my Parole Officer or other representative of the Division of Parole.

6. I will notify my Parole Officer immediately any time I am in contact with, or arrested by, any law enforcement agency. I understand that I have a continuing duty to notify my Parole Officer of such contact or arrest.

7. I will not be in the company of, or fraternize with, any person I know to have a criminal record or whom I know to have been adjudicated a Youthful Offender, except for accidental encounters in public places, work, school, or in any other instance with the permission of my Parole Officer.

8. I will not behave in such manner as to violate the provisions of any law to which I am subject, which provide for a penalty of imprisonment, nor will my behavior threaten the safety or well-being of myself or others.

9. I will not own, possess, or purchase any shotgun, rifle, or firearm of any type without the written permission of my Parole Officer. I will not own, possess, or purchase any deadly weapon as defined in the Penal Law or any dangerous knife, dirk, razor, stiletto, or imitation pistol. In addition, I will not own, possess, or purchase any instrument readily capable of causing physical injury without a satisfactory explanation for ownership, possession, or purchase.

10. In the event that I leave the jurisdiction of the State of New York, I hereby waive my right to resist extradition to the State of New York from any state in the Union and from any territory or country outside the United States. This waiver shall be in full force and effect until I am discharged from Parole or Conditional Release. I fully understand that I have the right under the Constitution of the United States and under law to contest any effort to extradite me from another state and return me to New York, and I freely and knowingly waive this right as a condition of my Parole or Conditional Release.

11. I will not use or possess any drug paraphernalia or use or possess any controlled substance without proper medical authorization.

12. Special Conditions:
    I will seek, obtain, and maintain employment and/or an
        academic/vocational program.
    I will submit to substance abuse testing as directed by the P.O.

I will participate in a substance abuse treatment program as directed by the P.O.

I will participate in an anger management program as directed by the P.O.

I will abide by a curfew established by the P.O.

I will cooperate with a mental health evaluation referral, and follow-up treatment as directed by the P.O.

I will not associate in any way or communicate by any means with (associates Conrad Hall and Giovanni Dupre) without the permission of the P.O.

I will cooperate with all medical referrals and treatment recommendations.

13. I will fully comply with the instructions of my Parole Officer and obey such special additional written conditions as he or she, a member of the Board of Parole, or an authorized representative of the Division of Parole, may impose.

I hereby certify that I have read and that I understand the foregoing conditions of my release and that I have received a copy of this Certificate of Release.

Signed this 15th day of June 20 02

Releasee Tariq Batista

Tariq Batista

Witness J. Beardsley

J. Beardsley

3010PRS (12/00)

7

Reentry

Isabel sits in the front seat of a car, her painted toes wiggling out the window. On the dashboard, the vents are probably tilted upward so that the AC blasts up her skirt, cools off her crotch. Isabel stands on the corner, eating an arepa. Her chin shines with grease, which she doesn't wipe off, which is not like her at all. Isabel sits in the back of a cab. Isabel climbs the stairs to the 7 train. Isabel pushes a baby carriage—but no, no, no, no, that's impossible, it's too soon. The rear doors of a van swing open and Isabel steps out, leaps to the street. The van advertises Carpet Cleaning Services, but Isabel holds no vacuum, no broom or mop. Isabel walks out of one of the jewelry stores on Seventy-fourth Street. She carries a little bag probably stuffed with gold chains, but wait a second, never mind, that woman is obviously not Isabel. That lady's Indian, which Isabel is not, and she's wearing high heels, which Isabel never wears. Isabel crosses the street at the intersection. Isabel jaywalks, gliding between moving cars. Stuck at the light, Isabel foolishly presses the green button on the corner. Isabel comes out of a pool hall, Isabel walks into a bank, Isabel sits behind a large plate-glass window while a Chinese lady files her nails, Isabel trips over her own feet and falls to the sidewalk, and when Tariq reaches out to grab her elbow and help her up, she pulls away from him and hustles down the street.

As he watches her run away, he feels something he's been feeling all morning, something like a lump of ice caught in his throat. The woman's handbag bounces as she motors down the block. The struts in her neck tighten. Tariq knows she wants to turn around and give him a look, but she won't—he sees this in her neck—because he frightens her.

Isabel walks toward him, gives him a wide berth so that they don't bump shoulders. He has been seeing Isabels all morning: at the Beacon train station; on the 6:50 a.m. to Grand Central; in the subway; out the windows of the elevated 7 train, many feet below the tracks, where Isabel was a lonely dot on the pavement. But there had been just one or two Isabel sightings at a time. Now that he's off that train and in Jackson Heights, he sees the slight upward tilt of her nose on every woman's face, her curly hair and copper skin, her mouth passing him on the right, the lips thick and full of blood. Everywhere he looks, he sees Isabel, and every time he sees Isabel, the ice in his throat turns to water.

But oh man this Isabel walking toward him, with her features all fuzzy . . . Tariq can't be sure. Incarceration weakened his eyesight. Too early every evening, all the Fishkill lights would click off, except for a small bulb at the end of the corridor, by the CO station, and this bulb shot a golden sliver into his cell. He'd get out of bed and sit on the floor and bring the Book into this sliver. With his face pressed against the bars, he'd read and reread, his eyes straining in the dark. And so now the Isabel coming toward him looks all fuzzy, but she walks *exactly* like the real Isabel walks, with her head down and her soft hands scrunched into fists. Get ready, Tariq. This Isabel might actually be her.

He throws himself into the nearest store, where he crouches down low and peeks out the window. Lights flicker off the glass, red lights and yellow lights and white lights, all of them flashing from inside the store. Motors whir, machines beep. Along one wall, a counter stretches toward the back of the store, and behind that counter are cameras, phones, TV sets, DVD players, answering machines, pagers, antennae, and, with his hands tugging at his beard, an Arab man in a loose-fitting cream-colored robe. Along the other wall: more electronics, another counter, another Arab man. It takes Tariq a moment to understand that these men are not twins. Only one man and only one counter exists. The store's other half is a mirror.

Tariq puts his hand flat against the window. He knows he's not afraid to see Isabel. Not at all. *Absolutely* not. No, the reason he ran into this store is because he's afraid she might see him. Before that can happen, certain moves need to be made.

From the Arab man, Tariq buys himself a wristwatch, which happens to be the very first item on his agenda. Coincidence? Is it some kind of accident that of all the stores on Roosevelt Avenue, he ducked into this one, an electronics joint he didn't even know existed? Of course not. There are no accidents, happy or otherwise. Tariq has been put on a straight path.

In addition to the clothes he's wearing (plain white T-shirt; natty, rubber-soled Converses; a pair of prisoner-made jeans that taper to an end just above his ankles), and in addition to the train ticket to Grand Central Station and the green sheet with parole stipulations and the nineteen Steri-Strips in his cheek, the Fishkill Correctional Facility gave Tariq upon his release two twenty-dollar bills. Gratis. For time served. Thanks for the memories. Earlier today, he used one of these twenties to buy a MetroCard, and the machine spat out his change, eighteen gold dollar coins that he'd never seen before in his life. He goes away and they change the currency? Seriously? Instead of Washington or Lincoln, the coin shows a young girl, with a baby asleep on her shoulder. Even she, this moonfaced girl, reminds him of Isabel. With her coins he pays for his watch.

It is a Casio F-91W, a water-resistant model (not quite the same as waterproof, but so what?) with an alarm, stopwatch, digital numbers, and a light rubber wristband. At a cost of twelve dollars, it is the only watch he can afford. He presses a button on the side, which should cause the time to illuminate. *Don't worry,* the Arab man tells him. *That particular function will work better at night.* After paying for the watch, Tariq turns away from the counter, embarrassed by the width of his grin.

When exactly did the lights click off at the Fishkill Correctional Facility? Tariq doesn't know. It never mattered. Calendars, sure, to mark the passing of days—but wristwatches? Hours? Minutes? What use could they have in a place of controlled movement, where there was always someone telling you when to line up for head counts and contraband checks and cafeteria meals of overcooked beef as leathery as a dragon's tongue. But it's a brand-new morning, Tariq. Today

marks the first day in two and a half years that he has had a reason to know the time. As the Book says:

It is He who gave the sun its radiance, the moon its lustre, and appointed its stations so that you may compute years and numbers. God did not create them but with deliberation. He distinctly explains His signs for those who can understand.

Tariq takes his Casio F-91W digital watch outside the store, where it looks flimsier under the sun's natural light. The wristband feels greasy, as if it's already been worn. He searches the watch's face for scratches. Obviously what's happened here is that the Arab man saw Tariq come into the store with his busted sneakers and his prisoner-made jeans, and he sized him up as some kind of punk. Sold him a cheap, used, worn-out, greasy Casio. Tariq moves the watch up and down on his wrist. If he were to go back into the store . . . although, of course, he won't. No way to *prove* the watch is used. And, more important, Tariq has his agenda to consider. But what if? What if he went back into the store and smashed this watch against the man's face? His nose would shatter, of course. And probably his lips and teeth and jaw. And the watch? Would that break, too? Tariq suspects that it would.

Reentry day, baby. First day home. First day of freedom. In the early months of his incarceration he made lists of things he wanted to do on this day: go straight home and take a three-hour shower, drink beers at Budd's Bar, shoot pool, go bowling, sit in a recliner, walk down to Travers Park and dominate the handball courts, hit up Sammy's Halal, sleep in a bed with three dozen pillows, go to a Mets game, smoke a dub, go to Numbers, Records, & Tapes and buy the new Nas, the new Noreaga, the new Mobb Deep, visit his old grammar school, Our Lady of Fatima, and apologize to all the nuns, snort lines off a CD case, tear up some black and white and Asian and Latina pussy.

But things changed. He changed. Things he never imagined came to pass. Difficult things? Sure. Some of them. But one must adapt, right? That is, as the expression goes, the name of the game. Tariq's new and improved reentry day to-do list:

1. ~~Buy a watch.~~
2. Buy chocolates.
3. Get a haircut.
4. Pick up a more impressive, more stylish pair of jeans.
5. Remove Steri-Strips.
6. Buy and eat two delicious slices from Gianni's Pizzeria.
7. Be home by 1:10 for the start of the Mets-Yankees game, when everyone will be together, sitting in the living room.

He checks his Casio F-91W. Time to make moves.

From a bodega on Roosevelt Avenue he buys Kit Kat bars, Snickers bars, Charleston Chews (his favorite), Mr. Goodbars, and two fistfuls of Hershey's Kisses. Not only does it cost him all six of his remaining Isabel coins, but he also has to dip into his last twenty.

"Hope you got a good dentist," says the bodega man.

Tariq stuffs the candy into all four of his pockets, really jamming it in there. Outside he walks on the sunny side of the street, partly because it's so nice out, and partly because he wants the chocolate to get warm.

Everyone inside Jackson Heights' Headz Ain't Ready barbershop—the barbers, the men getting their hair cut, the men waiting for their turn, the men flipping through issues of *Source* magazine and *Sports Illustrated*, the men who, with felt-tip pens and management's permission, scrawl their graffiti tags onto the walls—they all turn to look at Tariq when he walks through the door. No one stops what they're doing. The clippers still clip and the buzzers still buzz and the boom box still blasts an Eminem song Tariq's never heard before. But just because the men in here don't stop what they're doing doesn't mean they're not eyeballing him. As Tariq knows, there's always time for that. Even the photographs tucked into the mirrors. Even the two-dimensional hair models—their glossy head shots pasted to the walls—even they seem to give him the once-over. *Look at the new guy in his Casio watch and his too-short jeans.* One kid in particular, a broom sweeper, a skinny little

bitch with sharp elbows and a pubic hair mustache—he can't *stop* looking at Tariq. The kid runs his hand over his mouth, hiding his toothy smile.

The Book says:

Do not disagree among yourselves or you will be unmanned and lose courage. Persevere, for God is with those who endure.

In an uncomfortable wooden chair, Tariq waits for his turn. The men around him talk about the upcoming Mets-Yankees game. With Roger Clemens coming to Shea and with the DH rule not in effect, everyone wants to know if the Mets will plunk Clemens for what he did to Piazza two years ago. No one asks Tariq for his opinion. When they've exhausted the Mets game, they talk about the Nas/Jay-Z feud and they talk about the molestation scandal in the Catholic Church and they talk about a young black kid who got himself killed last night in Corona. Tariq tries to read the *Queens Gazette*, but the words keep running together. He feels certain the broom sweeper is watching him.

"You up," the barber finally says, and Tariq takes a seat in one of Headz Ain't Ready's high leather chairs. The barber circles behind him. "Damn," he says. "Look at all these gray hairs! My man, you can't be older than twenty-two years old, am I right?"

"Shave it all off," Tariq says.

Through the mirror he sees the barber frown, as if he'd much rather give Tariq a shape-up or an ill fade, as if simply shaving a man bald is a waste of his talents. "You sure?" he says. "I can take it off, but I can't put it back on."

"Get rid of it."

"You the boss," he says. Around Tariq's neck, he ties a hair-catching smock. His breath smells like coffee, his fingers like Barbasol. As he buzzes off a sideburn, he says, making conversation, "That's a real beaut you got there. Fresh. Recent."

Tariq assumes he's referring to the two-and-a-half-inch gash in his face. The barber wants to know the story, but he clearly doesn't have the balls to come out and ask for it.

What is there to say? He was out in the yard, playing cards. With his Spades partner shooting for nil, Tariq had to cover the high cards and pick up as many books as possible, and that's exactly what he was

doing, scooping up his partner's queen with an ace, when he heard what sounded like the teeth of a zipper coming undone.

The other Spades players jumped up from the table. Tariq's hand came away from his face slick with blood. He was impressed—this was before the pain arrived—by how bright red his blood looked, almost like cartoon blood, a sign, he thought, of a healthy body. Then the pulse in his cheek jumped. He closed one eye—the left one, on the untouched side of his face—to make sure he could still see out of the other eye. While he held his cheek together, blood rolled down his arm, dripped off the tip of his elbow. He tried not to get any on the playing cards.

Arturo Sanchez rang him up with a toothbrush, buck-fifty'd him with intent to blind. Tariq doesn't know if he used a blade—he never got a chance to ask him—but if Arturo didn't use a blade, then he must've spent two or three nights sharpening the handle of his toothbrush against the walls of his cell. If he did use a blade—and it certainly felt like he used a blade—then he probably snapped the plastic safety off his disposable razor, pushed out the banger, and melted it onto the toothbrush with a Bic lighter, stopping every now and again to blow on the tips of his fingers.

He cut Tariq against the grain. The toothbrush entered the cheek just above his mouth, got yanked upward, tore through facial muscles, took a banana route around the orbital bone, and came out, the toothbrush did, a half inch shy of his ear. Arturo walked away, his hunter green pants spotted with blood. He let the toothbrush drop from his fingers. An against-the-grain buck fifty is deep, although inaccurate, and while Arturo must've been pleased to see the blood squirt out of Tariq's face in long, satisfying arcs, he must've also been disappointed to have missed the soft jelly of his eye. Not to mention how pissed Arturo must've felt later that night, forced to brush his teeth with his finger.

Tariq imagined that if he were a corrections officer, he would've been lounging in the back of an ambulance, on his way to the Beacon ER for reconstructive surgery. But instead he got tossed into the in-house medical unit, where he saw, for the very first time, his new, gashed-open face. He thought of his mother's disappointment. He thought of Isabel, and how much harder everything would be now. His cheek puckered open like the mouth of a fish.

But because he tries to strive in the way of Allah with a service worthy of Him, Tariq received the blessing of the FHS's most skilled doctor: a short, no-nonsense Korean with fingerprint smudges all over his glasses. A man respected throughout Fishkill, by both COs and inmates. As the doctor worked on the cheek, Tariq told him about Isabel and how important it was—how necessary, really—that the doctor fix him up right, that he get Tariq back to his old handsome self.

"Stop talking," the doctor said.

He didn't sit there with a needle and thread like in the old days, sewing Tariq's face back together with 150 stitches. Instead he compressed the gash, cleaned it, dried it, and reunited the cheek's two halves with something he called Steri-Strips. Tariq thought they looked like bones a dog might gnaw on. Except tiny of course, and sticky on one side. When the doctor finished applying the Steri-Strips, he jammed a tetanus needle into Tariq's arm, slapped a clear plastic Band-Aid on his face, and said, "Don't mess with it. Keep it clean. Keep it dry. The Steri-Strips should fall off on their own within seven days. That's their genius. Don't pull them off yourself before it's time. You'll get infected. And please—don't bother asking me for painkillers. Come back on Tuesday and I'll give you another Band-Aid."

"I can't," Tariq said proudly. "I'm moving out. Saturday morning, I'm going home."

The doctor grabbed Tariq's chin and tilted his head toward the light, just as Lizette used to do when she checked her son's ears for wax. The doctor inspected the left side—the clean side—of his face.

"Keep telling those psychopaths you're getting released," he said, "and I'll be seeing you in here tomorrow. Bleeding out the one good cheek you got left."

Tariq says none of this to the Headz Ain't Ready barber. He is told he's got a real beaut, fresh, recent—and all he says in response is *uh-huh*. He fidgets in the chair so as to better smush the chocolate in his pockets. The barber finishes the haircut in silence. When he's done, he holds a mirror behind Tariq's head, giving him a 360-degree view of his new, shaved, vulnerable-looking dome. Perfect. Tariq imagines he looks as bald and as clean as the day he was born. With a small brush the barber wipes the hair off Tariq's face, careful to avoid his cheek.

At the cash register, the skinny little broom sweeper rings him up. As he stares at Tariq's cheek, he passes his hand over his mouth, just below his pubic hair mustache. The haircut costs thirteen dollars, and when Tariq has to take the Kit Kats and Snickers bars out of his pocket to get at his money, the kid laughs, *hahahahaha*, and sticks his hand in a jar full of lollipops next to the register.

"Sweet tooth?" he says. "Here. Take some. You want a purple one, too? Go ahead. Take as many as you like."

Fight those in the way of Allah who fight you, but do not be aggressive: God does not like aggressors.

The broom sweeper actually grabs hold of Tariq's hand. He uncurls the fingers, shoves lollipops into his palm.

"Do you enjoy what you do?" Tariq asks.

"What?"

"I said, Do you enjoy what you do?"

"What do you mean? Do I like working in the barbershop?"

"No. That's *not* what I mean. I didn't ask, Do you like working in the barbershop? I asked, Do you *enjoy* what you *do*?"

The broom sweeper smiles. He doesn't try to hide it. His hands stay down at his hips. "I don't know," he says. "I guess I don't know what you mean. What do I . . . what am I doing?"

"Don't you know? Surely, my brother, you must know what you do. The broom? Yes? The hair on the floor? You sweep it up. You sweep it up into tidy piles and then you take it away. *That* is what you do. The question, my brother, is do you enjoy it?"

"Well," he says. He hits a button on the cash register and the drawer slides open, kisses his belly. Looking not at Tariq, looking down at the money in the drawer, he says, "I don't know. Why? What is this about?"

"What is this *about*?" Tariq puts his money on the counter. He counts out the bills. One two three four five six seven eight nine ten eleven twelve thirteen fourteen fifteen, which leaves him with exactly three dollars, just enough for a couple of pizza slices from Gianni's. "That's thirteen dollars right there," he tells the broom sweeper. "There's thirteen dollars on the counter, plus an extra two. That two dollars is for you. That's yours. You want to know why? Don't answer. I know you're not good at questions. That two dollars is me saying

thank you. For sweeping my hair off the floor. Because you seemed to *enjoy* yourself so much, I'm giving you two dollars of my money. What do you say? You say, *Thank you.* What do I say? Look at me. Don't look inside that cash register. There's nothing in there for you. Look at me. You say, *Thank you,* and I say, *No, no, no. Thank* you, *brother. You did a very good job.*"

1. ~~Buy a watch.~~
2. ~~Buy chocolates.~~
3. ~~Get a haircut.~~
4. Pick up a more impressive, more stylish pair of jeans.
5. Remove Steri-Strips.
6. Buy and eat two delicious slices from Gianni's Pizzeria.
7. Be home by 1:10 for the start of the Mets-Yankees game, when everyone will be together, sitting in the living room.

How fast does news travel from the streets to the prisons? You read letters. You make phone calls (collect; monitored; fifteen-minute max). You have dreams and nightmares. You stand on line at the commissary, waiting to buy another can of instant soup, and you look up and see a guy from the neighborhood, a guy you went to sixth grade with, a guy who used to steal Slurpees from little kids, and you say, *Hey! What's going on? When'd you get here? What's poppin back at home?*

And he says, *Haven't you heard?*

How fast does news travel from the cells to the streets, from Fishkill to Queens? It don't. Nobody cares . . . *Yeah yeah. Boo-fucking-hoo.*

Of all the shops in the Queens Center Mall, the Macy's department store has the most merchandise, the most men's and ladies' wear, the most jewelry, the most street-level exits, the most gifts-with-purchase, the most cashiers, the most security guards, the most women with the most makeup spritzing the most perfume onto the inside wrists of passersby, the most cameras, the most shoppers, the most crying babies, the most Isabels, the most cosmetic specialists, the most everything, and it is here, inside this mall-dominating superstore, that Tariq grabs off the shelf a pair of Rocawear jeans ($68) and carries them into one of Macy's many dressing rooms.

A young, pasty, pink-haired girl guards the entrance to the rooms. She folds one button-down shirt after another. A metal hoop pierces her lip, hangs from her mouth like the knocker to a door. The age and ethnicity work, Tariq thinks, to his advantage. He's not as sure about the pink hair or the lip ring. He worries she's the kind of young woman who lives to be unimpressed, who watches scary movies with her chin on her fist, who opens birthday presents with a snap of her gum and a roll of her eyes. That's not what he needs. His plans do not call for *under*whelmed reactions. Having finished with the shirts, the girl moves on to a series of khaki pants, folding them, matching hem to hem. This is her job. She folds the clothes people tried on and discarded, the clothes nobody wants. Then somebody else—not even her—takes them away and puts them back on the shelves. When Tariq approaches her folding table, the pink-haired girl hands him a card with a 1 on it (for the number of items he's trying on), and she points him toward a dressing room in back.

"Thank you," he says, because one should always be polite.

Inside the dressing room, he gets down on his knees facing east. Or at least facing what he hopes is east. For only the second time today, he prays. Allah has a plan and Tariq has a plan, and the trick for Tariq will be keeping those plans from a battle royal. Of course, as it is written, *the best of planners is Allah,* but what Tariq needs to do is sandwich his plan to His plan, so that they become plans *within* plans.

He tries on the Rocawear jeans, the bottoms of which cover the tops of his sneakers, just as they should. In an ideal world the jeans wouldn't fit so tightly, but in an ideal world the Fishkill Correctional Facility would've given him a belt. He peeps himself in the mirror, turning this way and that to admire his ass. Looking good, he thinks—and a good thing too, since that's a part of his physique Isabel's always appreciated.

He slips out of his dressing room and enters the one next door, which looks exactly the same: same mirror, same carpeted floor, same bench with wooden slats, same vanilla-colored walls. He looks up at the light fixture above his head. He wonders if it conceals a security camera, if there's a sun-deprived man in a tiny room jammed full of closed-circuit televisions, staring at the top of Tariq's head. Oh well. As the saying goes, *No reward without risk.*

He unwraps the Snickers, Kit Kats, Goodbars, Charleston Chews,

and Kisses. The chocolates—sun-battered, pocket-pressurized—have softened nicely. They smell sweet, strongly sweet, sickly sweet, and for a moment he feels dizzy. Because he can't help himself, he eats one of the Charleston Chews. The rest he smears onto the dressing room walls. Carefully, so as not to mess up his new Rocawear jeans, he shakes a soft, dripping Snickers bar over the bench, splattering its wooden slats. He streaks the mirror with Goodbars, leaves crescent moons of chocolate on the glass. While mashing Kit Kats into the carpet, he notices a feather in the corner of the dressing room. It lies on the floor, its two ends curled upward. Another crescent moon! Somebody must have been trying on a down jacket in here, and the feather popped out of a sleeve. Has it been here since winter? Tariq can't even imagine. He leaves it alone, rubs chocolate Kisses onto the dressing room's door-knob.

Not since Little League have his hands been so filthy. Not since he slid into second base on a mud-covered infield. He turns them over, these sticky, chocolate-smeared hands. The Hershey Kisses' wrappers—those thin, metallic sheets—have rubbed off on him, and now his palms and fingers sparkle with glitter. Time to clean up. He does the best he can with his hands by rubbing them against the rough insides of his Fishkill jeans. He sucks chocolate out from under his fingernails. The candy wrappers, the three dollars of pizza money, the parole paperwork—all of this he shoves into his new Rocawear pockets. With the old pants balled up in his fist and with his head held high, he leaves the dressing room and strides over to the pink-haired girl at the folding table.

"Who you been letting around back here?" he says.

"Excuse me?" She folds a plaid shirt against her chest. She keeps the collar tucked under her chin, making it easier for her to work, to finish this shirt and move on to the next one. "I'm sorry. I didn't hear you."

"I asked who you was letting around back here. Crackheads?"

"Excuse me?"

"Excuse *me*, but I'm just trying to figure out what's going on around here when you've got dressing rooms covered in shit."

She lifts her head to look at him, and the shirt falls out from under her chin.

"Feces," he says. "I'm talking about somebody's feces up on them

114

walls." He throws the Fishkill jeans down onto her table. He leans forward, closes the space between her body and his. "I'm walking around back there, I look into a dressing room and I see it's got shit all over it. Right back there. Hello? You hearing me? Somebody did diarrhea up on them walls. Understand? And I'm telling you so you can get somebody down here and clean it up." He pulls his head back, a natural-looking recoil. "Unless you already know about it," he says. "Unless you already *been* knowing about it and it's cool with you to work all day in a crack den, a place where the walls get themselves shat on."

"No," she says softly. She chews on her lower lip, her teeth clicking against the metal piercing. "I don't know nothing about this."

"Well that, at least, is some *good* news."

From the waist of her pants, the pink-haired girl unclips a walkie-talkie. But she doesn't speak into it. With the walkie-talkie in hand, she wiggles out from behind her folding table and heads toward the dressing rooms at the end of the hall. She walks slowly, toe to heel. The door to the dressing room yawns open, and when the pink-haired girl gets to it and peers inside she might scream or she might run away or she might drop her walkie-talkie or she might rip off her Macy's name tag and throw it to the floor. Tariq doesn't know. He doesn't know what she says or what she does because he's already gone.

In his stiff-legged designer jeans he walks through the menswear section and the handbag section and the unmentionables section. Two security guard fat-bodies in navy blue blazers run toward him. As they get closer, they split apart, passing him on either side. Walkie-talkies are pressed to their ears, giant grins plastered across their broad honest faces.

Who's chocolate going to fool? Nobody. Particularly if you get close enough to it. But who's going to get close enough? Who's going to bring their nose right up to those brown, nut-filled smears on the wall?

But that's not even the thing. Tariq knows that these kids—the pink-haired girl, the thick-necked security guards, every last one of the embittered employees of the Macy's department store, trapped in here on a beautiful late spring Saturday morning, working the complaints department, staring at doors, breaking penny rolls into cash registers, folding the pants and shirts nobody wants—they all absolutely *need* to believe in a dressing room smeared with shit. So that later tonight, after they've clocked out, these boys and girls can go

home and drink a beer out on the stoop or smoke a dub in Astoria Park or just drive in circles around Francis Lewis Boulevard, and they can turn to their friends and say, *Guess what, just guess, what the fuck happened at work today.*

A black guy with a Big Brown Bag heads toward the exit, and Tariq times it so that they push through the doors at the exact same moment. The alarm trips and beeps. Red lights flash. The black guy stops. Tariq doesn't.

Because the haircut has left him with brown and gray hairs all over his face, and because in the sweaty walk to and from the mall these hairs began to feel like so many swarming, mandible-snapping fire ants, and because he can't show up at home like that, looking like a face-scratching bum, Tariq goes down to Travers Park and sticks his head in the sprinklers. Around him, kids are leaping and prancing through the water, but Tariq stands still, cleans himself off for Isabel. His body temperature cools. Water sprays into his eyes, fills his open mouth.

Doused, he sits on a bench in the sun—what a beautiful day!—and yanks the Steri-Strips off of his face. Every time he tugs on one, his cheek tugs back. He rolls the strips into a gooey ball on his finger and flicks them away, as if he were airmailing boogers.

Two little white boys watch him. They don't run through the sprinklers or kick a ball or play saloogie with some smaller kid's cap. Faces blank, they just stand there, seemingly content to watch this bald man tear sutures from his face.

He pays them little attention. Instead, he stares across the park at a Guyanese man sitting on a bench just like his own. Actually he doesn't so much watch the man as he watches the dog at the man's feet, a beautiful brown pit bull, its face spotted with white freckles. The dog leans into its collar. Its tongue hangs out, as crooked as a question mark. When a ball rolls by, when a tennis ball or a softball or a soccer ball or a Sky Bounce blue handball gets away from some kid and rolls near the bench, the pit bull lunges after it. And because in parks balls don't roll by without kids close behind, chasing them with outstretched fingers, every time the dog lunges at a soccer ball, the dog also, in effect, lunges at a child. The Guyanese guy pulls up hard on the

leash. The pit bull snaps its teeth. And the children run away laughing and squealing. No one, Tariq thinks, seems to appreciate the danger. Except for himself. And the dog of course, whose legs strain forward with coiled bloodlust.

Tariq stands up off the bench, and the ground tilts. He throws his hands out in front of him. Light dances in his eyes. He feels a spirit of dizziness poured into his ear. No wonder! It is close to one and his stomach is growling.

Get this: the booths inside Gianni's Pizzeria are no longer booths. They are tables. Covered in red and white checkered *cloths.* The floors have been mopped. A sign on the door says Now Serving Iced Coffee! And the old movie posters on the walls—Stallone's *Nighthawks;* Stallone's *Rocky IV;* Stallone's arm-wrestling picture, *Over the Top*—have all been replaced by tastefully framed photographs of Italian hills and wooden gondolas and old ladies smelling luminous eggplants. Tariq grips the back of a chair, as if to make sure it actually exists. He never expected time to wait for him, to freeze in place, but he also didn't expect the skyline to look so very different, or the currency, or the inside of Gianni's Pizzeria. He never expected so much to have fucking *changed.* At least the ancient *Street Fighter II* machine still stands in the corner, where a crowd of Asian kids have collected around it to watch one of their own, a spiky-haired Korean, battle a heavyset black kid. And, most comforting of all, Gianni himself is still here. He stands sentinel behind the counter, kneading dough with his fists.

Tariq orders two slices, extra hot. He hoped to elicit a *Hey, where you been?* Or a *Nice to have you back!* Tariq wonders if Gianni can't recognize him because of the gash in his cheek and with his head shaved bald—or maybe, he tells himself, expecting hospitality from Gianni is expecting a little too much. While the slices bubble in the oven, Gianni preps a tray, covering it with wax paper, placing three napkins off to the side. Another comfort, another thing that hasn't changed. There are no napkin dispensers on any of the tables. Gianni, cheap bastard that he is, doles out all napkins himself in an effort to prevent paper overdrafts. You get three—if you're lucky—and if you want more you gotta go ask Gianni and deal with his harrumphs.

Tariq gets his money ready as the slices come out of the oven. The

crust has charred and bubbled beautifully. Here's the plan: Tariq will fold the crust down the middle and flip the tip back into the slice, so as to trap the oil. He will blow on the cheese once, maybe twice. Then he will bite in, burning the roof of his mouth so badly that for the next twenty-four hours he will regretfully prod the skin with his tongue. Oh well. What are you gonna do? Gianni throws the slices onto the tray and Tariq's cheeks fill with water.

"Four dollars even," Gianni says.

"I don't want a Coke."

"No Coke. Four dollars for the slices. You *want* a Coke?"

"Four dollars?" Tariq says. "For *two* slices?"

"Four dollars for two slices," Gianni says.

"My entire life it's been one fifty a slice."

"What do you want me to tell you? You want one slice?"

"You don't understand. I've been eating pizza bagels. Catsup and rubber cheese on a toasted bagel. On an English *muffin*." Tariq looks into his face. "I don't want one slice. One slice doesn't *mean* anything to me. I want two slices, please. For three dollars, please."

"Two dollars a slice. Two slices, four dollars. You want a calculator?"

"No thank you. I want two slices for three dollars, please."

The redness starts in Gianni's neck and rises past his chin and mustache and doughy nose all the way up to the crown of his head. He brushes his flour-covered hands against his apron.

"Hey!" someone says. When Tariq turns around he sees that the voice belongs to the heavyset black kid, the one who was playing *Street Fighter II*. The kid comes over and *throws his arm over Tariq's shoulders*. He says, "Hey, Gianni, cut this guy a break. He's a friend of mine."

Gianni points a wooden roller at Tariq's chest. "He needs to learn some manners."

"Ha ha," the black kid says. He tightens his grip around Tariq's shoulder, hugs him even closer. "Like I say, you gotta cut him some slack. He just got out of prison."

If Tariq turned to look at the kid, their faces would be touching. The kid would be able to breathe *into Tariq's mouth*.

"Figures," Gianni says. He talks to the black kid but looks only at Tariq, their heads floating on opposite sides of the counter. "You need to remind your friend here he ain't in prison no more. He's gotta get

rid of his joint mentality. You know what I'm saying? Out here there's something called etiquette."

"Ha ha," the kid says. "I'll tell him. I'll let him know."

So that Tariq may be guided out of his own darkness, he reaches, arms straining, toward the Book:

Hasten for the pardon of your Lord, and for Paradise extending over the heavens and the earth, laid out for those who take heed for themselves and fear God, who expend both in joy and tribulation, who suppress their anger and pardon their fellowmen.

"Excuse me," Tariq says, shaking the kid's arm off his shoulders. He walks away, leaves the slices untouched on the counter.

Outside, the dizziness returns. It drips down his ear, into his throat. Miniature suns float across his retinas. They burst, these suns; they burst and blood surges behind his eyes. He'd sit down if he could, if the streets didn't stink of piss and rotten fruit, if the sidewalks weren't clogged with garbage. Everywhere he looks: garbage. Garbage in the gutters, on the street, spilling out of corner wastebaskets, stacked high on the curb in black-bagged pyramids. One of these overstuffed bags has a tear in its side. Flies buzz around the hole. Brown liquid oozes out onto the sidewalk. Tariq stares at this hole in this bag, and he half expects a baby to fall out, its belly clawed open by pink-eyed rats.

The black kid has followed Tariq outside and he wants to know if everything is okay, if there's anything he can do.

"Go away," Tariq says.

"Don't you remember me?"

"Go *away*."

The kid takes a step backward and shows himself to Tariq. He spreads his hands out wide, causing the flesh under his arms to jiggle. He is man-sized—he is XXL-sized—and yet Tariq could drop him to the ground so easily. Knock that stupid Spider-Man hat off his head and push in his eye, smash his head against the sidewalk. He wears— loosely, and yet the outlines of his breasts remain visible—a stylish Rocawear T-shirt, which Tariq thinks would nicely complement his own Rocawear jeans. He wonders what Isabel might think of this shirt.

"You don't recognize me at all?" the kid says. He takes off his Spider-

Man hat and shows Tariq the top of his head, where the hair grows only in patches.

"Winston?" Tariq says. The kid smiles and quickly puts his hat back on. "You've gotten huge," Tariq tells him.

"I got fat. But you—you're ripped. I don't want to know what happened to the guy who opened up your face."

"Where'd you get that shirt?"

"You like it?" He pulls down on the hem, so that they can both get a better look at it. The shirt tightens, making Winston's breasts even more visible. "Alfredo bought it for me a while ago," he says. "Hey, have you seen Alfredo yet? Have you even been *home* yet?"

"Give me the shirt."

"It's nice, right?"

"Give it to me."

"What?" he says. He tries to smile. Half his face looks dry, but the other half sweats. Big beady drops roll down his cheek. He dips his head to his shoulder, wipes his face dry with the sleeve of his shirt. When he looks back up at Tariq, Winston's smile widens and brightens into the genuine thing. "You got me. For a hot second, you got me good. *Give me the shirt*, he says. Ha ha. You're hilario, Jose. Sorry, sorry. Tariq. You're hilario, *Tariq*." Still smiling, Winston shakes his head and looks around at no one in particular, like a sitcom straight man gesturing to the TV audience, as if to say *Get a load of this guy*. His eyes suddenly widen. "Holy shitballs," he says, pointing behind Tariq. "Would you look at that!"

Tariq suspects a lame schoolyard trick. Asked to give up his shirt, Winston points at the unseen world and says *Look at that!* and when Tariq does, Winston will take off running. But that's not what happens at all. Winston doesn't take off running. He actually comes closer, throws his arm once again over Tariq's bulked-up shoulders. He turns Tariq around and points across the street where a white Camaro plays HOT 97 out of its open windows, and where two halter-topped Isabels dance on the sidewalk, melting the ice in Tariq's throat, and where, behind a furniture store's plate-glass window, a sofa stares out at the street with an empty-cushioned, heartbreaking loneliness, and where the Mister Softee ice cream truck drives by and momentarily blots out Tariq's view, and where a black kid pushes a bicycle with two deflated tires, and where a young Isabel bites into a Jamaican beef patty, the

steam softening her face, and where—if Tariq follows Winston's extended index finger precisely—the Guyanese man from the park is walking down the block, his beautiful brown pit bull at his side.

"That's your dog," Winston says. Reeking of pot smoke, he squeezes Tariq tightly. "You talked to Alfredo yet? We been trying to find a dog for you all week. Like a present kind of? For the dogfight tonight? The welcome back party? You talk to Alfredo yet or what? I'm telling you, we been looking for a dog *just like* that one. And now, *poof.* Yabba-dabba-doo, man. You know what I'm saying? A pit bull. Right across the street."

The Guyanese guy holds his dog on a short leash. The pit bull doesn't trot or scamper beside him. The dog walks. He walks with his head held high, just as a man would walk. Between his legs swing an impressive pair of bright-red balls.

"It's like a sign from God," Winston whispers. He takes a plastic bag of pills out of his pocket. He reaches into the bag—without even looking at what he's grabbing—and pulls out a small white pill, which he drops onto the tip of his tongue. "You want one?" he asks, but before Tariq can say no, Winston has already sealed the bag and put it back in his pocket. "I'm quitting drugs," he says. "Starting tomorrow." He closes his eyes, pinches the bridge of his nose. "Here I am, standing right here with you for crying out loud, and a pit bull, *your* pit bull, walks across the street. Do you know me and Alfredo been looking for a dog like that all week? We found a nice one last night, a Doberman, but it was behind a fence and we couldn't get at it. All week. No luck. And now here I am with you, twelve hours from the dogfight, and . . ." He shakes his head. "It's like the gods be smiling. It's like the universe is on our side. You know what I mean?"

Tariq knows exactly what he means. Across the street, the dog and the man are walking away, nearing the intersection. They pause for the light, let the cars drive by, and then they move on, walking quickly down Northern Boulevard. From a distance of one full outer-borough block, Winston and Tariq follow.

"Stare at his shoes," Tariq says.

"Stare at his shoes," Winston repeats.

"You don't want to look at the back of his head. People can feel that

kind of thing. It tingles the scalp, don't ask me how. But if this guy feels eyes on the back of his head, then he's gonna turn around, and if he turns around—"

"Then we're sunk," Winston says. They walk in step, not faster or slower than the man and dog a block ahead of them. "So what we want to do," Winston says, "is stare at the shoes. Got it."

"Ain't no one ever felt eyes on the back of their shoes."

"And this guy ain't going nowhere without taking his feet with him."

"Exactly!" Tariq says, smiling. He feels good. He feels better than he has all day. "It's just a little trick, sure. But I'm telling you, Winston—it's little tricks that keep you ahead of the game."

"You pick it up in prison?" Winston asks.

Tariq shakes his head. He never had to follow anybody in prison because he already knew where everyone was going: the same place he was. No, shadowing people without getting caught was something he learned out here, in Queens, long before he ever got incarcerated. On Friday nights he'd meet up with Gio and Conrad—currently serving out their prison sentences at Otisville and Altona, respectively—and the three of them would follow the construction workers who stumbled off the 7 train, their jeans splattered with paint, their pockets jammed with payday cash, their blood Budweiser-thinned. *Stare at the shoes,* he'd tell Gio and Conrad. Amazing, ain't it? Years later, and he's saying the same shit.

The man and his dog turn the corner, disappear from sight for the very first time. Winston starts to hurry after them, but Tariq grabs at his shirt. He counsels patience. He explains that the guy might've stopped right around the corner, to chat with a neighbor or to scoop poop off the curb, and if Tariq and Winston were rushing they'd bump right into the guy, or they'd have to walk past him, lose their advantage, become the pursued rather than the pursuers.

"*Relax,*" Tariq says. He gestures to the Isabels passing them on their left and right. He points to the base of a maple tree, where pigeons peck at dried crusts of bread. "Take it easy, brother. Enjoy all this scenery."

When they eventually do turn the corner, they see the man and the dog halfway down the block. The guy has slackened his grip on the leash. In his free hand, he jangles a set of house keys. The dog makes a

sharp left toward a stand-alone, one-family house, a Queens residential specialty, and the man follows. They go through a fence—it is waist-high, with a latch door—and they head, the man and the dog, toward the backyard.

Winston and Tariq don't stop. They pass the house without looking at it. They go all the way around the block, taking their time, practicing their lines. When they get back to the house, they make the same sharp left the dog made. Tariq lifts the latch on the fence door as if he's been lifting it every day of his life. And what if the man hasn't gone inside the house yet? What if he's still in the backyard, sunning himself on a lounge chair, zinc oxide smeared on his nose? We're here for the party, they'll say. Told to come straight out back. You know. For the barbecue, the cookout for the Mets-Yankees game. Weiners and hamburgers? This is Rosario's, right? Tell me we've got the right house. This is Eighty-third Street, right?

Tariq holds the latch door open for Winston, who leads the way into the yard. Surprisingly calm, Winston walks right in without any apparent fear, and Tariq is impressed. More than impressed: Tariq is *proud.* He expected the kid to be shitting in his socks by now, but then—with unexpected and considerable disappointment—Tariq remembers that Winston's on drugs. Anti-anxieties, probably. Xanax, or something like it. See, that's the problem with these kids. Anxiety can be useful. Slowing down can be effective. Pay attention. Take your time.

The yard is a couple hundred square feet, small for a backyard, but a good deal bigger than a prison cell. The grass—like the hair on Winston's head—grows only in patches. Soil is exposed. Chipped clay pots line the perimeter of the yard. Nothing grows out of the pots except for the white plastic tags that indicate what *should* be growing out of them. Geraniums. Marigolds. Petunias. Rosemary. There's no lounge chair, no squeezed-out bottle of sunscreen. In one corner slumps a barbecue grill, covered in a tarp. In another corner a kiddie pool, which doesn't seem to be used for recreational purposes. Kids don't jump in the water or splash one another's faces. Instead, the pool seems to be for drinking. It serves as a big dish of water for the yard's only tenant, the pit bull. A metal chain connects the dog's collar to a steel rod buried deep in the ground, and this chain is just long enough to reach the lip of the pool. But the dog isn't drinking

any water. He's sitting in the patchy grass, watching Tariq and Winston with his jaws clamped shut and with his ears pinned to the top of his head.

Stone steps lead from the backyard into the house, where a door has been propped open to let in some air. TV noises spill out of the house. Tariq can hear it as easily as if he were in the living room with the Guyanese guy, sitting on his couch, their feet stretched out on the coffee table. It's the Mets-Yankees pregame show, and the announcers debate only one thing: whether or not Clemens will get beaned when he comes up to bat.

Next door, in the neighbor's yard, four tires stand in a rubber column, stacked one on top of the other. A sign hangs on the fence that separates that yard from this yard. The sign reads Parking for Millionaires Only.

The dog lifts his head to look over at Winston, who's got his hand balled into a fist, his arm reared back, one eye closed to the sun. Before he can complete the windup, Tariq grabs his arm. He pries open Winston's fingers and finds in his palm a tiny blue pill.

"What's this?"

"Sleeping pill," Winston whispers, as if afraid the man in the house—or maybe even the dog—will hear him.

"You're going to give the dog a sleeping pill?"

"No, I'm going to *throw* the dog a sleeping pill. I wouldn't *give* that dog the fucking time. I throw the pill, he licks it up. If he don't, we go cop some burgers and put the pill—"

"And then the dog falls asleep?" Tariq says, with his hand still gripped tight around Winston's wrist. "Yeah? Have I got that right? The dog licks up the pill and then passes out?"

"Correct," Winston whispers.

"Then what? We wait for it to fall asleep? To hit the hay? Then what? You gonna *carry* the dog back to my house? And after you've fed this sixty-pound dog a sleeping pill designed for adult human beings, who's gonna bring it back to life? Once it falls asleep, how's it ever going to wake up?"

"So don't throw the pill?" he says. Tariq stares at Winston, at his ashy skin, at the flecks of white spittle caught at the corners of his lips. "Tariq," Winston says. "You're hurting my wrist."

The Book says:

O you who believe, do not enter other houses except yours without first taking permission and saluting the inmates. This is better for you.

Which seems fairly clear-cut, sure. But Tariq knows a backyard ain't a house. A backyard is a backyard. Religious loophole? No way, this is New York State law. A backyard equals trespassing; a house equals burglary. This is a significant distinction that operates on both sides of the law: a search warrant that provides access to a residence does not necessarily provide access to the property around that residence, e.g. a garage, an alleyway, a run-down backyard.

Tariq walks toward the dog. He keeps his hand out in front of him, palm up, fingers spread apart. Under his feet, pavement gives way to patches of grass and dry soil. The dog sits up off the ground and leans forward on his two front legs. Both ears stand straight up in the air. Because the leash is tethered to the metal pole in the ground, there is a section of this yard in which the dog cannot reach Tariq. Keeping his back straight, Tariq walks out of that section. The dog watches him approach. Inside the house, the TV turns off, and the voices of the baseball announcers are replaced by the jingle of a Mister Softee truck a few blocks away. The dog's back legs flex. He exposes the small black pupils of his eyes. He smells greasy, which reminds Tariq of his father's hair gel, and the way it always stains both sides of the pillowcases. Tariq listens for footsteps padding toward the back door. He bends forward at the waist and the dog's mouth swings open. A yellowish string of saliva connects a top fang to a sharp lower fang. The dog growls, deep and low in his throat. Eyes closed, Tariq slides his hand into the dog's mouth. It feels dark and warm and moist. Teeth pinch his knuckles. A rough tongue slides across the meat of his palm. The dog jerks his head back and, eyes straining, greedily licks the tips of Tariq's fingers. Laps at his wrist. Tariq puts his other hand in the dog's mouth. If any chocolate remained in the spaces between his fingers, it's gone. The dog gnaws on the rubber wristband of the Casio watch. Good boy, good boy. He shoves his head under Tariq's hand, allows himself to be scratched behind the ears.

The hook connecting the leash to the metal pole unlatches easily. When Tariq pulls on the leash, the metal spikes on the pinch collar insinuate themselves into the dog's neck. So Tariq doesn't pull on the leash.

Winston is hugging himself. Watching Tariq and the pit bull approach, he massages his arms, squeezes himself so tightly that blood vessels rise in his knuckles. Tariq takes a quick peek back at the house. No one appears in the door. No one comes charging down the steps. When he turns back around, the dog—as if waiting for Tariq's attention—lunges at Winston. The leash hums in Tariq's hand. Winston backs into a corner, and the dog follows, pulling Tariq with him. Eyes bulging, ears pitched forward, he snaps at Winston's waist.

"Get it away from me," Winston hisses. He goes up on his tiptoes. His eyes are white and moist.

It occurs to Tariq that he needs to give this dog a name.

In the lobby of the Batistas' apartment building a sign on the elevator door says Out of Order—Fuera de Servicio. Underneath that, someone has written in pencil *Then fucking fix it!* Winston optimistically pushes the elevator button anyway. When it doesn't work, he curses under his breath, betrayed. He clearly doesn't want to be here, but Tariq made him come. He likes the idea of Winston entering the apartment before him, announcing his arrival.

They take the stairs, with Winston, like a good herald, going up first. Tariq tries to think of a time when he had the privilege of following Isabel up a flight of stairs, but he comes up with nothing, not one single time. Her ass would've been eye level, swinging from right to left, stretching the cloth of some tight-fitting jeans. One more thing he missed out on. Following Winston, however, offers its own pleasures. Nonsexual pleasures of course. With his shoulders as tense and as high as his ears, Winston takes the steps two at a time until Tariq snaps at him to slow down. The pit bull lurks unseen behind him. The dog nips at air, inches from Winston's meaty thighs. Winston's shoulders rise even higher. But he doesn't say anything, doesn't complain. He knows—how could he not?—that at any time Tariq can let go of the leash.

8

Batista Bros., Inc.

No, no, no, no, no," Lizette says. "Please. It's fine. I don't need any help."

Cookware crowds her stovetop: a pot of her famous habichuelas guisadas simmers in the back; a frying pan waits for tostones, a slab of butter islanded in its cast-iron center; and the signature dish—spicy chicken and rice—cooks in one large pot, a pot Lizette mysteriously found under the sink, when she damn well knows she left it in the cupboard. Evil spirits are rearranging her kitchen, up to no good, testing her sanity.

Isabel lifts the lid off the chicken and rice. As an added layer of protection, heavy-duty aluminum foil covers the pot. Isabel goes to work on unwrapping it. When she peels back a corner of the foil, she allows heat to escape from the pot. Puffs of steam swirl around the bulb on the ceiling. "If you want," she says, "I can stir the rice."

"No, no, no, no," Lizette says. She snatches the spoon out of Isabel's hand. "You stir the rice too much and it goes all amogollao. Yeah? It gets all *sticky*."

"I like sticky rice," Isabel says. Actually she doesn't like sticky rice, but she's willing to start. She's willing to rejigger all her grain-related preferences, just to be contrarian. "I think it tastes better that way."

"No you don't," Lizette says. "Nobody likes sticky rice. The Chinese maybe. But even them, I'm not so sure."

She rewraps the foil around the lid, traps the steam in the pot so the rice grains will pop evenly. Normally Lizette wouldn't bother with the foil—Trade Fair is selling it for $2.99 *apiece*—but the arroz has gotta slide right off the fork tines. The chicken, the tostones, the red bean stew, the sofrito, the meal, the seating, the day—it all has to be perfect. Earlier this morning, she ran down to the Indian girls on Thirty-seventh Avenue and got her eyebrows threaded. Then she jaywalked across the street to the Korean nail salon for a ten-dollar pedicure. While they worked on her feet, she read the *Post,* the ink coming off on her fingers. Rescue workers finally stopped searching for bodies at Ground Zero. Iraq might have links to the 9/11 attacks. Pakistan and India are staring at each other over the tips of nuclear warheads, a Utah teenager got herself kidnapped, some rapper named Nas called Jay-Z "Gay-Z." An editorial made the argument that because of 9/11, intracity race relations are better than ever. *Okay,* Lizette thought. She read all the articles on the Catholic Church scandal, saw something about repressed memories, and wondered if her altar-boy sons ever got . . . oh Lord, don't even go there. In culture: MOMA's Queens opening was just two weeks away, and modern art lovers are griping about the temporary outer-borough location—even Picasso, it seems, can't drag the snooty into Queens. In sports: the Mets lost to the Yankees (4–2), but they'll go at it again today, game two of their three-game series. And in the Irrelevancy Department: the stock market took a hit. Lizette read these articles and others—or if she didn't read a particular article, she at least scanned the punny headline—but nowhere in the paper's hundred-plus pages did she see anything about the day's real story. Not that she expected tabloid coverage, of course. But the omission cast a pall over the paper's other, supposedly more important news items. Who cares about Enron? Who cares about the possible smoking ban? The *Post*—and every other paper in this city—failed to report what was in Lizette's personal edition the extra-extra, read-all-about-it, front-page splash: the return of her son, her eldest baby boy, Jose Batista Jr.

If he ever got here. The clock on the kitchen wall reads a couple of minutes past one. Lizette started cooking early because Junior's letter

said he'd be released in the morning. Plus, she's got to go to work soon. She works full-time—thank you very much—at an eyeglass shop, and while Dr. Remmelts, the optometrist, gave her the morning off, he needs her to come in for the afternoon. His wife is nine months pregnant or some such thing, and because apparently for pregnant people the whole world and everyone in it has to come to a goddamn screeching halt . . . forgive her! Forgive her the blasphemy! *The Father, the Son, and the Holy Spirit,* Lizette mutters under her breath. She's stressed, that's all. He should've been here hours ago, and now, who knows? Forget the expense, forget the inconvenience—Lizette should've taken a train up to Fishkill and picked him up. And now, because she didn't, Junior has probably kicked a hack guard in the ear and gotten himself tossed right back behind bars. Lizette knows the rate of recidivism. She reads the paper. She knows the ex in ex-con is only temporary, Indian-given; she knows the prisons have cells on the inside and revolving doors on the outside. The only thing that will keep her baby out of that spinning vortex is good old-fashioned Family Values: unified parents, Junior's favorite foods, a clean kitchen, fresh towels, cloth napkins that smell like fabric softener. Given its importance, she wishes this first meal was a Batistas-only affair. Not to be mean or anything, but Lizette wishes Isabel would suck it up and move back in with her mother. For a little while. At least till the baby is born. Is that so horrible? Does that make her a bad person? Maybe, but Lizette is more concerned with being a good mother. With Junior's personality, with the state of incarceration, well, it's going to be hard enough keeping this family together, repairing the boys' relationship, without Isabel coming in and out of the shower, walking all pregnant through the hallways.

Lizette turns down the heat on the habichuelas guisadas. In five minutes—oh why did she start cooking so early?—the chicken will be done. Lizette will take it off the burner, of course, but if she lets it sit too long the rice will get mushy, or worse: cold.

"You need the sofrito?" Isabel asks. The girl opens the freezer and pulls out an ice cube tray. Lizette makes all the sofrito herself in a food processor—nothing comes out of a jar in this kitchen—and she keeps the green peppery sauce in ice cube trays. Sure it makes the freezer stink of onion and garlic, but what are you gonna do? Lizette needs easy access to her sofrito. She doesn't cook anything without it.

Isabel turns the ice cube tray over onto the counter, so that its blocky plastic asses stick straight up in the air. She's about to bang out all the little green cubes when Lizette seizes her by the wrist.

"Someone cleans these counters, you know." Lizette turns the tray over, right side up. "Just flex it, see? Just a little pressure and the cubes slide right out. No mess, see?"

"How many cubes you want?"

"Oh, I already did the sofrito, sweetie. I used two cubes to sauté the jamón. Twenty minutes ago." Lizette inhales deeply. "You smell it?"

Because Isabel—of course—left the freezer door open, the cranky, ill-tempered refrigerator begins to hum, announcing its neglect.

"Put this away," Lizette says as she hands her the ice cube tray. "You know, dear, this kitchen's awfully small for two people."

Isabel pulls her shirt down over her belly. The poor thing's got no maternity clothes. She wears one of Dito's old Our Lady of Fatima T-shirts, and the bottom keeps riding up on her stomach, exposing a small sliver of skin. A pair of dirt-stained sweatpants have been cinched tightly around her waist. She wears no makeup or jewelry. Her hair is pulled back into a severe, face-tightening ponytail.

"You don't like what I'm wearing?" Isabel says.

Lizette smiles, upset that her thoughts have been so easily penetrated. "You look fine," she says brightly.

"I woulda wore my Versace," Isabel says, "but it's still at the cleaners."

"I think you look *perfectly fine.*"

Alfredo comes into the kitchen from the living room, where he'd been watching the Mets-Yankees pregame show with his father. Alfredo didn't even know he was walking toward the kitchen until he got here. His legs and nose had apparently brokered some kind of side deal, arranged all by themselves to carry the rest of his body into Mama's kitchen, where red beans stew in a thick, fragrant paste of olive oil, garlic, and cilantro, where chicken falls off the bone. And now that Alfredo's here, he sees he's got some work to do.

The two women lean slightly forward at the waist, moving toward each other by millimeters, like a pair of tectonic plates. *Got here just in time,* Alfredo thinks. In his mother's smile and in his girlfriend's clenching hands, Alfredo reads—quickly, accurately—that Isabel's trying to help and Mama's having none of it. So Alfredo will give Isabel something to do. So that she feels useful, wanted. So that she may keep

herself momentarily busy. So that her hands will unclench, he will ask her to do something for *him*. Give to her what his mother has denied.

"Hey, baby? Can you pour me a glass of water?"

"Your legs broken?" Isabel says.

"I'm just trying to—"

"You want water," Lizette says, "get it yourself."

"Wow," Alfredo says. "Forget it. I'm not even thirsty."

Isabel tilts her head, thinking that if she changes her angle on Alfredo, he might change as well. She could murder him. In the movie version of her life, Isabel's not in this kitchen. She's on a Greyhound bus, a balled-up sweatshirt between her head and the window. *Come on*, Christian Louis says. *Has it come to this? That even in your fantasies, you can't afford a pillow? Fuck that noise!* In the movie version of her life—and we're talking Hollywood now, no Sundance independent camcorder bullshit—in the big budget, wide release movie version of Isabel's life she's not in this garlic-reeked kitchen because she's on an airplane to Paris, up in first class, sipping on a fountain Coke, and while Alfredo is with her—he's gotta be—he's all the way back in coach, in a middle seat, between the two fattest air travelers of all time. These wide-bottomed men eat blue cheese sandwiches and sneeze into their armpits.

If only. She and Alfredo had their chance to leave last night. But Alfredo rolled over on the sofa bed and explained that he could leave Jackson Heights like Captain Britain can leave the UK. Which is to say not at all. Alfredo grew up here, he's never left here, his family's here, his friends are here, his business is here, he's written his name in the wet cement of these sidewalks. Isabel asked who the fuck Captain Britain's supposed to be. *A comic book character*, Alfredo said, and Isabel stopped listening.

"You guys want to do something useful?" Lizette says.

"Not really," Alfredo says.

"Move the table—pick it up so you don't leave streaks on the floor—and place it, gently, in the middle of the kitchen."

That's not right, Alfredo thinks. The table—flimsy, rectangle shaped, propped up on four thin metal legs—hugs the kitchen wall. That's where it *lives*. When the family eats dinner together—which is every night, work schedules permitting—they sit on only three sides of the table, Lizette and Jose Sr. on opposite ends, Alfredo and Isabel

next to each other. To move the table now is to change everything, is to block Jose's access to the bathroom and bedrooms. But Isabel has already picked up her end, and Alfredo can't have his seven months pregnant girlfriend schlepping furniture all by herself. Together, they wobble the table into the middle of the kitchen. Open on all four sides now, the table stands exposed. It seems to float. An island in the sky. Alfredo feels like he's been dropped into some other family's kitchen. Near the wall, on the linoleum floor, four clean little squares—where the table's legs used to stand—stare up at him. "Is this permanent?" he asks.

Lizette reaches into the hallway closet for the second time today. Earlier this morning she went in here to get a bath mat, to replace the one that had mysteriously gone missing. ("What bath mat?" Isabel had said under questioning.) This time, Lizette pulls out a gray metal folding chair.

Jose Sr. wheels himself into the kitchen. He'd come in here to tell Alfredo the game's about to start, but when he sees the obstruction in the middle of the kitchen he stops. "Whoa," he says. He runs his hand along one end of this new, four-sided kitchen table. "What's going on? Is this permanent?"

Lizette sets the table, muttering to herself. She puts out the good forks, knives, and plates. Instead of the usual paper towels, she gets her nice cloth napkins, recently laundered.

"We're eating dinner *now*?" Jose says. "It's one o'clock in the afternoon. The game's starting."

"The chicken's almost done," Lizette says. "When the chicken's done, we eat."

"But Junior—"

"Tariq," Alfredo corrects.

"He's not even here yet," Jose tells Lizette.

"Then we eat without him," she says, and she has to keep her hands from flying to her hair. "Does anyone know where he is? Because I haven't the faintest. And the tostones. I haven't even *started* the tostones."

Isabel grins. "I can fry them."

"You know," Lizette says. Her hands fold in prayer under her chin. "This is an awfully small kitchen."

The doorbell rings. Jose spins his chair around, and Lizette shoots

past him into the living room. Almost immediately, however, she comes back and does something Alfredo hasn't seen her do in a long time, months maybe, possibly even years: she gets behind her husband's wheelchair and pushes it. Jose rolls, she steers, and the two of them move, together, toward the living room. The doorbell rings again.

Isabel pulls her shirt down over her belly.

"You ready?" Alfredo says.

"It's not too late."

"Oh no?" He moves closer, gives her a bright, brilliant smile. "Have I got anything stuck between my teeth?"

"Is my breath bad enough?" she asks. Alfredo sticks the tip of his nose into her mouth. He sniffs her lips, and then, a rabbit in a lettuce patch, he canvasses her entire face, trying to get her to laugh, sniff-sniff-sniffing her cheeks, her forehead, her eyeballs. "Maybe I should suck on one of your mother's sofrito cubes," Isabel says. "Get my breath ass flavored."

"It's not your fault you're beautiful."

"There's always the fire escape in your father's room."

Alfredo smiles again, a less brilliant smile, a smile without teeth. He grabs Isabel's hand, which feels surprisingly warm. Heat flows out of her body and into his. He leans toward the living room, dragging Isabel with him, and he wants to say something cool and reassuring, something confidence inspiring, but he doesn't say anything. He gets distracted. His mother is screaming.

"Don't worry!" Tariq says. A dog—a pit bull!—lunges at Alfredo's mother. Elbows out, Jose Sr. wheels away and bangs into the coffee table, upsetting a small vase of lilies. Stalks spill onto the floor. Again the pit bull lunges, and Tariq yanks on the leash. The dog's front legs come up off the carpet. They flail at nothing, these legs, as if the dog were storming up a flight of invisible stairs. Lizette doesn't step away because, it seems, it hasn't yet occurred to her that she should. Her hands stick straight up in the air, her fingers splayed, her face bemused—a law-abiding citizen who finds herself suddenly, inexplicably, under arrest. Isabel holds her belly. In the corner of the living room, behind the front door, Winston—*Winston?*—looks down at the

ground. He is hugging himself. Vase water drips onto the carpet. The dog growls at Lizette.

"Put your hands down," Tariq tells his mother. "You're making him nervous."

Alfredo grabs a plush parrot off an end table and tosses it under-hand—Winston style—into the rumpus. Like an overeager infielder, the dog tries to snatch it out of the air, but he closes his jaws too soon and misses. The parrot bounces off his freckled snout and skips across the floor. The dog chases after it, traps the bird's beaked face under his paw. He dips his head over the parrot's body, as if in mourning, and tears open its stomach. White bits of stuffing explode into the air.

"You're going to teach him bad habits," Tariq tells Alfredo. The dog chews on the parrot, and when Tariq tries to pull it away, a wing comes off in his hand.

"My God," Lizette says. Her face is red, her forehead shines. She looks up, past the parrots on wires, at her cracked ceiling, where a tea-colored bubble of plaster sags down.

Tariq gets down on the ground and wrestles the parrot away from the pit bull. The dog's wet nose is matted with cottony stuffing. He licks Tariq's face. Tariq pulls him close, blows air into his eyes, scratches him behind the ears. With the dog squirming, playfully nip-ping at earlobes, Tariq ties his leash to a leg of the sofa. They both seem to be laughing, sharing some private joke.

"Hi, Winston," Alfredo says.

"Hello."

"I was worried you might be dead."

"No," Winston says, sounding almost sorry to disappoint. "Hey— but my phone's dead." He reaches for the cell in his pocket—as if to prove his claim, as if he were presenting evidence before a judge—but Alfredo waves him off. No time for nonsense. The living room pulsates with noise, and Alfredo strains to hear everything at once: the dog growling, the Mets game blaring, Jose telling Tariq that their mama doesn't care for dogs in the house, and Isabel—where's Isabel?— hovering in the kitchen doorway, silent, speaking to no one.

Lizette seizes Tariq's chin. Her fingers flexed like a claw, she leads him away from both Jose and the dog. "Baby, what happened to your face?" she asks, sounding less concerned than annoyed, as if her son's face were not his own but rather something she let him borrow,

and now, years later—would you look at this?—he returns it with a deep scratch right down the middle. "That dog mangle your face, baby?"

Tariq puts his arms around her. For a moment her head pulls away from the hug—fighting, straining to get a good look at her baby's cheek—but eventually she slackens. She has waited too long for this. She rests her head against his chest.

Over his mother's shoulder, Tariq watches Isabel, who continues to hang suspended in the doorway, halfway between the kitchen and the living room. With his eyes on her she feels conscious of her feet, her hands, her awkward elbows. She presses her knees together. She wishes she didn't *have* knees. She wishes she'd worn a long-sleeved shirt. She wishes the hair on her arms were darker, and more plentiful. She wishes . . . *shhhhh.* Curled up in Isabel's ear, Christian Louis—God bless him—hums a cradlesong. The Internet taught her the lullaby, and she passed it on. Between stanzas, he says, *At least, Mama, your feet are covered.* Earlier this morning, Isabel put on socks with holes in them and then immediately changed into new ones, thinking ahead, knowing that in this moment, this first encounter, she would not want a toe exposed.

With a final squeeze, Tariq releases his mother and moves toward Isabel. He comes at her as a gorilla might, sideways, in profile, showing her only one half—the clean half—of his face.

Alfredo steps in front of him. He extends his hand, and Tariq slaps it away. Hard. He is smiling. He throws his arms around Alfredo's body and holds him close—no handshakes here, no stiff, one-armed back-slapping. Not knowing how to react, Alfredo allows himself to be hugged, his arms frozen at his sides. Tariq smells like Papi, like sweat and Barbasol and peanuts and tattered old newspapers. In Alfredo's ear, he makes low grunts of pleasure. *Been a long time,* he murmurs. Is that right? *Been a long time? Been too long?* Something like that. If Alfredo had gotten more sleep last night, then he might have heard what his brother said, and he might have zinged back with an appropriate reply. Tariq pulls him closer, tightens his grip, and when Alfredo feels the acceleration of his brother's heartbeat, it occurs to him that if Tariq's eyes are open, then he's staring directly at Isabel.

"All right," Alfredo says, squirming to free himself. "Come on."

Tariq releases Alfredo and swims past him toward Isabel. She leans into the doorway and tries to look brave. Both Alfredo and his mother

are rushing over. They flank Tariq as he stands in front of Isabel, his body listing to one side, his thumbs hooked through his belt loops in what seems to be a forced attempt to look casual. He stares down at her and she gamely stares back for as long as she can, but eventually her back stiffens and her eyes drop to the floor. He wets his lips before speaking.

"You're further along than I thought you'd be."

"Oh yeah?"

"*Yeah*," he says, using her word, spitting it back at her. He reaches out and puts his hands on her stomach.

Instinctively, Alfredo slaps them away. He feels the sting on his fingertips. In the far corner of the living room, the dog starts barking. Tariq turns to look at his brother.

"Listen," Alfredo says. He's prepared no speech, no explanation. "Listen to me."

"I'm listening," Tariq says.

"Jose?" Lizette says. She pulls on the sleeve of his shirt. "Where'd this dog come from? What're we going to do about this *dog*?"

He ignores her. Still looking at Alfredo, he reaches out, places his hands back on Isabel's stomach. "My nephew's in here," he says. "Or is it my niece? Let me tell you something. It *feels* like a boy, the way it's kicking the shit out of my hands."

"It's a boy," Alfredo says.

"Good work," he says. "And what's this boy's name?"

Alfredo shakes his head. He refuses to say the name out loud, afraid Tariq might somehow pollute it. "We don't know."

"You don't know?" Tariq says. "You gotta have a list of possibles at least. How about Alfredo Junior?"

"We'll consider it," Isabel says. She takes his hands and forces them down to his sides. She backs away into the kitchen, and as she goes she pulls her shirt over her stomach. Tariq is beaming, almost panting. He takes a step forward to follow her, and Alfredo, who has to say something, says, "What happened to your face?"

Tariq turns to him. Alfredo has a hard time maintaining eye contact and so he stares at the knot of Tariq's Adam's apple, at the little hairs encircling the collar of his shirt. Tariq says, "What do you *think* happened to my face?"

"I don't know," Alfredo says. "You cut yourself shaving?"

"Bingo," Tariq says. "You got it. On the very first try. I cut myself shaving."

Lizette goes up on her tiptoes and kisses Tariq's shoulder. "Are you hungry, baby? I made my rice."

"What do I win?" Alfredo says. "For guessing—on my very first try—about your mangled, fucked-up face?"

"*Alfredo,*" Lizette hisses.

"What do you want?" Tariq says. He tilts his chin toward the pit bull. "You want the dog? You want him, he's yours. My gift to you."

Jose Sr. says, "Your mother doesn't want dogs in the house."

"Oh would you lay off that already!" Lizette says.

Alfredo steals a peek at his brother's pit bull. Leashed to the sofa, the dog lies down with his stomach flat on the carpet. Alfredo is afraid of many things. He's afraid of eating chocolate because he's afraid of getting zits. He's afraid of moving away from home. Every day, as he slips on his Timberlands, he's afraid a mouse will be camped out at the bottom of one of his boots. He's afraid of starting the crossword in the *Daily News* because he's afraid he won't be able to finish it. He's afraid of not knowing. He doesn't know what his best friend is doing here with his ex-con brother and a pit bull terrier, and he is afraid of asking for details and advertising his ignorance. He's afraid he enables Winston's drug addiction. He's afraid of awkward silences and poisonous snakes and another terrorist attack in New York—but who isn't afraid of those things? He's afraid of his brother. He's afraid of cars. He's afraid of farms, in particular being trapped inside a silo with grain pouring down his throat—although he's never actually seen a silo in person, or even been to a farm. Isabel takes three to four shits a day, and Alfredo contributes two dumps himself, and in all DNA likelihood Christian Louis will inherit this defecatory gene, and Alfredo worries he won't be able to afford enough disposable diapers. He's afraid he'll be a cold, inattentive father, although Isabel assures him that the very fear guarantees he won't be. He's afraid he works too hard for too little gain. He's afraid of being a nine-to-five schlub, a regular guy with modest dreams. He's afraid of miscarriages. He won't even say the word out loud. When separated from Isabel, he's afraid of the sobbing sirens of ambulances. He's afraid his father's body—like the bodies of so many paraplegics—will confuse below-the-waist immobility for end-of-the-line mortality and just give out. When Alfredo

thinks of the way he kicked Vladimir in the neck, Alfredo is afraid of himself. He's afraid Vladimir—or someone Vladimir knows—killed Curtis Hughes. He's afraid the bone-knuckled Alphabet Brothers—Alex and Bam-Bam—will blame him. He's afraid of the head-tilted look Isabel gives him when he's disappointed her. He might be afraid of the dark; it's hard to tell around here, in a city where lights are constantly burning. He's afraid that Isabel—and he knows he's a fucking idiot for even thinking this—he's afraid that Isabel will leave him for Tariq. He's afraid of cats. Well, not all cats. Just one in particular, a soot-backed calico who stalks the alleyways at night, wherever Alfredo and Winston are getting stoned. Alfredo worries—in his paranoid, THC-addled state—that this cat might actually be Lizette, metamorphosed via some Santeria witchcraft for the purposes of keeping an emerald eye on her pot-smoking, misbehaving son. And dogs. Alfredo is afraid of dogs, especially this one. His eyes look like a man's eyes, with plenty of white around the pupils. That's what's so scary. These eyes bulge in their sockets, as if they want out, as if they want to return to the human face from which they came.

Wake up, Alfredo. This isn't the time.

While he was midreverie, his family agreed to make a mass movement toward the kitchen. Isabel's already in there. Lizette drags a protesting Winston by the wrist, and Jose wheels behind them, complaining about supper's ludicrous start time. Excluding the pit bull, only Tariq and Alfredo are left behind in the living room. They stand on opposite ends of the kitchen threshold, where the carpet gives way to linoleum.

"After you," Tariq says.

Alfredo reaches down and pulls a long clear plastic strip off the back of Tariq's jeans. The strip says *Rocawear* with the numbered measurements—*34 × 30*—repeating themselves all the way down to the bottom. Blue denim fuzzies float on the sticky side of the strip.

"Oh," Alfredo says. "Did you want to keep this on there?"

"See, I didn't know." His face softens, goes peaceful—an expression Alfredo recognizes as dangerous. Tariq reaches out and gives his brother's shoulder a squeeze. "Case you haven't heard, I've been away for a while. I don't know nothing. I thought keeping tags on the jeans might be the new style."

"No," Alfredo says. "It ain't."

With considerable disappointment, Lizette realizes she's going to have to skip the tostones and serve regular old bananas instead. She picked up some nice ripe ones at the store yesterday. She'll peel them and leave them exposed on the perimeter of everyone's plate. The tostones would've added a nice crispy texture to a meal full of mushies, but what're you gonna do? She doesn't have the *time* for tostones. She'd have to defrock the plantains, slice them, fry them, dip them, fry them again, blot them dry on paper towels, and sprinkle them with salt. If she made the tostones, she'd be up at the stove for whole minutes at a time, her back to her family like a substitute teacher writing the multiplication table on a blackboard, worried about the unseen class behind her, worried about spitballs and note passing and hell-raising young boys. Lizette peels ripe bananas instead of plantains, and she knows that already her meal has been tarnished. Already, things have begun to unravel.

"This is where the table lives now?" Tariq says. "In the middle of the kitchen?"

Jose wheels himself to the head of the table. To his right sits Isabel, and to her right sits Alfredo, both of them in their usual seats, where they can, if necessary, covertly hold hands. Winston sits opposite Alfredo. He plops down into the seat heavily, as if exhausted from a full day's work of drug taking and *Street Fighter II*. With the spot at the table's other end reserved for Mama, there's only one chair left. Without complaint, Tariq sits down to the left of his father and across the table from Isabel.

Lizette finishes the final preparations. She pours the red bean stew into the chicken and rice pot, and with a large wooden spoon she turns everything over. It pleases her to mix it all up, to acquaint the different food items with one another before they make the long dark journey through her family's digestive tracts. She sets the pot down in the middle of the table, on top of the *Post*. The pot's heat and moisture warp the paper's cover photograph: the swollen, guilty, apologetic mug of New York's Catholic archbishop. His Excellency might not object to this sizzling pot on his face if he were actually in this kitchen, if he could smell the oregano and chopped cilantro and puffs of paprika. Much to Lizette's satisfaction, the people around her table take deep,

appreciative sniffs. No one speaks. Taking turns, they all help themselves to food, except for the perpetually sedentary Jose, whose plate is prepared by Alfredo and passed down.

"Hey, Isabel," Jose whispers. "You interested in this baseball game?"

"Are you kidding?"

"Well, what I'm saying is, if you're not interested one way or the other, how about we switch seats. Cause look—you got a view where you can see straight into the living room."

Lizette, whose hearing is uncanny, particularly when Jose whispers, says, "This isn't a bar, you know. You don't sit down and watch a game on TV. You sit down and eat dinner."

As if to demonstrate, Winston shoves a forkful of food into his face. Rice—a consistent problem for him—dribbles out of his mouth and gets stuck to his chin. His jaw seems to be working independently from the rest of his face.

"First of all," Jose says, turning away from the boy, "people don't eat dinner at one o'clock in the afternoon. Okay? Second, I'm not trying to watch a game. I'm trying to watch an *at-bat.*"

A couple of years ago, during a subway series game, the Yankees' ace pitcher, Roger Clemens, beaned the Mets' superstar slugger, Mike Piazza, right in the melon. Piazza is Italian and good-looking and wildly popular in Queens, and Mets fans claimed the beaning was intentional, Piazza having had significant statistical success against Clemens. Yankee fans called Mets fans overdramatic crybabies. The debate intensified in game two of the 2000 World Series, Mets vs. Yankees, under the lights in the Bronx, with Clemens facing Piazza again. Clemens threw an inside fastball, and Piazza swung, making poor contact. His bat broke—no big deal, happens all the time, but a chunk of wood made its way toward the mound, and in a fit of teeth-gritted rage, Clemens picked up the shard and threw it at Piazza. An on-the-field confrontation ensued, which is rare in World Series play, but then again so is bat throwing. Clemens pointed menacingly at Piazza, who had to be restrained by his teammates. Mets fans lost their perpetually aggrieved minds; their team lost the game, and then, unfairly, the series. The injustice of it all!

But now. Now Clemens is coming to Shea. And in a National League ballpark, without the protection of the designated hitter rule, Clemens will have to slither into the batter's box and hit for himself.

Many in Queens expect a tit-for-tat head beaning; more than one Mets fan hopes Clemens will be killed.

Jose Sr. doesn't hold an intense, personal grudge against Clemens, but he does know that the Mets season—and in effect the satisfaction he might wring out of the upcoming summer months—all rides on this one at-bat. Whether or not the Mets plunk Clemens, whether or not he goes down to the dirt with a baseball-sized bruise on his ample rear end, will determine whether or not the Mets return to the play-offs. Simple as that. And so Jose doesn't want to hear about this at-bat secondhand, as it seems he must experience so much else in his life. He needs to *see* the at-bat live, as it happens. If his legs still worked, he'd be at the ballpark, just to avoid the televisual delay. He'd buy a ticket in the upper deck and he'd sneak down to the blue seats in later innings. He'd be part of a crowd. He'd stand for the wave. When it came time to cheer *Let's . . . go . . . Mets,* Jose would be stomping his feet.

"So, if you don't mind switching," he asks Isabel.

"You want my seat?" Alfredo says.

"From where you're at, you can see into the living room, but you can't see the TV. I scoped it already. All you can see is parrots, and what do I need to look at parrots for? Listen," he tells Lizette, who grips the edges of her plate. "I don't *need* to switch seats with Isabel. I could always ask her for updates every couple of minutes. Who's pitching? Who's up? What inning is it? Where's Piazza? Where's Clemens? Of course I'll have to give her a physical description of Clemens so she'll know who I'm talking about. But if I could just sit there, my dear, if I could just move two feet to the right, I won't have to bother nobody, not my lovely daughter-in-law, not my lovely wife. I could keep one eye on the game, one eye on this fine-smelling chicken you prepared, and who knows—every now and again I might drop in a line of sparkling, dazzling conversation."

"You know," Lizette says, half admiringly, "you're a real piece of work."

Jose and Isabel switch places. Alfredo watches her get up and drag her chair to the head of the table, next to Tariq. As if suddenly shy, Tariq won't even look at her. He fiddles with the wristband of his watch.

Inside Alfredo's pocket, his phone begins to ring. He'd turned the volume up last night, when he thought Winston might call, or the

police somehow, with news of Winston's murder, and Alfredo forgot, this morning, to set it back to vibrate. It rings now like a bell clapper, sounding the alarm of his anxiety. With Winston and Isabel already here at the table, the most likely caller is Baka, Alfredo's connect—and if this is Baka, he's probably calling about the money Alfredo owes him, or the infinity-branded X he may have sold Vladimir Shifrin, or (*brrrrrring, brrrrrring*) he might be calling with the intent to lure Alfredo out of the house, as he may have lured Curtis Hughes last night. Alfredo wishes he could talk to the fat fuck. Not over the phone, but in person, to look him in the eye and get the info he needs.

"Your phone," Lizette says. "It's ringing. At the *dinner table.*"

"Sorry," he says as he silences the phone in his pocket. Of course there's a pit bull in the living room, devouring parrots—but so what? That's fun. That's hilarious. But Alfredo's phone ringing at the dinner table? God forbid! And God forbid Isabel gets to sit where she wants to sit. She stares at her plate of food. Although she shows no outward signs—her jaw stays rigid, her cheeks don't pucker—Alfredo knows she is grinding her teeth. "It's business," Alfredo says. "The call, I mean."

"Can we get this show on the road?" Jose says. Except for Winston, who's got a mouthful of chicken, no one has eaten anything yet. "Who's the youngest here?"

"I am," Alfredo says. Two months younger than Winston, a full year younger than Isabel. And so, the responsibility falls to him. "Bless us, O Lord, and these Thy gifts which through Thy bounty we are about to receive." Usually, when giving grace, Alfredo stuccos the words together like an auctioneer. But today he enunciates. He watches Isabel, who could not be farther away, and he watches his Muslim brother, whose eyes are closed and whose head is politely bowed. "Through Christ our Lord," Alfredo says. "Amen."

Winston swallows heavily. All around him forks and knives meet plates. They get together, say *clackety-clack*. Winston, however, puts down his utensils. He's mortified. Is this what families do? They say grace before dinner? In 2002, for fuck's sake? It never even *occurred* to Winston that he should wait. At home it's just him and his ma dukes; they never eat together, and they most definitely do not pray together. Oh shit—just thinking about it makes his throat go tight. He takes a sip of water, but it's lukewarm, and so all of a sudden he's up at the

freezer, searching for ice cubes. As the cold air blasts his face, it occurs to Winston that this too is rude, rooting in someone else's freezer without asking permission. He mixed ketamine and coke earlier today, and now his heart is trying to sneak out of the house, shoulder its way through the bars of Winston's rib cage and leap clean out of his chest. Winston's got to give the bag of scrips in his pocket back to Alfredo. He's got to quit drugs tomorrow. The uppers and downers have jumbled his brain, stolen his appetite. Maybe Winston has even taken drugs he doesn't remember taking, some hallucinogens perhaps, some magic mushrooms. *I must be trippin' balls,* he thinks, because as he sits back down in his seat he realizes his water, with the ice cubes floating in it, has fucking turned green.

Lizette turns away from Winston, shaking her head. Best to ignore it. "I was going to make an avocado salad," she announces to the table. "But the Koreans are charging three dollars apiece. Has anyone heard of such a thing? Three dollars for an avocado?"

Tariq hasn't eaten anything yet. He moves his fork around his plate, flipping over grains of yellow rice, a forty-niner prospector separating silt from gold. He spears an oil-rimmed brown square of meat and lifts it up to his eyes. "Mama, what's in this rice?"

"It's my rice," she says.

"Yeah, but is there any pork in it?"

"A little ham. For flavor."

"Oh," Tariq says.

"Oh," Lizette says, suddenly understanding. "Oh, *honey.* Can't you pick around it?"

Tariq pushes the plate away from him. He closes his eyes and little vertical lines form between the brows. Little frustrated folds of skin. His face flushes, and it looks to Alfredo as if Tariq is holding his breath, counting down from one thousand.

"It's delicious, Mama," Alfredo says. He talks with his mouth full of chicken and rice and red bean stew. "You don't know what you're missing, big brother. Right, Dad? Right? *Papi.*"

"Huh?" Jose says. He looks around the table, unsure of whom to address. He settles on Winston, the guest, the only one not staring his way, the only one who doesn't seem to *expect* anything from him. "Bottom of the second," Jose says. "One out. We're getting close."

"The food," Alfredo says. "What do you think of the food?"

Jose leans back in his wheelchair and pats the sides of his stomach. "Best meal of my life." He says this every night. "A new standard, Ma."

"That's what I'm saying," Alfredo tells his brother. "You sure you don't wanna try it? I'm telling you, you can't even *taste* the ham."

Tariq stands. He seems to lose his balance for a moment and has to brace his hand flat against the table. He smiles, as if to communicate to everyone that there's no cause for alarm. *Keep moving,* he seems to tell them. *Go about your business. Nothing to see here.* He scrapes the food off his plate and dumps it back into the communal pot. A chicken leg plops down heavily, causing red sauce to splash out of the pot and onto Lizette's floral-patterned tablecloth. Tariq doesn't seem to notice. He drags his fork over the plate long after it seems necessary, and it makes a terrible sound, a nasal squeak, as if one of them, either the fork or the plate, were crying out in pain.

"You want my banana?" Alfredo says. "It hasn't even touched the ham. I swear."

Tariq sits down. He crosses his fork and knife over his plate, making an X, and he pushes the whole thing away with the palm of his hand. "That's nice of you to offer," he says. "But no thank you."

Lizette asks if she can fix something else for him. A tuna fish sandwich maybe. Or a plate of macaroni. He doesn't answer. He sits in his seat, his lips moving silently, as if he were casting a spell or chanting a prayer. Lizette tries asking why it took him so long to come home this morning. Did he see some people he knows? Drop in on some old friends?

"What friends?" Alfredo says.

"Did you see, uhm . . . ," Lizette trails off. She wants to keep the table talk impersonal. She wants to keep long-harbored grievances out of the air, and so, in an attempt at conversational misdirection, she tries to get everyone to talk about the people they know, the friends they all have in common. She wants to give and receive benign updates on mutual acquaintances. *Is so-and-so still living at home? Did his mother ever get that kitchen repainted?* The problem, however, is the Batistas don't have any mutual acquaintances. Alfredo's right. What friends does Junior have? And it's not just him. Jose doesn't leave the house, Isabel's a veritable orphan, and Lizette's coworkers don't run in the same circles as Alfredo's deadbeat cronies. But wait!

"Did you see Ear Man," Lizette says suddenly, happily. "When you were walking up the block, did you see his new shirt?"

Of course! The neighborhood crazies! Everyone knows them, right? Lizette performs for her son, fills in the gaps of his knowledge. They took away the bench in front of the post office, she explains, and so now all the bums have scattered like pigeons. Popeye—remember him?—he smokes his Parliaments now out of a hole in his neck. The legless alky and the teenaged Rasta who panhandles while listening to a Discman have switched spots, panhandling in front of Baskin-Robbins and the Jewish Center, respectively. And the Flying Nun? Surely Junior must remember her. That woman who painted her face white and screamed at all the children? Well, she all but disappeared. Got knocked up, Lizette explains. Raped in one of the Woodside homeless shelters.

"Who'd wanna rape her?" Tariq asks.

"How's Gio and Conrad?" Alfredo asks. "You talk to them at all?"

"Far as I know," Tariq says, "they're still incarcerated."

Above the table floats a heavy cloud of familial silence. For a few long moments, no one speaks. Isabel takes wolfish bites of her chicken, some of which is for her, some of which is for Christian Louis. She's never met Conrad or Gio, but she's heard the rumors. Not at the beauty parlor or in the stalls of the girls' bathroom, but on the streets. *Dropped a dime on his brother,* people said. *Just to get at a girl.* Isabel's never asked Alfredo if the rumors are true, because she knows he wouldn't lie to her, and she hasn't yet decided which answer she'd rather hear.

On top of the table Tariq's hand lies close to hers. The dinner conversation has fragmented: Alfredo and Winston are talking about someone they both know, while Lizette asks Jose what he wants for Father's Day. No one sees Tariq's hand moving closer. No one bears witness. Isabel forgot how big his hand is, how heavily it used to weigh on her own. Dark wires of hairs uncurl from his knuckles. She thinks that if all he wants is her hand, then she'll give it to him. No problem. She'll grab her knife and saw her arm off at the wrist.

"It's bad, I know," he whispers. He turns his cheek to her. The skin around the gash is puffed up, a pair of pink ropes knotted at the ends. "But I've heard that some women like scars."

Under the table his other hand moves between her legs. He prods the fabric of her sweatpants, the cotton of her underwear. She looks across the length of the table at Alfredo, who appears distracted, still talking to Winston. Just turn your head, Alfredo. Just turn your head and see what's happening, but of course he doesn't notice because no one ever notices, no one ever notices anything. She stares at the network of flowers printed on the tablecloth. She knows that if she stays here and deals with it and lets Tariq paw her, then eventually it'll be over. He tugs on her pubic hair, and a breathless Isabel jumps out of her body. She sits up on the counter, next to the stove. Legs dangling, she watches her body, that girl Isabel, at the head of the table. The body goes completely still. The body drops a fork, which clatters against her plate, but no one bothers to care. The body grabs hold of Jose Sr.'s arm (oh good for you, girl) and shakes it. In a voice that sounds like Isabel's but is somehow calmer, stronger, the body says, "The game, Papi. The game, the game."

"The game!" Jose says. He squints into the living room. "Clemens—he's on deck!"

Alfredo stands and so does Isabel. She shoots out of her seat so suddenly that her chair tips over and crashes to the floor.

"Be careful!" Lizette shouts, and Winston's head snaps forward as if he's just been jolted awake. In the living room, the dog starts barking.

"He's on deck!" Jose says. Alfredo races to the back of his father's wheelchair, as if he wants to stake his claim as the favorite son. They slide out of the kitchen, Jose grinning, Alfredo hunched over, his head bobbing, looking like a jockey on a horse. Behind them, Winston stomps his heavy feet and Tariq trails, as if he were stalking the three men in front of him. On his way out of the kitchen, he loses his balance and bangs into the doorframe.

Left alone in the kitchen, Isabel and Lizette stare at each other across the length of the table. In the living room, the dog continues to bark. The television plays at a riotous volume.

"What do you think he wants?" Lizette says.

Before Isabel can ask what she means, the downstairs neighbor, Mr. Pettolina, starts banging on his ceiling with a wooden broom handle. *Bang, bang, bang, bang.* He's complaining about the shouting, the barking, Winston's heavy footsteps, the toppled-over chair, the ubiquitous smell of sofrito in the hallways, his shitty court stenographer job,

the wife who left him seven years ago. He raps at the ceiling, his small white teeth presumably gritted.

"Oh for fuck's sake," Lizette says.

Bang bang, says the broom handle.

"Shut up!" Lizette screams. She grabs the table for leverage and kicks down at the floor with the heel of her foot. Her hair flies. Her leg goes up and down. When the banging continues, when it becomes obvious there's no way to stop it, she collapses into her chair. Her chest heaves. She looks miserable. "I should've made the tostones," she tells Isabel. "You think he wants a sandwich?"

Isabel grabs the sides of her stomach to remind Christian Louis that his mama's still here. The broom's vibrations rise up out of the floor and tingle the bottoms of her feet. Mr. Pettolina must be really mad. She imagines him down there. He hits the ceiling so hard the plaster must be coming loose. White dust drifts down onto his face, into his hair, coats the tips of his long, delicate eyelashes.

Meanwhile, Roger Clemens enters the batter's box. In Corona, Elmhurst, East Elmhurst, Jackson Heights, Cambria Heights, Astoria, Hollis, Glendale, LeFrak, Queensbridge, Jamaica, Rockaway, Fresh Meadows, Kew Gardens, Malba, Maspeth, Ditmars, Douglaston, Howard Beach, Beechhurst, Bellerose, Rosedale, Richmond Hill, Forest Hills, Floral Park, Ozone Park, Rego Park, College Point, Hunters Point, Willets Point, Breezy Point, Bay Terrace, Bayside, Sunnyside, Woodside, Woodhaven, Ravenswood, and Ridgewood, revenge-mongers lean forward in their seats. Beat cops on Thirty-seventh Avenue stare at a TV through the window of the Headz Ain't Ready barbershop. In Whitestone, at a bowling alley, Baka watches the TV set up behind the bar; in Corona, Alex and Bam-Bam Hughes sit on their couch, an empty space between them; and in Elmhurst, the game plays on a television suspended above Vladimir Shifrin's hospital bed. It ain't all TVs, of course. There are the radio listeners: drivers stuck on the BQE and Grand Central Parkway, Con Ed employees, dishwashers and doormen working in Manhattan, a little boy on a sticky tar roof, Max Marshmallow behind the counter of his candy store. And at Shea Stadium? The hot dog vendors and peanut slingers do what they've explicitly been instructed not to do: they turn around and face the

field. The fans have all been standing since the top of the third inning. They cheer the Mets and boo Clemens, but they're holding back, these fans. They're keeping a little something in their pockets, waiting for the release, the consummation of long-anticipated violence.

The Mets pitcher throws at Clemens and misses. It happens that fast. The ball sails three feet behind him, lands in the dirt, and rolls to the backstop. That was it—their one chance. Piazza hangs his head while the umpire issues warnings. Clemens smirks. He tips his helmet at the pitcher, and an entire borough deflates.

"Season's over," Jose says. "We're done."

"It's June," Alfredo says. "There's like a hundred games left."

"We're *done,*" Jose says. The next pitch is a fastball right down the middle, which Clemens fouls off. "You see?" Jose says. He waves a disgusted hand at the television. "You *see*? We missed him, now we pitch to him, and the season's all gone straight down the drain. You need confidence to play this game and we've lost all confidence. Aw Christ, Dito," he says, as if Alfredo's naïveté was not only obvious but blameworthy, responsible for the long stretch of winless baseball games in front of him. "Don't you understand?"

"Seasons don't end in June, Papi, just because we missed hitting a pitcher in the ass."

"*Don't you understand, Dito?*" Tariq says, perfectly mimicking their father's Nuyorican accent. He scratches his dog behind the ears and smiles at Alfredo, who doesn't know if his balls are getting busted here or if Tariq is winking at him over their father's head. "*You need confidence to play this game,*" Tariq says.

Jose squeezes Tariq's hand and looks up into his face. "Here's the problem," he says, his voice dropping, and it seems to Alfredo that Jose is suddenly addressing Tariq not as a father addresses a son, but as if they were peers, two guys from the neighborhood, sitting across from each other at a dominos table, sipping on cans of Modelo and bullshitting about cars and sports and women and the perpetual disappointment of children. "The problem is Dito doesn't know because he never actually played baseball."

"I played!" Alfredo says.

"Yeah, but your wrists were always too thin," Jose says.

"What the hell does that mean? My *wrists*?" With every word, Alfredo's voice rises, and he hates himself for it. At least Winston gives

no indication that he's seen or heard any of this. He lies in the recliner—at a safe remove from the dog—with his legs up, eyes closed, and mouth open, like a patient in traction. He snores loudly, crashing after a two-day-long drug binge. So as not to wake him up, Alfredo lowers his voice. "You're ridiculous," he tells his father. "You don't know what you're talking about."

"What are you getting so upset for?" Jose says. "Not everyone's gonna be a top-dog ballplayer. You're good at other stuff. What's fifteen times seventy-three?"

"How about this number?" Alfredo says. "Zero. The number of times you've seen me play baseball in your entire life. How many? *Zero.*"

"What's he getting so upset about?" Jose asks Tariq.

"He was pretty good," Tariq shrugs.

"Thank you," Alfredo says.

"Sure," Tariq says. Alfredo knows his brother has never actually seen him play an organized game of hardball either, but the two boys, when left alone in the house, used to play Wiffle ball. And that kinda counts, right? With a pillow on the sofa serving as the strike zone, big brother batted and pitched left handed, just to give little brother a chance. One time Alfredo hit a hanging curveball so hard he knocked three parrots off the ceiling.

"He had a strong arm," Tariq tells Jose. "And he could run, that's for sure."

"*Thank* you," Alfredo says.

"You were no superstar either," Jose tells Tariq. "You had the tools, sure. My genes. But not the work ethic. I'm sorry, but am I wrong? You weren't lazy. I won't say you were lazy, but you never really tried." He holds his hand above his head, as if he were measuring off the height of baseball stardom. "You never pushed yourself hard enough to get to that next level."

"See," Tariq says, "all these years, I didn't know you was a baseball scout."

"And he knows all this—have you noticed?—without ever having seen us actually play in a game. Not one fucking time."

"No cursing," Jose says. "It's a sign of ignorance." The two prime-of-life boys stand close to Jose, crowd him, look down on him in his wheelchair. On the television, Clemens has just gone down swinging.

149

Still smirking, he struts back to the safety of the dugout. "Go get a bat," Jose tells his sons. "You two think you're so smart. Go get a bat and I'll show you what's what. I'll strike out the both of you. Three pitches for Dito. And for you, my oldest, maybe four pitches. Maybe you foul one off. You understand? I'll show you. Go get a bat."

If there was a bat in this apartment, Alfredo tells his father, Mama would've brained him with it a long time ago. Tariq starts laughing.

"Go downstairs," Jose says. "Go downstairs and grab that broom out of Pettolina's fucking—excuse me—out of Pettolina's hands, and bring it up here, and swing *that*. Okay? Swing and strike out with that. A broom handle. Because that's what I had. I had a broom handle for a bat and a piece of cardboard for a glove, and I was a *player*. I walked the field with confidence."

"How about this?" Alfredo says. "How about we all go outside? Have a base-running contest."

"Ho shit!" Tariq says. He reaches out, laughing, and he and Alfredo slap palms.

It's been some time since Alfredo's had an ally against the Axis of His Parents. There's Isabel, of course, but she is by necessity a silent ally. She's an outsider, an exile living abroad in this tyrannical nation-state, and while she can use the tools of cunning and subversion, she cannot outwardly criticize. Not without fear of having her visa revoked. But Tariq, on the other hand. Tariq is a sibling—check the DNA!—and siblings, like war vets, share the common ground of fox-hole experience. He can fight back, strap on a helmet, get dirty. Over their father's head, Tariq smiles at Alfredo, and Alfredo, with a jolt, realizes that a secret part of him has desperately missed having his big brother around.

From the kitchen doorway, Isabel watches. She looks down to find her arms folded in front of her chest.

"Papi, are they teasing you?" Lizette says. She squeezes past Isabel and comes into the living room. "Are you boys teasing him? Don't you know it's Father's Day tomorrow? Tell them what you want, Jose. Tell them what you were telling me, you old pervert. Look at him. He won't even acknowledge me. Your father, for Father's Day, wants, as a gift, a sex machine. This is what he tells me. He wants a machine for sex, a strap-on penis."

"Not a strap-on," Jose says sourly. "A machine that straps *onto* your penis."

"Onto *my* penis?" Lizette says in mock horror.

"How much it cost?" Tariq asks.

"Thirty-nine ninety-nine," Lizette says. "Or so he tells me. There's an installment plan. They take all major credit cards."

"We'll buy you two," Alfredo says. "Case you wear out the first."

"My man goes, 'We'll buy two,' " Tariq says, laughing. "In case he wears out the first!"

Again the boys slap palms, but this time they do it the way they used to: two quick pats, then a fist bump.

"You got a name for that dog yet?" Alfredo says, but before Tariq can answer, Alfredo's phone starts ringing. Baka's number flashes across the screen. Not his name, just his number—Alfredo's too paranoid to save a business contact to his phone book. What if the DEA were to get ahold of his cell?

"Little brother's been big pimpin' since I was away!" Tariq says. "You blowing up, Dito. Another business call?"

"Yeah," Alfredo smiles. "I guess."

Tariq claps his brother on the shoulder. "You were always mad smart, Dito. I'd be telling people how my brother's gonna be *running* shit one day. I'm serious. Don't look over there. Look at me. You're pulling down mad weight, am I right?"

"I'm doing okay," Alfredo says.

"You wanna know something? I used to tell people that I'd be working for you one day. I'm being serious here. Man, look at me. You gotta bring me back into the fold, Dito. I wouldn't even know where to start."

Tariq's eyes are shining, set deep in a face with two mouths, the one he uses to smile at Alfredo, and the other mouth, the crueler one, sliced into his cheek. He has changed in these last couple of years. There is the scar of course, but also the bald head, hard as a razor, and the city of muscles under his shirt. This, Alfredo thinks, is a body capable of terrible power.

Alfredo fiddles with the phone in his hands. He thinks of how differently things might've been had Curtis gone out last night with big brothers Alex and Bam-Bam.

"You feel like coming with me somewhere?" he says. "I'd ask this guy"—he gestures to Winston snoring lightly in the recliner—"but . . . well, you know."

"Absolutely," Tariq says. "Where we going?"

"There's dessert," Lizette says nervously. "There's ice cream in the freezer."

"Is it pork flavored?" Alfredo asks.

"You've got some fucking mouth on you," Tariq says, still smiling.

"No cursing," Jose says.

"Chocolate," Lizette says. "Chocolate ice cream. Your favorite. Right in the freezer. Come on."

Tariq punches Alfredo hard in the chest and then punches his own, creating an invisible cord between them. "Sorry, Mama," he says. "We got moves to make."

Christian Louis has fashioned a knife out of something, some contraband he's smuggled into Isabel's body, and either he's stabbing her uterine walls with the knife or the knife keeps slipping out of his teeny hands, but either way it hurts. She runs to the bathroom, locking the door behind her. She sits her bone-wearied body down on the toilet seat, and then jumps back up, as if something in the water leapt out and bit her. She rattles the doorknob. To be positive. To make sure. To double-check. But don't worry, Isabel. It's locked. Okay? The door is locked.

9

The Many Loves of
Vladimir Shifrin

She taught preschool in the city of Novorossiysk, right off the Black Sea, in the last-gasp days of the Soviet Union. She had long blond hair and played the acoustic guitar. Vladimir doesn't remember her name, but she was, and always will be, the first.

In the pictures he finger-painted of the two of them, they'd be holding each other's stick-figured hands, or sitting behind the large bay window of a house, or standing on a yellow sun in insulated boots. While the other children napped, he feigned sleep on a mat near her desk. At snack time, he offered her sips from his milk cartons, which she politely declined, citing germs, citing the necessity of calcium for the building of healthy bones, but she always commended his willingness to share.

One day Vladimir decided they should live together. As he got ready for school, he doused his hair with tomato juice. With his mother's eye shadow, he painted a bold black circle around his eye. Mama didn't ask. She lay perpetually in bed around this time, her body a battleground for poisons, chemo vs. cancer.

Vladimir's brother, Misha, a ninth grader, walked him to school that morning. Like Mama, Misha didn't question the eye shadow or the tomato juice. Vladimir was a *choknutiy*—the familial odd duck destined, Misha thought, for great things. When they reached the pre-

school, Misha reluctantly let go of his little brother's hand. He kissed him on the forehead. Asked him to please stay out of trouble.

Vladimir went straightaway to the pretty blond teacher and told her he was being abused at home. Lookit. A black eye. Blood in my hair. Vladimir, whose theatrical skills were precociously pronounced, could cry on command, but he held back this time, thinking restraint would play better than hamming. Besides, he didn't want his eye shadow to run.

The teacher pressed his small body against hers. Vladimir thought she smelled like ripe tomatoes (although, more likely, he smelled like ripe tomatoes). She brought him into her office and sat him down in her chair. Her hands were shaking. She gave him construction paper and crayons. She told him to sit tight. She told him she needed to think. She needed to think this whole thing through.

One shudders to imagine that her figurative blindness here—eye shadow and tomato juice, lady!—might be explained by the possibility that she herself had been abused as a child, and as a grown-up had dedicated her life to protecting the innocent bodies of children.

"I'm afraid to go home," Vladimir said.

"Oh, you poor sweet thing."

Things were going well.

After she left the office—she needed to think; she needed to make some calls—Vladimir drew pictures of the rainbow house they'd live in together. He'd miss his parents, obviously, but love requires certain sacrifices. He wouldn't miss his brother, however, because—in Vladimir's master plan—his brother was coming with him. Vladimir drew an extension off of the side of the house for Misha to sleep in.

An hour later, the teacher (what was her *name*?) tiptoed back into the room, as if it were Vladimir's office and not her own. A man trailed behind her, wearing dark pants and a flannel shirt. He looked like a carpenter, but he had the thick-bristled mustache of police inspectors around the world. The teacher put a hand on his chest, afraid, perhaps, that he might bolt at Vladimir and scoop him away.

"Here he is, honey," she said. "The boy."

Honey came forward, cracking his knuckles. He licked his thumb and rubbed a streak of eye shadow off of Vladimir's face. He bent his nose to Vladimir's hair.

"Vegetables?" the man said. He smiled at the child and then smiled

even wider at the teacher, with the easy condescension of a boyfriend. "I think what we have here is a young boy who likes to tell tales."

"Vladimir?" the teacher said.

He had one card left to play. "My mom," he said. "She's sick."

Years and years later, well into the future—when Vladimir Shifrin is a paunch-bellied assistant professor of Slavic languages and literature at a small midwestern college—he will tell this anecdote in his lecture on Anton Pavlovich Chekhov's short story "The Kiss," using his own experience with early disillusioned love to segue to the end of Chekhov's story:

> And the whole world—life itself seemed to Riabovich an
> inscrutable, aimless mystification . . . Raising his eyes from the
> stream and gazing at the sky, he recalled how Fate in the shape of
> an unknown woman had once caressed him; he recalled his
> summer fantasies and images—and his whole life seemed to him
> unnaturally thin and colorless and wretched . . .

But this will be a bit of pedagogical exaggeration on the part of Assistant Professor Shifrin, a lie, another tale told. Because when the pretty blond teacher sent him out of her office, he did not become unnaturally thin or colorless or wretched. He did not, as Riabovich did, cast himself upon his bed, wroth with his evil fate. No, Vladimir grew only hungrier for love. Not for the love of the teacher—with the short-term memory of children and romantics, he had moved on from her almost immediately. Instead Vladimir grew hungrier for the love of women he had never met, women whose faces he had never seen and whose names he did not yet know.

Names like Jessica Yoffe and Tonya Valit and Marina Duvenskaya. Girls who lived in the apartment next door, who sat in front of him at school with little blond hairs on the backs of their necks. In the fourth grade, Vladimir had a crush on a girl named Elena, but Andrei (Vladimir's best friend) also had a crush on her so Vladimir redirected his amorous energies toward Svetlana, but then Sergei (the class's monstrous bully) laid claim to Svetlana, and so Vladimir was forced to back off. A love poem he'd written her (well, plagiarized actually) lan-

guished in his desk till the end of the school year, when a janitor threw it away, unread. In the fifth grade he asked Olga Guseva to the end-of-the-year dance. She accepted, which precipitated a burst of elation, followed by the sharp stabs of anxiety, for this would be Vladimir's first date and he did not yet know how to dance. Then the blonder, more popular Anastasia Domani broke up with her boyfriend, and things really got complicated. An on-the-rebound Anastasia had her friends indicate to Vladimir's friends—through a series of cryptic notes and whispered hints—that a Vladimir-Anastasia merger might be possible, and when the stock proved solid, he broke up with Olga and started dating Anastasia. Within days, however, Anastasia broke it off. When Vladimir re-asked Olga to the dance, she told him to get down on his knees and beg for it in front of the entire school. With his classmates watching him, jeering him, he dropped down to the ground, hands clasped in front of him. Oh where had his confidence gone!

And he still didn't know how to dance. If his mother were alive, she could have put on a record and taught him. *Hold my hand. Here, like this. Don't look at your feet. Here, Vladimir. Like this. Yes, beautiful. Now move your feet. Wonderful. Oh, my wonderful little man.* But all Vladimir had was Misha. He didn't teach him how to dance, but he did buy Vladimir a corsage. He even showed him how to tie it to Olga's pale thin wrist.

That summer, the summer before he and Misha boarded a plane to John F. Kennedy International Airport, Vladimir got himself ready by watching subtitled American movies. None of them made any sense at all. It was like homework, except thankfully with beautiful Hollywood actresses. At the end of one these movies a blond-haired woman jumped out of an American automobile and ran into the dark mouth of an American forest, and Vladimir, watching from home, felt a strong compulsion to chase after her.

"Who's that?" he asked his brother, who knew everything.

"Why?" Misha laughed. "Do you *like* her?"

Noooooooooooo.

Her name was Mariel Hemingway, Misha explained. The grand-daughter of a famous American author.

Vladimir loved Jessica, Marina, Olga (well, not so much her any-more), Tonya, Elena, Svetlana, the unnamed teacher, and Anastasia—but he loved them in a purely nonsexual way. He wanted to be around

them, pick them lilies, stare at them through the frosted window of his apartment, but he did not want to kiss them. At most he wanted to be the kind of person who *used* to kiss girls, who had a long history of smooching and could therefore treat the subject with nonchalance. But Mariel Hemingway, this American blonde? Vladimir wanted to do things to her. He wanted to run his thumbs over her thick dark eyebrows.

America! Misha and Vladimir took a cab from JFK to their new studio apartment in Manhattan. The Big Apple! The City That Never Sleeps! Within weeks, Misha had Vladimir enrolled in a nearby public school. Misha bought him pens, folders, and three-subject notebooks for his first day of sixth grade. But this American school was not what Vladimir had expected. With its giant asphalt yard and clock tower and fence-lined perimeter and uniformed guards and metal detectors and no-talking zones and cafeteria slop and lineups and mandatory periods of exercise and with its explosive undercurrent of tension, the school felt less like an enlightened educational institution and more like a Soviet penal colony. On the morning of his first day, a girl twice Vladimir's size pushed him up against the classroom wall and grabbed his balls through his pants. In the afternoon, he watched an eighth grader drive a pair of scissors into a sixth grader's skull, using his lunchbox as a hammer, the scissors as a nail. Vladimir came home with his teeth chattering.

Misha pulled him out of classes right away and decided to send him to Catholic school. They picked one in Queens, where the price tags were lower—Misha, through his connections, was making good money, but not yet Manhattan tuition money. Besides, he reasoned, Queens probably had fewer black people and more immigrants, and a school with an immigrant-heavy population might be more accepting of a pole-thin Russian boy with middling (although quickly improving) English skills. And indeed the teachers were nicer and the classmates friendlier and Vladimir's Manhattan residence gave him a certain amount of cachet, but there was one demerit, a problem almost as serious as steel-tipped scissors puncturing one's cranium: Vladimir's new school was *all boys*.

They smelled like he did, like sweat, like feet, like poorly deodorized

armpits. They didn't carry a soft down of blond hair on the backs of their necks. Some of them didn't even *have* necks. In class, Vladimir stared at the blackboard.

At lunch he name-dropped Mariel Hemingway, but his new friends looked at him as if he were an alien from the interstellar Kingdom of Herbs. Vladimir learned new names: Alyssa Milano, Yasmine Bleeth, Jennifer Love Hewitt. "What about blondes?" he asked. You want blondes? Rebecca Romijn, Donna D'Errico, Gena Lee Nolin, Pamela Anderson. Yes, Vladimir wanted to say, but what about real blondes? Do you guys, like, know any actual girls? Do you have sisters, cousins, particularly horny housecleaners? The *Baywatch* babes are nice and all, don't get me wrong, but I can't exactly smell their Coppertone.

One time, a cluster of girls were smoking in Astoria Park, and Vladimir and his friends—at Vladimir's urging—approached them, asking to bum a cigarette or two. One of the girls slipped a Camel between his fingers and proffered her lighter, but when he saw the chipped nail polish on her fingers and when he smelled the smoke on her wet mouth and when he remembered the touch of her hand on his, he felt a stiffening in his too-tight parochial pants, and then Vladimir became very nervous indeed, and that's probably why he stuck the wrong end of the cigarette in his mouth, and tried, unsuccessfully, to light its mentholated filter. Which everyone—the boys, the girls—thought was absolutely fucking hilarious. *The filter! You were gonna light the* filter? *Oh my God! Har har har!*

"This is how we smoke in Russia," he said miserably.

It was not one of his better lies. Worse, for the next few months, it gave his friends' taunts an organizing principle. Vladimir answered a question wrong in math class? *Hey, is that how you find the radius of a circle in Russia?* ("Russia" always receiving a heavy, Boris-and-Natasha inflection.) Vladimir shot an air ball in gym class? *Does that count as a three-pointer in Russia?* Vladimir mispronounced "subsequent"? Vladimir mixed up "orgy" for "orgasm"? Vladimir neglected to supersize his Extra Value Meal? *Is that how you order fast food in Mother Russia?*

"That doesn't even make sense, twat-face."

"Do you even know what a twat is?"

"Do you?"

"Do *you*?"

They were his friends. They were mean to him. That's okay. He was mean to them, too. *Do you have HBO at home? Hindu Body Odor? Har har har!* They were eighth graders.

At home, while eating Chinese takeout, Vladimir said, "They want to know what you do for a living."

"Who does?" Misha said.

"The kids at school."

Misha looked relieved. "Tell them to mind their own business." There were rules, Misha had explained. Don't talk about what I do. Don't talk about anything that has to do with the family. "You know who talks?" he asked. "Blacks, that's who. They run their mouths and don't shut up and that's why they're always getting arrested."

"Can I tell them about Mama?"

"What about her?"

"Can I tell them about Dad?"

"Yeah, tell them he's drunk in a snowbank somewhere. Oh, come on. Don't make that face. I'm sorry. Hey, stop it. I'm *sorry.* Tell them whatever you want about Dad."

"Can I say he's in the KGB? That'd be phat."

"Don't say 'phat.' "

"What do I say about you?"

"Vladimir. You say nothing about me."

"You don't understand! This is how you make friends." It felt perverse—and strangely empowering—to instruct his brother on something. "They ask you questions, you tell them stories."

"Tell them I'm a student."

"You're too old."

"Vladimir," Misha warned.

"Well, you are."

"Tell them I'm a grad student."

"In what?"

"Perestan' bit dabayobom!"

"All I'm saying is if they ask, I want to have my story straight. Jeez. What if they tell their parents and then the parents meet you at, like, a PTA meeting or something, and they're, like, 'Hey, how's the grad life going? You're studying blankety-blank, right?' I want you to be pre-

pared, that's all. I want you to know what's coming. Maybe you're in graduate school for business? Huh? Chemistry, maybe?"

"Are you being a wise guy?"

"No! I swear!"

"Tell them I'm studying literature," Misha said. He liked the sound of it. He imagined a life of quiet study, term papers, sitting between the wings of a library carrel, hunched over old-smelling books, his nose in Gogol's "Nose." "Tell them I'm studying Russian literature."

"That's wack."

"Don't say 'wack.' You know who says 'wack'?"

Yeah, Vladimir thought. *I know.*

For high school he went to McClancy's in East Elmhurst, another Catholic all-boys school. He could've gone to school in Manhattan— his brother, at this point, was making enough bank to afford two tuitions, but some of Vladimir's friends were going to McClancy's, and so he wanted to go there too. He didn't want to start over. He was tired, he told Misha, of starting over.

New school, still no girls. The only women walking McClancy's halls were the nuns, and while Vladimir considered himself an atheist, unafraid of divine retribution, there were boundaries even he could respect. The sticky-seated porno theater of his mind screened practically everything and anything, but nun flicks stayed in their titanium canisters, unwatched. Fair game, however, were the women on the subway. And at night, before his brother came home, Vladimir spent long hours humping the bed, fantasizing about Jess Yoffe and Tonya Valit and Marina Duvenskaya. Like an FBI supercomputer, he age-advanced their faces and bodies, approximating how they might look in 2002. He even entertained fantasies of the girl from his Manhattan school, the giantess who pushed him up against the wall and grabbed hold of his privates. At least she showed interest!

It wasn't all sex, however. He thought he'd be a good boyfriend—a great boyfriend. He'd open doors and pay for things. He'd tell her he loved her. He wouldn't flinch or joke when she complained of menstrual symptoms. He'd kiss her shoulders. He'd sit with her in comfortable silence, sharing sections of the newspaper in a breakfast nook with sunlight streaming through the window (not that Vladimir had a

breakfast nook or ever read the paper). But man oh man, what he really wanted was someone to confide in. He'd tell his girlfriend he doesn't remember what his mother looked like. Unless he was looking directly at a photograph, he had to think of moms from TV and super-impose their faces onto a generic, housecoat-wearing body. It's a shameful secret that he's never told Misha, but when he gets a girlfriend and when the time feels right, he'll tell her. *If* he gets a girlfriend.

His clothes didn't help. Five days a week he wore wool pants, poly-ester shirts, snot-green ties one step above clip-ons. Talk about the Kingdom of Herbs! With his ample allowance, Vladimir invested in a new look. He bought black baseball caps at the Queens Center Mall and 1980s basketball jerseys off eBay. He scoured vintage shops in the Village looking for the same type of baggy jeans Dr. Dre wore when *The Chronic* came out. Like the names on the basketball jerseys—Barkley, Drexler—Vladimir's fashion sense was about twenty years out of date. Which is exactly why it's cool, he thought. Wearing the clothes under his Catholic uniform, Vladimir received a negligible boost in popularity and a zero percent increase in attractiveness to females. So like a home-born American, Vladimir doubled down. He reinvested. He soothed his frustrations with the ointment of more spending, more shopping.

Someone on eBay was selling a pair of the super-hard-to-get series III Air Jordans, mint condition, for only $245.

"No way," said Misha, who himself had a closet of wildly expensive shoes. But his objection to the Air Jordans wasn't the price, but rather their status as signifiers. "What are you, *black*?" Misha asked. "Pick up your pants, bro. Air Jordans are for eggplants."

So what? Vladimir wanted to say. His favorite all-time athlete was Dominique Wilkins; his favorite movie star, Will Smith. He burned Nas CDs off his friends and kept them in jewel cases labeled "Van Halen." So black people wear Air Jordans? So what? Vladimir *wanted* them. They were *cool*. If need be, he'd pay for them himself.

He stole a beeper full of Ecstasy from his brother. His brother only had, like, tons of them. Misha gave them to dealers, who used the beepers to sneak E past bouncers at Webster Hall and Club Exit. Vladimir brought it to school, where he sold the X at a price he hoped wasn't too high. Ten dollars a pill.

Vladimir's popularity skyrocketed, as did the general mood of the

Monsignor McClancy Memorial High School. He bought the Jordans and kept them in his locker. He started hanging out with juniors and seniors. He pinched a couple more pills off his brother. He'd have to be careful here. He couldn't get greedy. He bought an Orlando Magic Bo Outlaw jersey off the Internet.

In the spring, with the pheromones poppin' and the birds a-tweet-tweet-tweetin', Vladimir met a girl. Let that sink in for a while. Her name was Vicki Rodriguez and she was the little sister of one of Vladimir's new upperclassmen friends, George Rodriguez, McClancy's starting point guard and a tenacious defender who had a habit of barking at opposing players. Vladimir had gone over to George's apartment to sell him three pills of E and to play his new Xbox, and he met Vicki in the hallway, the two of them converging on the apartment's only bathroom.

"Are you going to be long?" he asked her.

"It's my fucking house," she said.

Vladimir grinned. When she came out of the bathroom he pestered her with questions—What school did she go to? Did she have to take the train there? What sorts of music did she like?—and Vicki, flattered by the attention and moderately intrigued by the accent, provided dutiful answers. Eventually, however, he ran out of things to ask. His bladder, so close to the bathroom, was throwing a tantrum, which made it difficult to concentrate. He and Vicki looked at each other and then looked away. Smiling politely, she started to slip past him, and Vladimir—confused as to why anyone would want to leave so perfect a hallway—asked her where she was going. To the mall, she said. To get a new wallet. Her old one, a pleather facsimile of the Dominican flag, had fallen apart at the seams, literally.

"I can walk with you," he said. "Over to the mall. If you want."

"Do you have any idea how fucking awkward that'd be?"

"We could brainstorm names for our children. I'm thinking Victor, Vincent, uh, Vance maybe, Viggo. Fairly unusual names for a girl, I know, but . . ." If he'd had his tie on, he would've fiddled with the knot.

At the mall, Vladimir tried to pay for her new wallet, but she wouldn't let him. She did, however, allow him to buy her a cinnamon pretzel from the food court. As they walked through the mall, people stared—or at least Vladimir felt as if they stared—at their racial incongruity, the clash of their pigmentation. So what? A Dominican girl, Vicki had

dark dark skin, as dark as skin gets outside of Africa, and while that certainly must have appealed to Vladimir, while it must have sated some unrecognized fratricidal craving, he felt attracted to this girl for reasons beyond that. She smelled like cream and ginger, and her hair looked soft, and she bit her cuticles just like he did, and she stood the wrong way on mall escalators so that the world seemed to get farther away, and when she took bites of the pretzel Vladimir could see the pink muscle of her tongue, and she had big boobs that she tried to cover up (if he hadn't already fallen in love with her, he might have crassly referred to them as a sneak rack), and while she didn't laugh at Vladimir's jokes she at least knew they *were* jokes, and on the surface of her chin a pimple had formed, the pus of which was rising volcanically, and she told Vladimir that she was really, *really* looking forward to popping it. There are young men who did not find these habits and admissions attractive in the opposite sex, but in one afternoon at the Queens Center Mall Vladimir discovered he was not of their number.

He walked her home, and when they got to her door she put a hand on the side of his face, as if the city had gone suddenly dark and she needed to make sure he was still there, in front of her. "I like you," she said.

"I like you, too."

Come on, you idiot. Kiss her.

He didn't. He went home, loving her and hating himself. The next day they saw a movie together. The day after that, they went to a pool hall on Northern Boulevard. The day after that, she couldn't go out because she flunked an algebra test, so they talked for three hours on the phone. In the following days they went back to the mall, saw another movie, ate slices of pizza, sat on a bench in Travers Park with a clear view of the handball courts. And still they had not kissed. Every unconsummated minute brought Vicki and Vladimir closer to Friendship Status. At home, Vladimir stared at himself in the mirror, wondering if he should shave his widow's peak like Misha did, if maybe that would make him irresistible to Vicki, because clearly Vladimir stood incapable of making that first open-mouthed move himself, because he was a spineless, dickless, ass-licking loser. On Thursday—June 13, 2002—Vladimir, again, walked Vicki to her door, and again failed to kiss her. This time, however, she didn't go inside. Instead, they turned back around and she walked him to the train station, where she

passed through the turnstiles—like him, she had a student Metro-Card, so the swipe was free, but still!—and she stood with him on the platform, keeping him company as he waited for his train home.

They didn't say much. Under the ground, through their rubber-soled shoes, they began to feel the first soft rumblings of an oncoming train. Vladimir stepped up to the cautionary yellow line, leaned out over the tracks, and peered into the mouth of the tunnel. The rumbling grew louder. On the tracks, newspaper sheets and magazine pages twitched nervously. The air changed. Still no actual, physical train, but across the walls bloomed a heraldic light.

Vladimir decided he'd rather be the kind of guy who tries to kiss the girl and strikes out than the kind of guy who doesn't try at all. Wetting his lips, he turned to Vicki, who had already opened her mouth.

She tasted like she smelled, like ginger and cream. He clicked against the ridge of her teeth. He felt the slick underside of her tongue. Halfway through, Vladimir and Vicki remembered to close their eyes. It was the first French kiss for either of them, and not knowing when there'd be a second, they felt reluctant to stop. Eventually, however, they ran out of oxygen.

The train had come, the E express. The doors had opened, the commuters had stepped off.

"So," Vladimir said. Down by his hips, his hands opened and closed, grabbing at nothing. "I guess I'll see you."

She smiled and ran up the stairs.

By any objective criterion, it wasn't the world's greatest kiss. But don't tell Vladimir that. Or do. Tell him that kissing, like most things, only gets better with practice. Tell him that and see what happens. Because as the E express lurched toward Manhattan, Vladimir could barely keep his feet on the ground. If he was to jump—just a little hop, that's all—Vladimir would've smashed through the ceiling of the train car, through the tunnels, past the rats, past the mole men and Morlocks, up and into the East River that separates Queens from Manhattan, and once in that murky black-green water, he would've whooped it up, scissor-kicking his legs, using his hands to high-five the steroidal fins of radioactive fish.

He wanted to tell his brother so bad. Despite all of Misha's money, they still shared a room, and only two, maybe three feet of space separated their twin beds. That night, with the lights turned off, Vladimir

tried to find the courage to tell his brother that only a few hours previous he went underground and stood on a subway platform, and while trains whistled behind his back, he kissed a girl for the very first time. But Vladimir felt afraid. He worried Misha might find the confession too intimate, too feminine; he worried Misha might think it took Vladimir too long to nab his first kiss; he worried Misha might ask the color of Vicki's skin. Because while she wasn't Black, she was black, and Vladimir knew that would disappoint. And if Misha asked, Vladimir couldn't lie. He could steal from his brother and think the occasional evil thought about him, but he couldn't lie to him, not even in the dark. Nor could he disappoint him. So he didn't say anything. He went to bed burdened. He didn't tell his tale and somehow that made the kiss less real.

But Vladimir tells Misha now. He lies in a different bed, a hospital bed, with injuries consistent with blunt force trauma, as if Vladimir had been in an automobile accident or beaten with a pipe: cracked ribs, unfairly on both sides of the cage; a bruised sternum; a shattered bone in his left hand from trying to defend himself; and, worst of all, a broken jaw the doctors had to wire shut. He'll have to eat smoothies for months, but at least he can still talk. In a voice that sounds strange to him—slower, deeper, more distant—Vladimir tells his brother everything: about the kiss, the E-beeper, the Air Jordans, the cloudy features of their mother. Talking with a wired jaw doesn't hurt so bad, but crying does, and his whole body shakes from the effort of trying to stop.

Misha climbs into bed with him. A ponytailed nurse appears in the door, but Misha waves her away. He puts his arms around his brother's body. He collects the hospital gown, that flimsy thing, in his fists. He wants to spoon Vladimir. He wants to feel the delicate wings of his shoulder blades. But there are doctor's orders. With broken ribs, Vladimir must lie flat on his back.

"Shh," Misha says. "I love you. Okay? You're my brother. I love you."

Later in life, when Vladimir thinks of his brother—which will be *every single day*—he will often think of this moment. He will be pouring a cup of bitter coffee in the faculty lounge and all of a sudden he'll feel the ghost arms of his brother take hold of his body.

"You can never do anything wrong," Misha says. "Do you understand? We'll invite this girl over for dinner. Would you like that?"

"I won't be able to kiss her anymore," he says. Because he can barely open his mouth, the words come out muffled. "She won't even *want* to kiss me like this."

To keep himself from squeezing tighter, Misha lets go. His hands—still damp from a recent scrubbing—hover above Vladimir's body, unsure of where to touch down. Where do you put them? When your brother's ribs are broken and his chest is bruised, when he can hardly breathe, when his jaw is wired shut and his hand bandaged, where do you put *your* hands? What can you do that won't make the pain worse? Misha rubs the inside of Vladimir's elbow. He pours all his love into this one spot on his brother's body, and for everything else, for the rest of the world and the people in it, he feels only an unspeakable rage.

10

The Department of Worry

Alfredo and Tariq push through the bowling alley's heavy glass doors, and an air pocket pushes back, as if the building doesn't want them here. That's fine. Alfredo doesn't want to be here either. The carpet smells like cigarettes and chicken grease. Balls strike pins with the thunderous monotony of a roadside chain gang pulverizing rocks. And these balls don't glow in the dark, as they would at a schmancy Manhattan bowling alley. There is no dark here. Every bulb in every socket burns brightly, giving off the creepy orange gleam of fast-food heat lamps, and at each lane, under the pressure of these orange lights, the same painful tableau is enacted: men, women, and children, whether they're here on a second date or for a league game or a birthday party, whether they've picked up a strike or a gutter or some quantity of pins between the two, all the bowlers having bowled their balls and registered their scores, turn around now and make the exceedingly awkward walk back to their parties. The bowlers seem to wither under the scrutiny of observation. They have been watched, their roll judged, and now, not knowing what to do with their hands or where to put their eyes, not knowing how to act, these bowlers perform, and, of course, they perform disingenuously. They shrug. They pump fists. Overwhelmed with panic, they convert their thumbs and index fingers into pistols, take aim, and fire, *kapow kapow,* some of these

poor unfortunate souls going so far as to raise their fingertips to their lips and blow out invisible wisps of smoke. Alfredo, painfully self-conscious himself, hates to see others collapsing under the strain of painful self-consciousness. This is what happens, he thinks, when management leaves on the lights.

Tariq points to a lane in the back. "There's Baka," he says.

Like Alfredo, Baka is a self-conscious paranoiac, but unlike Alfredo, he wasn't born that way. An athletic child, Baka dominated Elmjack baseball. He stole bases standing up, spiraled footballs at eleven, drove his mother crazy with in-house ball playing and kitchen wind sprints and room-to-room dribbling, employed a patient, monotonous handball style, forcing no issues, striking no killers, simply keeping the ball in play from baseline to baseline until lung-scorched opponents gave up midpoint to bend over and take hold of their knees. And then at fifteen years old, he was diagnosed with Cushing's syndrome. A rare endocrine disorder, it caused his adrenal fight-or-flight mechanism to behave erratically. Even worse for young Baka, the Cushing's inflated his body to 250 pounds. Although increasingly unlikely, an athletic career remained technically, theoretically possible. At sixteen, he weighed more than 300 pounds. At twenty-eight, he no longer bothers with scales. Baka is centrally obese, which is to say the Cushing's has expanded his trunk and face while sparing his limbs. Which is to say he looks like a big black lion. He sweats too much. He bruises easily. Fatty pads layer the back of his neck, giving him a buffalo hump. And as is understandable for a man who once hoped to play center field for the Mets but can now no longer fit in the stadium seats, Baka has taken on an air of cynicism. He knows that bad things—missed beanballs, double-crossing business partners, terrorist attacks, nonhereditary endocrine disorders—suddenly poof into existence. And so he acts accordingly. To minimize risk, he doesn't go to drug dealers' houses, nor does he have drug dealers come to his. Instead, he prefers to meet in large public spaces, and because his competitive spirit remains, those large public spaces tend to be pool halls, pubs with dartboards, arcades with skee ball, bowling alleys like Whitestone Lanes. A couple of years ago, in the dimly lit parking lot out front, an upper-level drug dealer from the Bronx got himself shot in the head; Baka may or may not have been the executioner, but the very possibility tightens Alfredo's scrotum.

"Pretend you don't see him," Alfredo says.

"Yeah right," Tariq says. "Look at the size of him."

A young black kid, the latest protégé, rests a hand on Baka's considerable shoulder. They stare at Alfredo, and Alfredo stares back. He crinkles his eyes. He squints past them, watches an attendant scuttle out to the no-man's-land of the pins, watches a curly haired white girl bounce a ball off the bumpers. With his head moving like a sprinkler, Alfredo scans the lanes to Baka's right, lane 37, lane 38, lane 39, all the way to the end of the bowling alley. When he finishes, he turns and gives Tariq a big vaudeville shrug.

"You don't see him? He's right over—"

"Hold up," Alfredo says, flipping open his cell phone. He lowers his brother's arm. "Don't look at him. Look at me."

"You're *calling* him?"

"Not really." Alfredo keeps the phone on his ear for as long as it would take another phone to ring a few times and click into voice mail. "I don't want him to know we've seen him already. So I'm pretending to call him."

"Put your finger in your other ear," Tariq says. "It'll look more authentic that way."

After Alfredo hangs up the phone, he leads his brother to the shoe rental counter, where a white guy stands sentry on an elevated platform like a pharmacist. Alfredo asks him how much it costs to rent a locker.

"Fifty dollars for the year."

"Well, come on now," Alfredo says. He has a whopping two hundred dollars—the entirety of his life savings—at the bottom of his sock, but he ain't about to blow a fourth of it on a bowling alley locker. "How much for a one-day rental?" he asks. To keep himself sharp, Alfredo does the math himself: if the rate remained constant, a locker should cost a little less than fourteen pennies a day.

"We don't rent lockers by the day," the man says. He avoids eye contact, as if the news he's delivering is too terrible to bear. He picks up a shoe and sprays disinfectant into its insides. "We only have yearly rentals, I'm afraid. And that's fifty dollars. Like I was telling you."

"Where they at then? I wanna check them out before I throw down fifty dollars."

The man leans his head out over the counter, revealing a scalp

freshly mobilized with hair plugs. Each troop of implanted hair stands at attention, as if these were the first awkward days of boot camp. He points to a row of lockers that are close to Baka's lane but, thankfully, not too close.

As they make their way toward the lockers, Alfredo whips a white envelope out of his pocket. He flourishes it, as a magician might flourish a tricolored hanky. At a waist-level locker, he kneels down and his head dips close to his brother's body. Tariq smells clean, overwhelmingly so. Before they left, he took a "quick shower" that turned into a ninety-minute shower, where, judging by the smell of him, he must've used a full bar of soap. Plus a couple spritzes of Alfredo's cologne. Which is kind of flattering actually. When he asked to borrow a shirt, an XL Mecca tee, Alfredo was happy to lend it. He kneels down by the lockers, smelling his brother, looking at his shirt, and Alfredo feels a surge of love rise into his chest. He didn't invite this feeling, and yet here it is, flooding him. He pushes the envelope through a slit on the locker door.

"How you gonna get it back out?" Tariq says.

"I'm not really worried about it," Alfredo says. "It's empty." They're walking back to the shoe rental counter. "I owe Baka five hundred bucks, but it ain't like I've got that kind of money."

Tariq stops walking. "You don't have five hundred bucks?"

"No, no, no, no, no. What I mean is that I'm not gonna hand over that kind of money to a fat fuck like Baka just because he asked me to. But I think he might start some shit—"

"Because of the money you owe him."

"Over some other shit actually. But if he thinks I've got his cash in one of them lockers, then that'll check him. Know what I mean? He won't start any shit till he gets his money."

"Oh," Tariq says, nodding his head. "Well, I hope you got a Plan B."

Alfredo tells the white guy behind the counter that he ain't interested in them raggedy-ass lockers, but he would like to rent some bowling shoes. He requests a pair of size tens (he's actually a size nine, but he doesn't like anyone to know that, not even a potentially sympathetic stranger with hair plugs), and as is New York bowling alley policy, the man asks for Alfredo's Timberlands. He needs to keep them behind the counter as collateral against theft.

"You're kidding," Alfredo says. The bowling shoes sport a dizzying

design of red leather squares alternating with tan leather squares. The heels are frayed, the laces blackened with dirt. Even the insoles have gone missing. Nothing will separate Alfredo's feet from fungus but the thin cotton of his athletic socks. So as to ensure he won't steal these ridiculous bowling shoes, Alfredo has to relinquish his prized pair of Timberland boots.

"Well, I guess we only need to hold on to one," the man says. He offers a boot back, which Alfredo gladly accepts. "And you, sir? What size do you need?"

"I ain't wearing them shoes," Tariq says.

The man looks down at Tariq's prison-issue Converses. "I'm sorry, sir. But I'm afraid you can't bowl in sneakers."

"What do you mean, you're 'afraid'?" Tariq says. "Seriously. Explain that to me. You're afraid of what?" When the man doesn't say anything, when he just turns around and sticks Alfredo's boot in the cubbyhole, Tariq says, "You think you're a big deal? Standing up on your platform?"

Alfredo pulls his brother away. He wants Baka to see Tariq while he's like this, combustible. Alfredo figures that at some point in the last two and a half years, Tariq took down the pictures of Isabel he had taped to his cell's wall, and while Alfredo doesn't fool himself into thinking Tariq removed those photos calmly—he imagines Tariq vented his spleen on some poor inmate, as he vented his spleen just now on that poor shoe-rental guy—but after some quiet, religious reflection, it's possible Tariq decided that blood is indeed thicker than water. Right? There's *gotta* be something to that effect in the Qur'an. But Alfredo doubts there's anything in that holy book protecting overweight drug dealers.

As they approach Baka, Alfredo throws up his hand as if seeing him for the first time. Out of the corner of his mouth, he tells Tariq, "Try to look intimidating."

"Ah," he says. "I'm the Plan B."

When they get within earshot, Baka says, "Maybe we oughtta get you a new pair of glasses." He lounges in a leather booth skirting the perimeter of the lane. As befits his standing as a gentleman of leisure, he wears a tracksuit, and as befits the tracksuit wearer, his default mode is ball busting. "If you need new glasses—which, let me tell you, you obviously do—I can hook you up. I know a lady, works at an

optomalamadingdong shop. She can get you a sick discount. Little Puerto Rican lady. Tell her I sent you when you go. Drop my name."

"I tried calling you," Alfredo says.

"Negatory. Didn't get a call."

"Let me see your phone."

"You don't believe me?" Baka says. Tariq has taken a seat next to Baka on the booth, and Baka has to turn his body to talk to him. "I'd know, right? Believe me—when your brother calls, it's like an event around here. I write it down in my diary. Like a lunar eclipse, you know what I'm saying? Does not happen every day, am I right? Most definitely does not happen *twice* a day. Unless he needs something. Then, yeah, sure—I'll get a call. But he never calls just for friendship. And if I call *him*? Start leaving messages, which I never like to do? And then these messages start getting more and more frantic as I get more and more crazed? Forget it. I might as well be the girl with acne on the night of the prom. I start to get offended, if you know what I mean."

"Maybe he's trying to offend you," Tariq says.

"Maybe he is." Baka shakes his head mournfully. "It occurs to me. In my darker moments. The worst is when I worry that something's happened to him. Pierre here—have you met Pierre?" He gestures to the young black kid sitting in a chair with his back to them. The kid scratches his neck and enters names on the lane's computer keypad; either maliciously or not, he's spelled "Alfredo" as "Alfraido." "Pierre," Baka says, "tells me I've got a catastrophic imagination. You've heard of this? Catastrophic imagination? Me either. Which is cause for alarm, right? Because I start worrying where Pierre's heard this shit. In a fucking book? Impossible. And then, Jesus, don't get me started—I get to worrying if Pierre is smarter than I am. Which is a scary thought. Just wait till you talk to him. I'm up nights. I mean, I'm up nights anyway, but I'm bugging out over this, and the point is that all this bugging out over catastrophic imaginations is I guess a pretty good indicator that I actually *have* a catastrophic imagination, and so when I call and call and don't hear from your brother, I start to think, Aw Christ, oh no, maybe the big Dito got himself hurt somehow."

"Why would you think that?" Alfredo says.

"How *you* doing, by the way?" Baka asks Tariq. "Good to be home? Good to have you back, let me say that much. You look good. Hitting the weights, that's obvious. Let me tell you something—you go to

prison strong, you come home stronger. It's like a supervillain factory, am I right? Of course I wouldn't know. Anyway, you look good. Other than the cheek, which is infected by the way. That's some shit I do know about. Pierre, baby. Get over here. You're being very, very rude."

With his wiry arms and bony hands, Pierre looks a bit like a young Curtis Hughes. If Alfredo had to bet, he'd put the kid at sixteen years old. Maybe even younger. He's much taller than Alfredo, and by the looks of his oversized feet, he's only going to get bigger. He probably wakes up every morning with stretch marks on his shoulders and new coils of hair on his chest, probably outgrows his clothes every three months. Which is why he's got to invest in shirts like the one he's got on: a long white tee that comes to an end a few inches above his knees. Across the chest is a picture of Al Pacino, a Technicolor still frame from *Scarface*. Alfredo's never seen the movie—who's got the time?—but he's watched enough rap videos and heard more than enough impressions to be at least familiar with the scene on the shirt. An orange tulip of gunfire blossoms from the tip of an enormous gun, and Pacino, like Baka, tenders introductions: *Say hello to my little friend.* Alfredo and Pierre slap palms.

"I don't think I've ever met a black guy named Pierre before," Alfredo says.

Pierre inflates his chest. "Funny story, actually—"

"What is *that*?" Alfredo says. He leans in close to look at Pierre's neck, where a red constellation of bumps blotches the skin. Like fingers, the bumps reach down the collar of his shirt. "What the fuck is wrong with your neck?"

"My neck?"

"Poison ivy," Baka says, sounding impatient. "We gonna bullshit all night or are we gonna talk business?"

"We do need to talk some business," Tariq says.

"Poison ivy?" Alfredo says.

"Yeah, me and my boys? We was doing some graffiti shit over by the Maple Grove Cemetery, and we got into some bushes and whatnot, tagging this big—"

"Are you kidding me?" Alfredo says. "That shit is contagious."

Pierre shakes his head. "I looked it up online. They said it wasn't." He looks to Baka for support. "Right? The Internet? They said it wasn't catching."

Alfredo wipes his hand against the front of his shirt. "It's contagious, man. That's what poison ivy *does.*"

"Don't worry," Pierre says.

The kid, obviously, has no idea who he's talking to. For the purposes of spatial efficiency, Alfredo's neurological Department of Regret splits an office with the interrelated Department of Worry. They've got separate desks and filing cabinets but share the same frosted glass door. Many of Regret's overcaffeinated staffers work freelance in Worry, almost all of them preferring the latter job as it requires the use of more creative faculties. They wear green visors and chew unlit cigars—there is no smoking in the brain, for obvious reasons—and they draft worries on triplicate forms, each worry, like each correct response on *Jeopardy!* phrased in the form of a question. For instance: What's the incubation time on poison ivy? What are the dangers of exposing a pregnant woman to it? Did Pierre kill Curtis Hughes? Did he use a metal bat or a tire iron to compensate for the Alphabet Brother's knockout fists? Did Curtis, at any point, think Pierre kinda looked like a younger version of himself, or do people not recognize that kind of thing?

"The Internet said I'd be fine as long as I took a bath every day in tomato juice."

"That's for skunks," Alfredo says.

"What is?" Pierre says.

"Baths in tomato juice."

"Why would a skunk take a bath in tomato juice?"

"See?" Baka says. "This is the guy who comes to me with 'catastrophic imagination.' Can you imagine?"

"We need four ounces of cocaine," Tariq says. He sits hunched over on the edge of the booth. Between his knees, his hands dangle in a way Alfredo finds disconcertingly nonthreatening. "Nothing stepped on," Tariq says. "No filler. We want it by Tuesday at the latest. And we won't pay more than seven hundred an ounce. Which is what? Twenty-eight hundred dollars? I get that math right, Alfredo?"

No, Alfredo thinks. He sits in the swivel chair next to the computer keypad, away from the men in the booth. No, that math is not right. Well, okay, yes, the *math* is right, but the numbers are ludicrous. An ounce at seven hundred would be a pure gram cost of twenty-five, which is maybe what it costs off the boat when the shit comes into the

country, but to demand those prices now, from Baka, in a bowling alley in Flushing? And what would he even do with that much coke? Cook it in Mama's cast-iron frying pan, smooth out the bubbles with Mama's butter knife, store it in Mama's freezer till it hardened into crack rocks? Type in an ounce on a pusherman's calculator and you get 168 rocks. Four ounces then makes 672. Sell that on the street for ten dollars a rock (*well* . . . let's say fifteen a rock, considering Alfredo's salesmanship), and you've got $10,080, or a profit of over seven G's, which is probably how Tariq arrived at the original number, saying to himself, *Boy, I'd sure like to make seven thousand dollars—how do I do that?* Unless, of course, seven hundred an ounce was a reasonable price before Tariq went away, in which case Alfredo completely missed out on the porous-bordered heyday of drug dealing. If he were three years older and if he had the stones to sling rocks, Alfredo and Isabel would have their own apartment by now, with a flat-screen TV and a Sub-Zero refrigerator.

From his sitting position, Baka lightly kicks the boot in Alfredo's hand. "You're clutching that thing like a teddy bear," Baka says. "You didn't want to let the nice shoe rental guy hold on to it?"

"You kidding? I'm not gonna give that high school dropout *both* my boots."

"Aren't you a high school dropout?" Baka says.

"Yeah. And I'd steal somebody's boots."

"He didn't hear me?" Tariq asks Alfredo. Tariq won't even look at Baka. "He didn't hear me ask him for four ounces?"

"Maybe he's trying to offend you," Alfredo says.

Baka smiles as he wags his finger in Alfredo's face. With his free hand he waves over the waitress. She is a big-bottomed, middle-aged Latina. Alfredo's never seen her before, which isn't surprising considering Alfredo's never seen any of the waitresses here more than once. Whitestone Lanes employs one server at a time, converting them into perpetual motion machines, bouncing them from one end of the bowling alley to the other, age accelerating their weary bodies. Alfredo imagines that when this particular waitress came to her job interview she was a long-legged teenaged bombshell—almost as pretty as his Isabel—and she got hired on the spot. That was probably a week ago. Within the hour she'll have gray hair and arthritic knees.

Baka orders a strawberry milk. Pierre gets nothing—he's wandered

off toward the ball rack—and Tariq doesn't get anything either, which surprises Alfredo, considering Tariq didn't eat any dinner. It's like he doesn't even know the waitress is here. As he stares down at his hands, his lips move silently.

"What can I get you, sweetie?" the waitress says, and it takes Alfredo a moment to realize she's talking to him. He orders a beer, and she asks for some ID.

"I'll have a Coke," he says. She slips the nibbled pencil behind her ear and hustles away, toward another party in a different lane.

"So what's the story?" Pierre says. He hugs a giant black ball to his chest, his arms quivering with the effort. "We bowling, or what?"

"I don't think so," Baka says. His voice softens. "I don't know if the big bad Batista brothers have come here to play games."

"Are you serious? I already put everyone's names on the computer!"

"I know," Baka says. "I know. But how about you go and bowl for everyone. Yeah? Take our turns for us. See who wins."

The three of them watch Pierre slink away to the lip of the lane. He spreads his feet wide and cradles the ball between his legs, as if it were an elephantine testicle. He pitches it down the lane, and the ball breaks left, dropping heavily into the gutter. The pins stand erect, unimpressed. Not that Pierre seems to care. He races back to the ball return machine. He scratches his neck as he stares into the machine's black mouth, waiting for it to belch back what's rightfully his.

"We don't need to go through you," Tariq is telling Baka. "If you can't pull down that much weight, we'll go to somebody else. We came to you first as a favor."

"And I'm very, very flattered." Baka pats Tariq's knee. "Nice jeans. Expensive jeans."

"Maybe we've come into some dough," Alfredo says. He lets his eyes drift toward the lockers.

"Great," Baka says. "You can pay me the money you owe me." He squeezes Tariq's shoulder, and Tariq winces under the contact. "What'd you guys do?" Baka says. "Take out an advance on your gambling winnings tonight? That's a bad habit, let me tell you."

"What gambling winnings?" Tariq says.

"The dogfight," Baka says. He sounds surprised. "The party in your honor."

"Right, right," Tariq says. "The party."

"See?" Baka says. "You know everything. You're so fucking smart."

Tariq mutters under his breath, something about insolence or indolence. Something about—Alfredo can't be quite sure about this—rending the earth asunder.

"I'm not so sure the party's still on," Alfredo says.

Baka says, "The Alphabet Brothers—or at least the two that are still alive—they seem to think it's still on." He straightens the cuffs of his tracksuit. "I called them to offer condolences. You called them, right? To pay respects? No? Well that's not very nice, Fredo. Funeral's gonna be at Conway on Northern. Hope to see you there, God willing." He smiles at Tariq. "Or Allah willing, am I right? Anyway, the ABC bros told me they're still coming tonight. Apparently their dog was really Curtis's dog, first and foremost. He was the one who fed it and picked up its shit. So they're putting the pooch in the ring as a tribute to Curtis. I don't really get it. My opinion? I think they're grieving in an unhealthy way. They tell me they've got some aggression to work out."

"What's that supposed to mean?" Alfredo says. "They said that about me?"

Baka's cracked lips smile. "What do you mean?"

Alfredo looks to his brother for help, but Tariq is staring off into space. Alfredo closes his eyes. He needs a quiet room. He needs to crawl into this ball return machine and follow its underground tunnels to the magmatic center of the earth. Once there, he can prop his feet up on some stalagmites and figure this whole thing out.

The waitress puts a beer in Alfredo's hand. Stubborn ice crystals cling to the bottle's neck; the label has already started to peel off. Alfredo takes a long sip. The beer tastes cold and necessary. He wants to thank the woman who brought it, but having already dropped off the check and Baka's strawberry milk, she's disappeared.

"That was nice of her," Alfredo says.

"That *was*," Baka says. He takes the straw out of his milk glass and flicks it onto the ground. "People take a liking to you, Fredo. You ask Pierre what the fuck's wrong with his neck, and he doesn't even get mad. Tries to tell you a story. You steal your brother's girlfriend, knock her up, and he doesn't even look angry. Well, he looks a little angry, but he always looks like that. Oh, he's looking *real* angry now. Yikes. What's the matter? You didn't know about Dito and Isabel? Course you did. You know everything." Baka bends to his milk glass and slurps

pink foam off the top. He tells Alfredo, "That waitress could've lost her job giving you that beer. But she *liked* you for some reason. You've got a way, I guess. Now here I am. About to do you a very, very foolish favor myself. I got you a present, a beautiful snub-nose thirty-eight revolver that'll fit right in your waistband. A beautiful pistol. And you *gotta* take it. I already lost the receipt."

Alfredo never intended to be the kind of person who wants, much less needs, a gun. He looks over at Pierre, who bowls with perfect form: bent forward at the waist, left arm horizontal to his body, right leg tucked, head straight, fingers outstretched. The ball spins down the lane and knocks down all the pins but one. Up on the TV screen, an arrow points to Pierre's name. When bowling for himself, Pierre knocks down nines; when bowling for anyone else, he throws gutters. In a contest in which he's the only participant, Pierre cheats. He's the kind of guy, Alfredo realizes, who'd bring a bat to a fistfight.

"What do I need a gun for?" Alfredo says.

"Why does anyone need a gun? Self-defense!" Baka spreads his legs wide apart, settling into his story. "The kid you put in the hospital yesterday? His brother calls me up. Asks me who I sell drugs to in East Elmhurst. I say, 'Why?' He says, 'I'm looking for two black kids and a Puerto Rican.' I say, 'Jesus, you're kidding. That's everybody.' He says, 'One black kid hits like a motherfucker, the other one wears a Spider-Man hat.' You notice how this guy fixates on the black people? I'd get upset—well, that's not true. I *do* get upset, but what are you gonna do? I tell him one of the kids has gotta be a Hughes brother. And the other one is Winston, no doubt about it. I tell him Winston's Haitian, not African American. But he doesn't care. He wants to know about the Boricuan now. I tell him, 'If Winston was there, the Puerto Rican's gotta be Alfredo Batista. He's a nice guy.' See? I put in a good word for you. Well, maybe I didn't. Who can remember? So then the guy says—"

"This is the chemist we're talking about?"

"Chemist?" Baka says.

"Winston told me the kid's brother was a chemist."

"Winston told you?" Baka says.

Oh God. Winston? Winston thinks the expressions are "nip it in the butt" and "one foul swoop" and "play it by year." He says "eck cetera." He once bet Alfredo money that the arcade prodigy in "Pinball

Wizard" is a deaf, dumb, and black kid. He dropped out of high school in the eleventh grade, in the middle of midterms, when he opened up his exam booklet and discovered, with a sunken stomach, that he stayed up the night before studying the wrong subject. He told Alfredo that Boris was a chemist, that there was nothing to worry about, and Alfredo believed him because he wanted to believe him.

"Who," Alfredo asks, "is Vladimir's brother?"

"Mike Shifrin," Baka says triumphantly. "He's a drug dealer."

"I don't know who that is."

"Well, when he woke up yesterday he'd never heard of you either. What a difference a day makes, huh?"

"So call him up," Alfredo says. "Call him up and tell him you won't sell him any more drugs unless he backs off and leaves me alone."

"I don't sell him drugs."

"He's got your logo on his X."

"I got his logo on *my* X," Baka says. "I buy drugs from *him*. Actually, I buy drugs from a guy in Chinatown, and he buys drugs from Mike Shifrin. This guy's a Russian gangster. The real deal boss hog."

"This isn't fair," Alfredo says. He turns to Tariq. "I only hit the kid one time. I was getting the drugs for you. To give to you. I didn't even hit him that hard."

"Where's the gun at?" Tariq says.

"Queensbridge," Baka says. "The Ravenswood Houses. Pierre will drive you there. The both of you. Take you ten, fifteen minutes."

Alfredo peels the label off his beer bottle. "I don't want to go to Queensbridge."

"Oh, don't worry about that," Baka says. A foamy pink mustache lies slithered above his upper lip. "Queensbridge ain't as bad as the rappers make it seem."

"You know where this Shifrin guy lives?" Tariq asks.

"I'll find out. But first things first. Go to Ravenswood and pick up the pistol. Afterwards, Pierre—who's a very responsible driver, by the way—will drive you home. Save you a bus ride." He turns his round, leonine face toward Alfredo. "I don't give a shit that Curtis got merked. He was always too . . . brutish. But you? I *like* you, Fredo. You dance around shit. You crack jokes. You know how to flirt with my ass, which I've always appreciated. Know what I mean?"

Alfredo doesn't know anything. Maybe Pierre will drive him and his

brother to Ravenswood, and they'll park in front of a hydrant and run into the projects, and when the elevators don't work, because they never work, the three of them will take the stairs, and it'll be there, in a stairwell that smells like urine, that Pierre will open up their throats with a box cutter. Or maybe they never even get to the car in the first place. Maybe Pierre kills them in the dimly lit parking lot of White-stone Lanes, and somebody reads about them in the paper and says what Alfredo said when he read about that poor kid from the Bronx: *Oh shit, Whitestone Lanes—I've been there!* Or maybe—who knows?—Baka isn't setting him up. Maybe they really will go get a gun. But that won't have anything to do with Alfredo being likable. If Alfredo kills Mike Shifrin, then a vacancy becomes available, and Baka gets to creep up the drug-dealing ladder. And if that's what Baka wants, then maybe he made all this shit up. Maybe it's just a story he told. *But that can't be right,* Alfredo thinks. Mike Shifrin killing Curtis Hughes and then coming after Alfredo has gotta be true. In a weird way, Alfredo wants it to be true. It confirms his original theory, corresponds exactly to his worldview: there are boogeymen out there, lurking in shadows, plotting attacks.

If he gets killed, Isabel will never ever forgive him.

"What about the money?" Alfredo says. He's torn the beer label to bits. Little white pieces congregate on his T-shirt; the glue sticks to his fingers. "What about the five hundred I owe you? I've got an envelope."

"An envelope," Baka says, smiling.

"Yeah. I got your money in an envelope. Right over there. In one of them lockers. But listen, I'm not gonna give it to you unless you talk to this Shifrin guy. Okay? You gotta talk to this Shifrin guy, because if I get killed, how you gonna get your money, you see what I'm saying?"

"Sunken costs," Baka says. "I just won't send flowers to your funeral."

"But the envelope," Alfredo says.

"What about it?" Baka says. "What am I gonna do with an envelope? My African pen pals don't write back to me anymore. I pay all my bills online. The jerk-offs at the post office, they raise the price of stamps three fucking times a month. An envelope? Please, Fredo. That's the last thing I need. Hey, Pierre, you don't look so good. Too much bowling?"

Pierre has wandered over. Having finished all forty frames, his arm

hangs off his body as if wilted. He steals a big swallow of Baka's strawberry milk, drinks straight from the glass.

"What about the coke?" Tariq says.

"Ah," Baka says. "The coke." He puts his arm around Tariq's shoulders. "Forget about the insulting prices. Insulting prices can be negotiated. Forget about the fact that I think your business partner is going to be dead by Monday. I'm sorry. I'm not rooting for it, but come on, let's be real. Forget that I don't even think you *have* the three thousand dollars. Let me be real, my man. I ain't getting you your coke because I think you're going to be back in jail before I turn my fat ass around, and as a general rule I don't sell drugs to gangsters on their way to jail. But hey, listen—thanks for thinking of me. It's always nice to be considered. Now go to that big charitable drug dealer who can get you ounces at seven hundo, and go with my blessing, papi chulo. Thanks for coming down. Sorry you didn't get to bowl. Pierre? Baby? Do me a favor and drive these assholes to Ravenswood."

Pierre lifts the strawberry milk to his mouth, seemingly intending to drain it as payment for his services, when the shadow of a large black bowling ball crosses his face and the glass shatters in his hand. He drops down to his knees. Both hands cover his mouth, as if stifling a terrible secret. Blood seeps through the fingers.

The bowling ball dangles from Tariq's hand. A small cut has opened up underneath his eye, where a shard of glass must have ricocheted and caught him in the face. The red blood trembles. Tariq drops the bowling ball—it crushes the straw Baka flicked away earlier—and dabs at his cut with the tip of his pinky.

Pierre's cries are muffled, unintelligible. It's possible his lips have come loose from his face. Alfredo turns away, looks instead at the air vent on the ball return machine. He passes his hand over the slats. The air feels nice, but he wishes it was cooler.

"What are you gonna do now?" Baka says. He sounds as exhausted as his mother must have sounded when she came home from a double shift and found her house a mess, the vases broken, rugs trampled, her only son covered in infield mud. Still sitting in his big leather booth, he hasn't even made a move to help Pierre. "Where you think you gonna hide?"

Tariq pushes his face close to Baka, and the big man flinches. The Cushing's may have damaged his fight-or-flight response, but appar-

ently his body can still react instinctively when faced with a more dangerous predator. Tariq's mouth hangs open. His eyes are gleaming. He waits for Baka to say something else—but for once, he stays quiet. With a disappointed hitch in his shoulders, Tariq walks away.

Alfredo chases after him, just as, it seems, he's always chased after him. They pass lanes full of people. They pass the shoe rental guy, who has no problem making eye contact now. With a phone pressed to his ear, he glares at them, as if memorizing their eye color, their heights, their distinguishing characteristics. Alfredo glares back. He doesn't care about this guy—it's only the waitress he wants to avoid. He'd hate for her to regret her kindness toward him.

As soon as they get outside, Alfredo realizes he left his Timberlands behind. In these red and tan bowling shoes, he feels pounds and pounds lighter. He feels faster. And a good thing, too. Tariq dashes through the parking lot, his prison-built chest hardly heaving, and Alfredo struggles to keep up. While he runs, he peers into the windows of parked cars. He doesn't know what Mike Shifrin looks like, but he imagines an older version of Vladimir, a pale white face, a round head, a bottle of expensive vodka in the passenger seat.

"Hurry up," Tariq says.

When they reach the sidewalk, Alfredo feels as if he's burst through a forest, through dark trees and into a clearing. The lights are brighter. Tariq raises his arm, and the air all around him feels charged, pregnant with the threat of rain. Across the street, a squirrel runs by with half a hot dog bun in its mouth.

"Come *on,*" Tariq says. A gypsy cab has pulled over to the curb and it sits palsied at Tariq's feet like a giant nervous panther. "Let's go. Get in."

"What are we gonna do?" Alfredo whispers.

"I don't know," Tariq says. He slaps Alfredo hard between the shoulder blades. "But I'm sure you'll figure something out."

The brothers slide into the backseat. Over a dashboard-mounted walkie-talkie, a faraway dispatcher barks orders in a crackly, unintelligible Spanish. Or at least it sounds like Spanish, which is odd considering the driver has a turban wrapped around his head. Scented cardboard Christmas trees—each of them arctic blue—hang from the rearview mirror. They've all got the plastic wrappers still on them, some of these wrappers barely opened, others dangling from midtier

branches, as if the scented trees were exotic women in various states of undress.

"Where to?" the driver says.

Alfredo wonders if this guy is the father of the two little Indian girls in the park yesterday, the ones who walked with a swagger and had Mister Softee's schedule memorized. Alfredo tells the driver Jackson Heights, looking for some thrill of homecoming in the man's eyes. The cab takes off into the street.

"You thought Baka was setting us up?" Alfredo says.

"I don't know. But if he didn't want to fuck you up before, he'll want to fuck you up now."

"Oh great. Thanks."

"You're welcome," Tariq says. He reaches over and picks off the beer-label bits stuck to Alfredo's shirt. "It's important to know who your enemies are, Dito. If this Shifrin dude's big-time, you'll want him to act soon, while he's still mad enough to come solo. And now you know Baka will bring him to you."

"He doesn't know where we live," Alfredo says.

"But he knows where you'll be tonight, yeah?"

The cab lurches down the Whitestone Expressway. With the Mets game long over, traffic is only half bad. Up ahead a smattering of bleary red brake lights are glowing. The driver speeds up, cuts off a rival yellow cab, and both men lean into their horns.

Alfredo puts the E-beeper in his brother's hands. He tells Tariq that when you slide off the top, rows of pills suddenly materialize. *Welcome home*, Alfredo says without actually saying it. *Welcome home. This is my present to you.*

"How much does this sell for?" Tariq says.

Alfredo rounds up: "Fifteen hundo."

"That ain't enough," Tariq says and shoves the beeper into his pocket.

Alfredo doesn't know what he expected, but, well—he thought he might feel relief to relinquish an object that's brought him only bad luck. Or he thought he might take a gift giver's satisfaction in bestowing a present. At the very least, he looked forward to demonstrating the beeper's ingenuity, and by extension his own ingenuity in figuring it out. With all these pleasures denied to him, Alfredo stares out his window. There are two stickers stuck to the glass, one with the name of

the cab company, Mexicana, and the other with a warning: For Your Own Safety You Are Being Videotaped. Alfredo cracks the window open, lets the air outside toughen his face.

The Department of Worry crams his pneumatic tubes with questions. Fifteen hundred dollars ain't enough for what? If Alfredo is killed, will the mere sight of his dry-bristled toothbrush in the bathroom send Isabel into hysterics? Who will get rid of the tighty-whities under the sofa? The department comes up with many possible afterlives, but the one most frequently imagined is a small room without windows or doors, a black box where darkness fills your mouth like sand. Or maybe he gets to stay on as a ghost. He wonders if, years from now, he'll be hovering in the corner of a dorm room on the night Christian Louis gets too wasted and confesses to his roommates that all he has of his father are a couple of stories his mother told him and a few cheap Happy Meal toys he collected.

Alfredo turns to his brother, to ask him about the Muslim conception of the afterlife, but Tariq's eyes are closed. His breathing has deepened. Air whistles out his nose. Alfredo doesn't even know how this is possible. Less than five minutes ago, Tariq smashed a milk glass into Pierre's face, officially turning Baka against Alfredo. And now? Now his head sags into his chest. While Alfredo panics, while his stomach acid gurgles, Tariq catches up on some Z's.

"You're asleep?" When his brother doesn't answer, Alfredo says, "You gotta be fucking kidding me."

He wants to go home. He wants to fall into Isabel's arms and catch up on some Z's himself, sleep till all the world's vendettas are forgotten, till the ozone layer disappears and the earth explodes. Of course, at some point during that snooze, Izzy's water will break and Christian Louis will insist on his debut. But until then . . . Alfredo asks the driver if he can maybe go a little faster. I'm in a bit of a rush, Alfredo explains. The driver grips the wheel with both hands. He leans forward, his eyes framed in the rearview mirror. Alfredo isn't sure if he's somehow offended the man, or maybe he hasn't been heard. He's about to repeat himself when the car's sudden, extra acceleration throws him against the back of his seat. Wind howls into the cab, over the top of Alfredo's cracked-open window. With the exception of the ghetto car, Alfredo's never driven in his life, never had to worry about staying in his lane or keeping his eye on the road, and so, when in a car passing other cars,

he is free to stare out his window at all the people in all those other cars, who always seem to be moving backward, getting sucked into the past. He likes to catch them in some sealed-off moment of privacy—picking their noses, bobbing their heads to songs he can't hear. But when Alfredo looks out his window now, he can't see anyone clearly. Just a few blurry figures stooped behind a few blurry wheels. The cab is moving way too fast. With yet one more pleasure denied to him, Alfredo turns to his brother, who's still sleeping. A snore ripples out from the bottom of his throat. *What a bunch of bullshit,* Alfredo thinks. He picks at the stickers stuck to his window. *Videotaped? For my safety?* It doesn't even make sense, and Alfredo is starting to get a little tired, a little skeptical, of all these people claiming they got his best interests in mind.

By busting up Pierre, Tariq turned potential allies into definite enemies. *You're welcome,* he said. *It's important to know who your enemies are.* He provoked Baka so that he'll crash the dogfight and bring Mike Shifrin with him. *Here, tie this bull's-eye round your neck. Now you'll know for sure which way the bullets will be zinging.*

Alfredo realizes he's working with two possibilities here. Either his brother is a fool with a poorly conceived plan, or his brother is both smarter and more dangerous than he anticipated. Alfredo wishes he could come up with some rival explanations. Maybe if he were sitting someplace dark and quiet and isolated, where headaches aren't invited, he'd be able to think of something else, but right now this is all he's got: Tariq's plan only makes sense if its intent is not to protect Alfredo, but to nudge him into the crosshairs.

Alfredo—who constantly fights back exhaustion, whose job keeps him up nights, whose filing cabinet keeps him up past that, who gets three or four hours before the sun shoots through the blinds, before Isabel wakes him up for a prenatal appointment, before his father wakes him up for a favor, before his mother wakes him up with a grievance, before Winston wakes him up with a request to meet him at the park—watches Tariq sleep the sleep of the wicked. His eyes remain shut and his lips parted. With his head tucked into his chest, a small indent is made visible at the base of his neck. A little recess, deep enough for a thimbleful of water. A soft and familiar pocket. If given one thousand photographs of the backs of one thousand necks, Alfredo would be able to pick out his brother's every single time. The

skin around the indent seems to swell with pride. Red tiny bumps—presumably from the teeth of a barber's razor—encircle it, encroaching upon it dangerously.

"You know," Alfredo says out loud, "I'm not so sure you're as dumb as you seem."

Tariq's eyes snap open. Without emotion, as if reading lines off a cue card, he says, "We ain't never backed down from thugs and bitches. And you ain't gonna start now."

"Right," Alfredo says.

Contrary to street gossip, Alfredo never dropped a dime on the Virgil's robbers. Why would he have? To get rid of his brother? To get closer to Isabel? Come on! Before Tariq went upstate, Alfredo hardly even knew Isabel. He'd seen her around, of course, poised on the brick incline of the handball courts like some kind of talent scout, buying movie magazines at Max's candy store, gently stripping away the aluminum foil on a gyro as she waited for the traffic light to turn green, standing behind the blue police barricade at the Sunnyside Puerto Rican parade—but these moments only became charged by hindsight, reassembled *after* they'd fallen in love. Prior to Tariq's incarceration, Alfredo and Isabel had never even spoken, other than half-muttered hellos when they passed each other in the street. She was his brother's girlfriend. What could they possibly have to talk about? Besides, her physical appearance elicited a feeling previously unfamiliar to Alfredo: she made him feel shy.

And then, late one night, a month into Tariq's Fishkill sentence, she appeared, trudging through snow toward the candy store, toward Winston and Alfredo. She wore boots and mittens and a bubble jacket zipped up to her chin. A scarf completely covered the lower half of her face, and it seemed to Alfredo that this wasn't only protection from the cold, but a kind of disguise, as if she preferred to wander the streets incognito. But who could she fool? The eyes above that scarf could only be Isabel's. Her hair, exposed and dark, glittered with snowflakes.

Winston and Alfredo stood together under Max's red and gold awning. According to procedure, Winston should've been across the street, guarding the stash, but it was too cold a night to be all alone in the Alleyway, too cold to be outside at all, selling drugs *or* buying them. And yet there they were, in matching wool knit caps that Alfredo

had bought for them. They stomped their feet and breathed out smoke and watched Isabel come toward them through the snow.

She said something—it sounded like *hzgnoe*—and both Winston and Alfredo leaned forward and asked her to repeat herself. With obvious reluctance she pulled the scarf away from her mouth. What she had said, she explained, was hello.

"Oh," Alfredo said. "Hello."

"Hello," she said again. "I don't think we've met," she told Winston, as she extended her hand toward him. "I'm Isabel."

"Oh, I know that," he said. He grabbed her hand, not shaking it, just holding it, and while Alfredo looked on, frantically flipping through his conversational Rolodex, Winston *continued* to hold on to her hand, obviously reluctant to give it back. Tremendously stoned, he dropped his voice to a Casanova bass and said, "Let's stay like this forever."

"Sure is cold!" Alfredo said. It was the best he could do.

"It is," she said, pulling her hand free. "It is unbelievably cold."

"Freezing!" Alfredo said.

Winston tapped the bridge of his nose. "When it gets cold like this?" he said. "Oh my God, my nose hairs go buck wild. I can feel like each little hair up there. It's like they've gone stiff. Like they've turned into icicles. It weirds me out, but at the same time I kinda like it. This ever happen to you?"

"So," Isabel said, turning to Alfredo. "You talk to your brother lately?"

Ah. The reason for her visit. Alfredo had been worried she'd heard the neighborhood rumors and had come down here to jab her finger into his chest, to accuse him of doing her man dirty for financial gain. And so when it became clear that she only wanted to pump Alfredo for some Jose-related info, he felt relieved, although it was a relief tinged with disappointment. In the subsequent years, he's tried to pinpoint the source of that disappointment, and the safest explanation he can come up with is who the hell would want to talk to a beautiful woman about some other man? But that's what he did. He told Isabel that his mother had gone up to Fishkill, took the train and everything, but Jose asked her never to come back. Alfredo didn't describe Lizette's reaction to this, that when she got home she locked herself in the bathroom, nor did he share with Isabel his own reaction, that he thought it

selfish, not to mention cruel, but that he was, as always, trying to extend to Jose the benefit of the doubt, that maybe his brother was embarrassed and didn't want their mother seeing him behind Plexiglas, in those orange jumpsuits or whatever they've got on up there.

"Have *you* heard from him?" he asked her, although her presence here made it obvious that she had not.

"My mother the puta did something to our phone," she said. "It can't get collect calls or something."

"That sucks," Alfredo said.

"Yeah, right? It won't even give you the *option* of accepting collect calls. So like if he's trying to get ahold of me, I wouldn't even know."

"Was he trying to call you before your mother fucked with the phone?" When she didn't answer, Alfredo knew he should probably stay quiet, but he's always had trouble keeping his mouth shut, just as he's always had trouble resisting the urge to press his fingertips against walls with wet paint signs. "He's sent you some letters though, right?"

Her face darkened. "Jose didn't talk about you much," she said. "The only thing I remember him telling me is a story about how your father took you two on the subway for a funeral scam. And you started crying real bad."

"Oh yeah, you didn't know? I'm a real wuss."

"Getting colder out here," Winston said. He jerked a thumb over his shoulder toward the candy store. "I think I'm going to go inside. Where it's warmer? And, you know—"

"Less awkward?" Isabel said.

"Exactly."

Before the door closed shut behind him, a little heat from inside the store trickled out onto the sidewalk. A sign—ATM Available Inside—hung off the awning, and Alfredo slapped at it to give his hand something to do.

"I should probably get going," she said.

"I'll walk you home."

"And disappoint all your customers?" she said, laughing. "No, that's okay. I live right up the block."

"My father tells me that like fifty percent of your body heat comes off the top of your head. I don't know if it's true or not. But you know. That's what I've been told," and he handed her his wool knit cap.

Maybe 50 percent was an overestimate, a typical Jose Sr. exaggeration, but *man*: without his hat, Alfredo felt his body heat plummet. And he wasn't going to get any warmer either. Isabel looked at the cap in her hands as if it embarrassed her, and Alfredo's ears turned red, thinking he'd done something else he shouldn't have done. Later, he'd find out that she simply didn't have much experience receiving small kindnesses. "You don't have to take it," he said. "If you don't want to."

She dipped her nose to the wool and gave it a whiff. "You don't smell alike," she said. "You and your brother."

"No?"

"No. You're a little bit funkier." She slipped the cap over her head. It fit so snugly that she seemed to have a little difficulty tucking her ears under the wool. She smiled. As if she were at the supermarket, in the produce section, prodding a melon, she brought her mittened hands to his temples and gave him a squeeze. "You've got a really small head," she told him.

"Thank you."

"Sorry," she said, still smiling, looking not sorry at all.

She walked away from him, toward home, through the sidewalk's thin blanket of snow. She stepped in the footprints she'd made coming here, as if she were playing a game, or as if she wanted to leave behind as little evidence of herself as possible. When she got to the end of the block, she turned around and waved, and Alfredo's hand—without his permission, acting on its own—went up in the air and waved back.

The following night temperatures had dropped even further, and once again—procedure be damned—Winston refused to sit by himself in the Alleyway. If he was going to freeze to death, he at least wanted some company, someone he could talk to through their respective blocks of ice. And so he and Alfredo were together, in the exact same spot (outside the bodega), doing the exact same thing (selling drugs to nonexistent customers), when Isabel came around the corner again.

Under his breath, Winston said, "Don't do anything I wouldn't do." And then he disappeared. The bastard. Alfredo tried to grab him—*come on!*—but Winston wiggled away, hid himself inside the candy store. Abandoned, Alfredo watched Isabel approach.

From a distance of three or four feet, she tossed him his hat, which he fumbled, too eager as always. When he stooped to pick it up, he saw

that the cap looked cleaner, brighter, as if the time spent on Isabel's head had been restorative, a much-needed vacation.

As she had done the previous night, he brought the hat to his nose and gave it a whiff. "You washed it," he said.

"I just smell like that, actually."

"Really?"

"Nah, I washed it." Like Alfredo, she seemed to have a tendency to laugh at her own jokes. "Thanks for letting me borrow it," she said. "It was really nice of you. *Really* nice."

"Well, when I offered it to you I didn't think you were actually going to take it."

Instead of laughing like she was supposed to—it wasn't *her* joke, after all—she asked Alfredo if he liked dioramas, and Alfredo responded, naturally, by asking, "Dioramas?"

"I'm going to the Museum of Natural History tomorrow," she said. "In Manhattan? They've got these huge dioramas with antelopes and cavemen. Stuff like that. They got dinosaurs, too. The bones. I don't know. I thought if you like that kind of thing, you'd maybe wanna come with me."

"You have a boyfriend," he said.

"I'm not asking you out on a date, you dick." She pulled the hat out of his hands and put it on her head. "Don't you have any like female *friends*?"

"No."

He didn't really understand why she'd want to hang out with him— he still doesn't—but what he told himself at the time was that despite his slight edge in the funkiness department, he reminded her of Jose. That's all. With her boyfriend locked up, she settled for palling around with the next best thing: his little bro. The comparison flattered Alfredo. And the idea of a female friend actually sounded kind of nice. Maybe she'd help him pick out more flattering pairs of jeans, maybe she'd drag him out of the borough every now and again for some culture and shit, foreign films and art openings and diorama museums and opera boxes with them little mini binoculars on a stick.

Early the next morning, he picked her up at her place, and together they rode the E train, then the C, to Eighty-first Street. They wandered through the Museum of Natural History until he complained of

sore feet—*big wuss, remember?*—and then they ate bowls of chicken noodle soup in the fourth-floor cafeteria, where between slurps they agreed that the very best thing they saw that day was a ninety-four-foot-long replica of a blue whale, suspended from ceiling wires in the Hall of Ocean Life. They imagined what it would be like to be swimming next to one of those blubbery monsters, with its mouth gaping open, threatening to swallow them whole.

Over the next couple of weeks, with increasing frequency, Isabel and Alfredo went back into Manhattan, which seemed so very far away. They went everywhere. To Times Square and Union Square, Chelsea, Bryant Park, that roller rink the Guggenheim. They got hot chocolate at City Bakery. They sat in the lobby of the Pierre Hotel, where they pretended they were waiting for some glamorous friend. They went to FAO Schwarz, so Isabel could dance on the giant floor piano like Tom Hanks in *Big*, but the line was too long so they walked through Central Park instead. She even brought him to the video store where she worked, although they didn't go inside because what was there to see? On their first few expeditions they talked about Jose, and when they weren't doing that they tried to out-funny each other, top each other's jokes—but eventually, as Alfredo and Isabel grew more comfortable, those impulses faded. He told her about his considerable collection of phobias, and she told him about her history with her mother the puta and Raul the Cubano. When they discussed the future they agreed that they both felt ready for the ground to shudder under their feet, for life to bring them something different, some kind of dramatic upheaval, not yet realizing that this was their something different, their dramatic upheaval.

On a Saturday night in late February, Isabel and Alfredo—as friends, as friends!—went to Greenwich Village, where he'd made reservations at an impressively schmancy jazz club. For an hour and a half they sat in mandatory silence, drank seven-dollar screwdrivers (at least no one carded them), and listened to the supposedly world-famous Darren Gelato Trio. It was incredibly boring. At intermission, with the check on their table, Isabel pulled Alfredo outside for a cigarette. *You smoke?* he asked. *Not exactly,* she told him. Searching her purse for a phantom pack of cigarettes, she led Alfredo past the bouncers, ambled to the end of the block, turned the corner, and ran.

Alfredo chased after her. She'd never run out on a check before, not once, never done anything like it in her whole entire life. Drunk on adrenaline, she flew down the sidewalk. Tightness spread through Alfredo's chest. He heard the buzzing in his ears. Four vodka OJs and ninety minutes of jazz—all of it stolen. He knew that if he kept running, he'd collapse, right there on Sixth Avenue. "Hold on," he said, clutching her coat.

She turned around, steeled herself with a quick breath, and leaned toward him, her mouth parting softly. He thought she was trying to tell him something. So as to hear her better, he turned his ear to her face and she missed his lips, kissed him accidentally at the corner of his mouth. Miserably embarrassed, he tried to explain. *I thought you had something to tell me. I thought you were saying something!* She asked him to please stop squirming. She grabbed his chin and kissed him again—thank God—caught him this time flush on the mouth. When she pulled away, her eyes were wide open. She blushed, because it was her turn to be embarrassed.

"I'm sorry," she said. "It's just that, oh I don't know. I'm sorry. Is that okay? It's just that I *wanted* to, I guess. Is that okay? What I just did?"

He looked down to see his hands on her hips. His mind stammered. He pulled her toward him and together they fell backward against the fence of the West Fourth Street basketball courts. The chain links caught them, kept them up on their feet. She straightened the glasses on his face. Then she kissed him again, kissed his mouth, kissed his neck, slipped her thigh between his legs. Because she wanted to. He slid his hand into her coat sleeve, to feel the warmth of her skin. She laughed. She was wearing his wool cap, and he pulled it down over her eyes—confirmation, she later told him, that he was the right man for her. He felt calm. He felt happy as her kisses traveled up the side of his neck. Around the corner from the jazz club, only a few yards away from the mountainous bouncers, with that unpaid check still on the table, Isabel brought her mouth to Alfredo's ear and whispered, "What if we get caught?"

So there you go. Alfredo didn't initiate that first kiss and he never sold out his brother to the police, but he's initiated countless kisses since, and as he sits next to Tariq in the backseat of this cab, Alfredo decides

that he's going to sell him out tonight. Didn't drop any dimes two and a half years ago, but he's going to drop one now.

"Listen," he says, as the cab speeds toward the Northern Boulevard exit. "I got some shit to take care of. You mind if I drop you off at home?"

Tariq stares straight ahead, still and quiet, with his hands folded peacefully in his lap. Alfredo doesn't know how to read that. He hates the idea of leaving his brother in the same apartment as Isabel, but it's not like they'll be alone—both Mama and Papi will be there—and besides, you can't rat someone out while they're hanging off your elbow. Right? Since Tariq converted potential allies Baka and Pierre into definite enemies, then Alfredo—who feels as if he's gotten along just fine in this life doing whatever his brother wouldn't do—needs to convert some potential enemies into definite allies. Needs to invite some cruel motherfuckers of his own: the police. He plans to go down to the Dunkin' Donuts on Seventieth and Northern and wait for the Anti-Crime cops to show up, as they do every night, two or three times a shift. He'll ask them if they'd like to crash a dogfight. If they'd like to put their cuffs on his brother, the ex-con, the man on parole.

The cab exits the expressway and accelerates through Corona. With a string of green lights ahead, Alfredo and Tariq are getting closer to Jackson Heights, closer to home. Outside the window, the Langston Hughes Library gives way to a liquor store, which gives way to an Argentinean steakhouse, which gives way to a parking meter with a red canvas bag wrapped around its face.

Alfredo feels itchy all over, and he wonders if he's caught the poison ivy, or if this is just his mind attacking his body.

"You'll be okay?" he asks. "With getting dropped off at home?"

Tariq continues to stare straight ahead. "Where *you* going?" he asks.

"I gotta grab a cup of coffee with somebody," Alfredo says, which is both a lie and not a lie, one of his specialties. "I'm gonna be mad quick." He reaches over and taps the face of Tariq's digital watch. Alfredo wants this emphasized. How fast he's going to be. "Back before you know it," he says.

"You think you can fool me?" Tariq says. "Coffee?" His grin extends into the scar on his cheek so that it becomes one long lopsided smile. "You got a girl, Dito? A little something on the side?"

"See?" Alfredo says, scratching his neck. "That's what I'm talking

about. Right there. Maybe you didn't hear me before, because you were sleeping and all that. But I was saying that I didn't think you were as dumb as you seem. And now lookit: you got me nailed."

"You are, aren't you? You're going to see a girl. You little shit." He laughs. "I'm not as dumb as I seem, huh? You know what, Dito? I'm not so sure that's a compliment."

"It's comments like that," Alfredo says, "that prove my point exactly."

11

The Door Factory

Tariq knows that in a certain kind of book—not the Book, of course, but a pretend book, a make-believe book—a man in his spot would have to deal with moats and drawbridges and arrows and catapulted boulders and cauldrons of black tar and devils and demons and dragons and dwarves and bearded ogres and trickster brothers and who knows what else. This man, the hero of that make-believe book, would be standing out in the open air, just as Tariq is standing out in the open air, and he would look upon a large fortress-like structure, just as Tariq is looking up at his parents' apartment building, and blood would rush to the crown of that hero's head, just as Tariq's blood rushes, surges, leaving him dizzied. When the cab dropped him off, his brother gave him a set of house keys and told him, again, that he'd be right back. Sure, sure. Right back. See you in a jiff. These keys weigh heavy in his hand. The building pulls him toward it.

Not yet. Be patient. There are still moves to be made.

He walks down to a corner of Northern Boulevard previously populated with newspaper machines, all of them lined up like a squat robot army. Not anymore. People were apparently paying for one paper, opening the latch, and thieving them all. Just cause they could. And so

publishers, mindful of profits, took their machines off the corner. Besides the stench of garbage, the only thing left here are the free papers: the penny-savers, the *Queens Tribune,* the *Queens Gazette,* the job-hunting circulars. It doesn't look like a robot army no more. It looks like a bunch of cheap plastic row houses, with all the tenants inside calling out to Tariq desperately. *Take one! Grab one! Free! Free!!*

He goes to the end of the line, to a little green house with little attic windows jutting out of its roof. The door swings up. He finds inside two neat stacks of paperback books, which are all the same issue of *Apartment Finder,* June 2002. A sticker on the inside of the house— he's shoved his head all the way in, drawn by the plastic smell—says Warning: Destruction of This Property Will Result in Civil Fine or Imprisonment.

Okay, whatever. He sticks one of the books in his back pocket, where it crinkles his parole paperwork. He'd like to take all the books and toss them down the gutter, to disadvantage the apartment-hunting competition, but these little green houses are probably all over Queens. To make a significant dent, he'd have to go to each and every one, and really—who's got that kind of time?

Eight hours since Tariq bolted that Charleston Chew in the Macy's dressing room, and since then he's had nothing to eat. No pizza at Gianni's, none of Mama's spicy chicken, not even a burger at White-stone Lanes. And now it seems too late. He's missed out on his chance. While incarcerated, he'd often stay up two nights in a row, reading in the sliver with his cheek against the bars, and on the third night, although bone-tired, he'd feel too jittered for sleep. He feels like that now. Too hungry to eat. Standing outside the Laundromat, across from Papi's old store, Tariq wonders if his stomach has left him, transplanted itself into one of the bodies nearby, into the Chinese delivery-man who pedals past him, reeking of lo mein, or maybe into any one of the ants at his feet, disappearing down a sandy hole between sidewalk panels.

This is as it should be. The straight path is paved with hunger. Muhammad, peace be upon Him, fasted in the caves of Mount Hira and returned home the Prophet. Deprived of food himself, Tariq feels only a pulsing pain behind his eyeballs, and although he can live with

pain—and with scars on his face and specks of glass under his eye, and with betrayal and insult and disrespect, and with backbiters and maligners and jinn-possessed demons—he worries that this dull hunger will prevent his thoughts from proceeding in orderly ranks.

The sign on the Laundromat's door reads Change Is for Customers Only and it takes Tariq too long to understand they mean change as in quarters and dimes. As if embarrassed for him, his stomach grumbles noisily. Inside the Laundromat, a bald-headed black guy, one of those customers with the right to receive change, looks up at Tariq pushing through the door. The guy sits in a chair next to a washing machine, with his feet rudely propped up on another chair. He's working on a laptop. A real pro—his mother must be awfully proud, Tariq thinks—he doesn't need to look down when he types. Allowing him to stare at Tariq. And why? Because of these pathetic Converses? Because Tariq's walked in here without a laundry basket? Meanwhile, these Rocawear jeans alone cost ten times more than everything this black guy's wearing put together. And yet, unable to help himself, unable to summon the requisite pride, Tariq punks out and looks down at the floor. He doesn't know why. He feels an uncomfortable tingling, the same tingling one of them ants must feel when crouched under a magnifying glass.

Still tingling, he hurries over to the magazine rack, where he grabs a circular called *Rentals,* a circular called *Rent 411,* and, thickest of all, a circular called *The Real Estate Book.* He feels the guy's eyes on the back of his head. He hears his fingers striking the keyboard. He punishes that laptop, as if he were writing down everything Tariq's doing, narrating all of his movements.

When Tariq stops, the man stops, and he doesn't start typing again until Tariq walks past him, carrying the three rental magazines over to the bulletin board. Because everyone in this Laundromat conspires to annoy him, a fat Ecuadorian woman sits directly under the board. The TV above the dryers plays a telenovela, which the woman watches with her mouth hanging open and with her fingers absently worrying the beads of her necklace. Tariq has to lean over her—his crotch inches from her ear—in order to read the business cards thumbtacked to the board. Psychics next to personal injury lawyers next to massage specialists next to computer repairmen. A homemade flyer advertises babysitting services. The nanny's phone number is repeated on little

strips of paper, which dangle off the flyer like piano keys. Another flyer offers a reward for a lost dog, a floppy-eared beagle. Tariq leans over farther, brings his face closer to the cork of the board. *Classic 2 Bdrm for Rent.* Now we're talking. A two-bedroom is exactly what he's looking for—it'd be nice to have an office for his studies, with a little sewing machine set up in the corner for Isabel—but he doesn't take the flyer's dangling piano key because he knows "classic" is just a fancier word for old.

More apartment listings hang off the board, but in order to see them he'd have to sit on this woman's head. The guy stops typing. Waits for Tariq to make the next move. With all these dryers going, with all this static electricity in the air, the Laundromat smells like the first few minutes after a lightning storm. Tariq clears his throat to see if the guy will start typing again, maybe even write that down—*The monster clears his throat*—but instead the woman looks up at him. She flinches when she sees him leaning over her. He never meant to frighten her, but come on lady, who asked you to sit directly under the fucking bulletin board? Now that he's here, now that she's staring at his scar, he has to do *something* to justify his presence and so he reaches out blindly and rips a random piano key off the bulletin board. He's still muttering apologies when the Laundromat door closes behind him.

Because the frustration never ends, the crumpled piano key in his fist turns out to have nothing at all to do with apartment rentals. It says,

Meth Study
Queens College

Under that it asks him to call a 718 telephone number. Yeah right. He tears it up and chucks the bits of paper into the street.

He knows exactly where he is—he's escorted his mother to this Laundromat thousands of times; he used to *live* in that bodega right across the street—and yet he feels lost, as if he's only been told about this place, as if all his memories belong to somebody else. Apparently he exudes this confusion. A homeless man hustles over, eager to pounce.

Normally an expert at identifying the ethnicities of other men—

credit Queens, credit prison—Tariq can't tell if this guy is Indian or Pakistani or Bangladeshi or something else altogether. Despite the heat, the man wears a thick sweatshirt, as gray and dirty as his beard. Powerful drugs, or withdrawal from powerful drugs, cause his left leg to tremble. Head bowed, he asks for some spare change.

"Haven't you heard?" Tariq says. "Change is for customers only."

"What?"

Tariq reminds himself, not for the first time, that he should leave the joke-telling to others. He rolls up all the rental magazines, and the man takes a step backward, as if he were a spider about to be swatted. Tariq shoves the magazines into his back pocket. Both pockets are embarrassingly full now, a pair of unsightly bulges stretching out his Rocawear jeans. He expects the homeless guy to make some sort of crack, call him a peckerwood or something, and when he doesn't, Tariq gives him his last three dollars.

"Good luck, my brother," Tariq says happily, for as everyone knows the upper hand is better than the lower hand. "Peace be upon you."

Rather than dwell any further on his own benevolence, he walks away from the man and all of his thank-yous. It feels good to be moving. Up in the sky, the sun's purple light still lingers. Things are as they should be. Having given that man the last of his money, Tariq feels as if he's reclaimed his neighborhood. He could stroll through these streets indefinitely, humming a wordless tune, his hands in his pockets, but the Casio F-91W tells him he better hurry up. Let's see a little urgency in that gait. You're losing time you can never get back. Or as the Book says:

The Hour has come and split is the moon.

He breaks out into a jog. Keeps his head down, watches sidewalk panels disappear beneath his feet. Watch out, people! Get out the way! It felt good to be moving, but my oh my, it feels even better to run.

Three deadbolts protect his parents' door. He tries a square key, but it won't fit in any of the locks. He tries a different square key. He tries squat keys and round keys and skinny keys, but none of them fit, no matter how hard he pushes. Desperate, he tries a mailbox key. His

heart quickens when an extra-long key fits into the middle lock, but of course of course of *course* that key refuses to turn. He tries an eyeballed comparison between the teeth of the keys and the mouths of the locks, but it's hopeless, he can't see that well and the hallway lights are dim and there are just too many fucking keys, a massive jumble of keys, a janitor's wet dream of keys, keys his brother probably found on the street and stuck in his pocket, keys to their old apartment behind Papi's bodega, keys that lack any known function, unlocking doors that probably don't even exist anymore. This is just like him, Tariq thinks. His brother keeps keys past their usefulness because he wants to seem like a *romantic,* a man who stays up all night blinking back nostalgia. A thick metal hoop spears the keys, and dangling off that hoop is a cheap plastic bottle opener. The engraving on that cheap plastic bottle opener reads World's Greatest Dad.

Halfway through, Tariq loses track of which keys he's tried and which ones he hasn't, and so he has to start over. Black spots of mildew blemish the walls. One more thing that up in Fishkill, dreaming of his return, he failed to imagine.

The possibility occurs to him that no matter how badly he wants them to, none of these keys will open any of these locks. His brother may have intentionally given him a fake set as a joke, an attempt to humiliate him, to have him impotently scratching at locks, to make him ring the bell or knock on the door like an outsider, a Jehovah's Witness or a traveling salesman, a man with his hat in his hand and his dick tucked between his legs.

On the other side of the door, the TV plays loudly. Tariq thinks he hears laughter. And not the TV laughter of a simulated studio audience, but real laughter from real people *inside the living room.* Breathless, he presses his face to the door. His dog is whimpering, and yes, someone inside is definitely laughing. Truly right here, home and yet not home, he feels closing in upon him painful torment: fetters and fire and food that chokes. He bends one of the keys in half, which isn't easy, which leaves a ridged imprint on the meat of his thumb. Hands shaking, he reaches inside of himself, grabs hold of the Book:

Your Lord has neither left you, nor despises you. What is to come is
better for you than what has gone before; for your Lord will
certainly give you, and you will be content. Did He not find you an

*orphan and take care of you? Did He not find you perplexed, and
show you the way? Did He not find you poor and enrich you?*

So of course there are locks. Of course there are obstacles. Tariq knows
he's been put on a straight path, but not necessarily an easy one. With
the steady, guiding hand of Allah, the Most Merciful, the Most Compassionate, he tries again, one by one, and this time into the right locks
he drives the right keys. Orphans, all of them, they slide into their
chambers with the ripple of homecoming.

When he walks into the apartment, Isabel and Papi turn their plastic, mock-innocent faces toward him. They sit close to each other:
Isabel on the sofa with her feet tucked under her thighs, and Papi in
his wheelchair with a blanket covering his lap. Between them, on the
floor, sits an air mattress, shiny and inflated and looking as if it would
be easily punctured. Get this: Papi turns away from Tariq and directs
his attention back to the television. Apparently Tariq's return to this
apartment has become another boring, taken-for-granted, humdrum
affair. Apparently he can't compete with the TV screen, where a white
woman, her voice unnaturally amplified, shills September 11 com-
memorative coins: *We will never forget. Proud to be an American. A
necessary addition to any patriotic collection.*

At least the dog welcomes him. Still chained to the leg of the sofa, he
lunges to get at Tariq, and every time he lunges he gags on the spikes of
his pinch collar. Determined, smart, quick to adapt, he abandons the
lunging and instead takes small steps, one paw after another, with the
history of his breed defined in the muscles of his neck. The sofa inches
forward. He's dragging it across the carpet, and Isabel, who had been
sitting Indian-style on the cushions, sends her feet to the floor. The
dog leans into his collar. If Isabel stood up, the sofa would surely shoot
toward Tariq, but if she continues to sit, with her feet rooted to the
ground—and no reason to think that she won't—the dog will strangle
himself. This is a train for which Isabel's already paid her fare. This is a
test between her and the dog, and Tariq watches impassively, not
knowing whom to root for. The dog's legs are shaking. His tongue falls
out of his mouth.

"Where's Alfredo?" Isabel says. "Is he okay? Did something happen
to him?"

Despite his struggle, the dog doesn't even bark. Of all the things

Tariq admires about this animal, this is at the top of the list. He's all bite. Tariq goes to him and unclips the leash from his collar. *Thank you, thank you.* The dog jumps on him, hugs on him, almost knocking him over, his paws scrambling across Tariq's chest. Tariq plays their game where he blows into his marbled eyes, and the dog squirms away, pretending to be annoyed.

"Your mother don't want him off the leash," Papi says.

"Oh yeah?" Tariq says. He forces the dog's mouth closed, so he can't drool on his jeans or lick at his cheek. "And where *is* Mama?"

"In bed. Comatose. She tried to stay up till you got home, to tell you something . . ." He snaps his fingers. "What was she gonna tell him?" he asks Isabel.

She shakes her head, as if she cannot recall. But there's no way, Tariq thinks. There is no way she forgot.

To help himself remember, Papi closes his eyes and tilts back his head. A loose purse of skin hangs from his neck. Something evil, Tariq thinks, has drawn his father's gray cheeks into his face. It's as if Papi's been using one of those breathing machines, one of those clear plastic jockstraps that cover the nose and the lips. Except instead of providing oxygen, this cruel machine pulls it out. And now Papi looks like this, someone who's given up, who's already half gone, one paralyzed foot in the Cedar Grove Cemetery. The Book says:

> If one or both of them grow old in your company, do not say fie to them, nor reprove them, but say gentle words to them and look after them with kindness and love, and say: "O Lord, have mercy on them as they nourished me when I was small."

Yeah well, Tariq's first objection is that the whole nourishment part of this sura may not apply in his particular case. Second of all, Papi did not grow old in Tariq's presence. This happened during Tariq's incarceration. This happened, he is sure, *because* of his incarceration.

"I remember now," Papi says.

"Did you hear me outside the door?"

"Your mother wanted me to remind—"

"Did you hear me? Outside the door?"

Jose looks over at Isabel, and Tariq is careful to notice if anything

rises on his face—if his eyebrows arch, or if his flaky, dehydrated lips curl into a smirk. "What do you mean?" he asks.

"Did you hear me when I was out in the hall? Struggling with the locks."

"I guess."

"You're not sure?"

"We figured you were maybe a little—you know."

"No, Papi. I don't know. Can you please explain it to me?"

"I don't know, Junior. A little buzzed maybe? First day back, maybe you and Dito get a little drunk. Smoke a spliff or something." He draws a hit from an invisible joint, his pinky raised in the air. "Come home a little stoned and maybe you have some trouble opening the door. I don't know. We didn't really think about it, tell you the truth."

"You didn't really think about it? Don't look at her. Look at me. You didn't—"

"What right do you have, talking to me like this?"

"Please don't interrupt me when I'm speaking." Tariq forces the dog's head down into the carpet. "You say you weren't really thinking about me outside the door, fumbling with the locks like an *idiot*. But then what were you thinking about? What were you *laughing* about, Papi?"

"Laughing?" he says. He smoothes out the wrinkles on his lap, a clear giveaway. "What's the matter with you? You wanted me to get up? Unlock the door for you?"

"Here's the thing," Tariq says. He tries not to smile when he sees how closely Isabel is watching him. She sits on her hands, as if perfectly composed, but he's willing to bet dollars to donuts that if he put his ear to her breast he'd hear her heart wildly thumping. "Here's the thing," he says again, stepping closer to his father. "How would you feel if I laughed in the face of your pathetic moments? When you need help coming in and out of the bathtub. Or when you've pissed your pants in the middle of the day and don't even know it?"

"This subject is closed," Jose says. He points the remote at the television and raises its volume. "Your mother wanted me to remind you to call your parole officer. Before it's too late."

Tariq's on him before he even has a chance. He forces his hands behind Jose's knees and under his tailbone, and hoists him out of

the wheelchair. The old man weightlessly floats into Tariq's arms, as easily as cream rises in coffee. And then he starts fighting. He punches Tariq's ear, his face, his back, the cluster of muscles between his shoulder blades. *Put me down*, he says. *Put me down right now!* Imagine that. Granting this old man's request. How easily these thin legs would shatter. Tariq is laughing. He tosses him up in the air, as one might do with a baby. They are swirled together, father and son. Jose is still fighting and Tariq is still laughing. To protect the gash on his cheek, he sticks his face in Jose's armpit, which smells like sofrito. He carries him toward the back of the apartment. Tariq can't see where he's going—his face stays buried in Jose's armpit—but he doesn't need to see where he's going. This is his house. He knows where the parrots hang low and where sock-snagging nailheads stick out of the carpet. As they go through the kitchen, Tariq tilts his father's helpless body and walks sideways like a crab, so that Jose's dangling legs don't get clipped on a doorway.

Isabel says nothing. *I'm the main event*, Tariq thinks. *I'm the chaos she needs.* Like the perfect audience member, she sits still and silent in the dark.

He throws his father onto the bed, and Jose lands as a pile of shirts might land—with a soft thud, in a twisted heap. Grease-stained pillows bounce to the floor. The mattress springs creak. Rising up onto his elbows, Jose shows his son the face of an old man, red and swollen and accusatory. This face demands to know what right Tariq has. What right? What right? Tariq could ask him to elaborate, but he's too disgusted. He cuts straight to his father's lies.

"Where's Mama?"

Jose's lost his voice. The words come out thin and black, barely even whispered: "What right do you have?"

Oh please. Tariq gets down on the carpet and slides a hand under his father's dresser. The wood feels bumpy, as if infected with disease. Something contagious. Years ago, when Tariq was just a kid, he'd root around inside the dresser drawers for whatever his little hands could find: loose change, cough drops, porno mags, airplane bottles of Bacardi, an inexplicable yarmulke, condoms that he'd blow up like balloons. This time, however, Tariq searches for something specific: a

package he'd duct-taped to the bottom of the dresser. It should be right in the middle. A clear plastic baggie, it is full, or at least it should be full, with $930, his share of the Virgil's money.

When he can't find it, he crawls across the floor and checks under his mother's dresser. No money there either, and he isn't surprised. Nothing's safe around this family. He stands up slowly, brushes the dirt and dust off his hands. His father's thin chest trembles.

In the hallway outside his parents' bedroom, Tariq bumps into Isabel. He thought she would've waited for him in the living room, but of course not. She *had* to follow him here. Had to see what he might do next. Smiling, he moves toward her, and she backs away into the wall.

"What's the matter with you?" she says.

"I don't know," he says, still smiling. "What's the matter with me?"

"He's your *father.*"

"He's a liar. Did you know that? He said my mother had gone to bed when—"

"She sleeps in your old room."

"Please don't interrupt me when I'm speaking," he says. He looks down at her stomach, which presses against the zippered fly of his crotch. Oh, he wishes their positions were reversed, that it was him backed up against the wall, supported, unable to crumple to the ground. Isabel smells faintly sour, like milk on the day it expires. He'd like to wash the smell off of her. Shampoo her hair, lather her back. When he brings his face closer to hers, she turns her head and looks blankly out the kitchen window. The purple dusk that lingered throughout the early evening has been swallowed, devoured by darkness. Wise of him to have waited, to have delayed, for as the Book says:

Surely in the watches of the night the soul is most receptive and words more telling.

Twenty-nine months of imagined scenarios, and not a single one took place here, in this darkened hallway, with these familial pictures on the walls, with Isabel wearing his little brother's Fatima T-shirt. Can't complain, though. You tussle with what is, and you do the very best that you can.

"I got these for you," he says as he digs into his pockets. "I went down to the corner. And to the Laundromat, too."

He pushes the magazines into her hands, giving them to her one at a time, so as to prolong this moment for as long as he can. He watches her face. The book, *Apartment Finder*, he saves for last, sliding it over the top. He pats his pockets. That's it. That's everything. If not for that fat Ecuadorian bitch, he would've had more, dozens more, flyers and piano keys, a thick catalog of choices that would overflow Isabel's arms and cascade to the floor.

"If you look right here you'll see that the magazine's pages are color coded according to neighborhood. If I was you, Izzy, that's where I'd start. Choose a place to live first, and then go on from there. There's no place that's off-limits, okay? Don't worry about prices." He doesn't tell her that he didn't find the Virgil's money, or that he failed to get the grams of coke from Baka—those are his problems, not hers. "I like Astoria," he says. "And I'd recommend a two-bedroom apartment. It'd be nice, that extra room. But all the final decisions are entirely up to you."

He can tell by her face that he's not explaining himself very well.

"Here's the thing about that second bedroom," he says. "We could put a sewing machine in there for you. And I'd like to use it as an office. I'd like to learn Arabic, you know? So I can read the Qur'an the way it's meant to be read. I bet that's something you never thought I'd want to do. Am I right? Never in a million years, right? But that's what I'm telling you. I'm different now. It's like I've got words overflowing my head." He looks away, suddenly embarrassed. "I'm going to need that office," he says. "There are things I've got planned. Impressive things."

"Did something happen to Alfredo?"

Tariq would sigh if he had the energy. "At least ask it right," he says. "Don't ask if something happened to Alfredo. Ask if I happened to Alfredo. You see what I mean? Ask if he's not here with you because of something I did to him."

She's crying now and it makes him want to slap her face. "Did you hurt him?" she says.

"Who?"

"Alfredo."

"Try again. Do it right."

"Did you hurt Alfredo?"

"No I did not. But thank you for asking me so directly."

The dog follows Tariq into the bathroom. Not exactly his first choice—he'd rather have Isabel behind him, with a big fluffy towel wrapped around her body—but hey, whatever, it's nice to have the company. The dog's paws click on the tiles as he makes his way toward the toilet bowl. It sounds like a typewriter without paper, the keys striking an empty roll. He looks over at Tariq—*what kind of rules are we dealing with here?*—before plunging his face into the toilet and drinking its water. Tariq thinks he should probably yell at the dog, but the little beast is probably mad thirsty, and besides, Tariq's got his own problems to manage. He stares at his cheek in the mirror. What a mess. With a wad of wetted toilet paper, he dabs at the little eggies of pus embedded around the gash. Maybe if Isabel doesn't get too close, she won't see anything . . . but that's ridiculous and he knows it. Girl's a first-class noticer, just like himself.

Blood dribbles out of his nose. It's all this stress. He's been bugging out over appearances, over money, over trying to set everything up perfectly, trying to make all the right moves, and it's too much, he wants to scream, he wants to smash his face against the mirror. He grips the handles of the sink. Leaves little comets of blood all over the family's face towel. *Don't worry,* he tells himself. *Calm down. So you got blood on the towel? So what? Mama does laundry on the regs and it's not like you got hepatitis or HIV or some other junkyard shit. Right, doggy?*

The dog doesn't answer. Like a little explorer, he steps into the bathtub. His paws go *click, clack. Click, clack.*

Tariq walks out of the bathroom and into an apartment blazing with light. Every switch has been flipped, every lamp turned on. Bulbs shine in the kitchen and in the hallway and especially in the living room, where he finds Isabel haloed, scrutinizing a cordless phone. She's stopped crying and it looks to him as if her face has taken on an erotic intensity.

"You sweet little innocent girl," he says. He sits down next to her

207

on the couch, takes her flaccid hand in his. As he stares at her fingers, he imagines a world without razor blades, a world where Isabel would surely be the hairiest woman alive. He used to hound her about it all the time, teasing her until she started shaving her legs every day and waxing her forearms and upper lip and privates. She'd even Bic her fingers, so that when he held her hand he'd feel between her knuckles a dark gunpowder of stubble. Now, however, that powder explodes out of the skin. It feels wonderfully soft under his thumb, and for the life of him he can't understand why he ever asked her to shave.

"His phone's going straight to voice mail," she says. She won't look at him. The rental magazines lie next to her on the sofa in a humiliatingly small pile. "If you know where he is—"

"He went to go see a girl," Tariq says. "You happy now? That's all I know."

"Just tell me the truth. Please. I promise I won't be mad at you."

"Does this kind of thing happen a lot? Does he usually not come home until late at night?"

She pulls her hand away from him.

"Here's my question," Tariq says. "If he's working all the time—look at me. If he's working all the time, then where's all the money? You know what I mean, Izzy? Where's the *money* at? Why you two still living with my parents?"

"He has to take care of your father," she says.

"Or does my father take care of you? Is he the babysitter? Does he stay up with you all night till your hardworking man comes home? Come *on*. This has to have occurred to you. If it was just the two of you in your own apartment, you'd be staying up all night by yourself. Without any distractions. And then maybe you'd get to wondering what that boyfriend of yours is up to. Maybe you'd open your *eyes*."

The dog totters into the living room with his head slumped, as if he were ashamed to be interrupting them. And rightfully so! Tariq flies off the couch and backs the whimpering dog into the kitchen. While he's up, he decides to turn off all these romance-murdering lights. It's been a long time since he's been able to do this. Because of him, because of his hand on a switch, Con Edison's power meters are quivering. In control, reluctant to stop, he flips the switch in the kitchen on

and off. Up on the ceiling, his mother's decorative light covering, an insect crematorium, glows and then darkens.

On his way out of the kitchen he turns off the hallway light and then all the lamps in the living room so that only the television's bluey glow remains. While he was gone, Isabel maxed out the volume and changed the channel to a sports highlight show, a program she apparently thought might interest him. He turns it off.

"What happened to Winston?" he asks. He's whispering; under this burden of darkness he feels chastised into lowering his voice. "Did he go home?"

"Yes."

"Did you ask him to stick around? Were you worried I might come home alone?"

"What do you want me to say?"

"Why didn't you go somewhere? You gotta have someplace you could've gone. The movie theater, maybe? See? I remember. You could've gone to the movie theater, but you know what I think? I think maybe you wanted to be here when I came home. Maybe you knew I'd be showing up all by my lonesome."

"No," she says. "I never thought you'd be alone."

"Well, guess what?"

He kneels down on the carpet in front of her. She lifts her chin, stares into the empty space above his head. She can't see, he realizes. She can't see a thing and maybe she thinks he can't either, but he can, he can, his eyes have been institutionally adjusted to the dark. He sees everything: the outline of her jaw, the bulge of her stomach, her thighs pressed together, her hands bunching the fabric of her sweatpants. Her breath thickens as he peels off her socks. Innocent girl. She smells like the soil that anchors a potted plant. He grabs her sweatpants by the waist, and because she's still holding on, bunching the fabric, when he pulls them off, her body comes toward him. Her face hovers above his. Her legs feel cold and rough. His hands find the lanyards of brutalized skin, where the kitchen knife tore up her calves. You see? There are no secrets. His hands creep up, toward her thighs. Bruises dapple the skin. So fast, as always. Back in the day, he'd pull off her pants in the backseat of his van and he'd see his blue thumbprints all over her body and he'd be amazed, proud of his passion, that this was something he did just by squeezing and grabbing and pinching.

When he pulls down her white cotton panties, he finds underneath them another pair of white cotton panties. *Isabel,* he thinks. *You are an odd bird.* He pulls down the second pair, halfway expecting a third, but instead he uncovers the rich dark thicket of her pubic hair. No shaving here, it seems. But that's fine with him. That's even better. He leaves both pairs of panties tangled around her knees. He drinks the air coming out of her mouth.

She goes limp on the couch. Her bones have turned to soup and in order to reanimate her, to bring her back into her body, Tariq sticks her hand down the front of his pants. She screams. Her neck tightens as she calls out for help, bellows the name of his mother. *Lizette! Lizette!* He covers her mouth with his hand. He wants to tell her that Love will deliver her this instant from herself, and he wishes she'd understand that he *is* Love, her custodian and witness, sending his soul forward in order to save her from all of this, from his brother, from his parents, from this apartment strung with parrots and given to wickedness, from a life of mediocrity, bewilderment, the fire that is closed in, the spider's flimsiest of houses, the crack of doom, the stone-hurling wind. She bites the fleshy web of his palm, but he can always push down harder. The wings of her nostrils expand. A violent trembling swims to the surface of her face.

Outside the window, cars wash by, their headlights bleaching the walls. Tariq lifts his hand and Isabel calls out for Lizette. And so it's here we go again. One more time. His hand reclamped on her mouth.

He tells her to unbutton his jeans. He wishes he had a belt she could unbuckle, just to delay delay delay, but that's life. Fishkill didn't give him a belt, and besides, he's running out of time. He reaches into his pocket and pulls out the beeper. He tries to slide off its plastic top, but he can't manage it with only one free hand. For leverage, he pins the beeper under his chin and yanks on it. But it won't budge. He tries using his teeth, which doesn't work either. Isabel's fingers hang limp at his waist. He bangs the beeper against the carpeted floor, and then against the sofa's metal leg. He's banging and banging, a steel driver swinging his hammer, and a loud crash comes out of the kitchen—it sounds like pots getting thrown to the floor—and Tariq wonders if he's made this happen, if his banging in the living room created this unseen clattering in the kitchen.

The beeper cracks open. Little round pills spill across the carpet. He

picks one up and wants Isabel to swallow it, but that requires taking his hand off her mouth, which gives her another opportunity to cry for help, but he tells her that if she does, he's going to drag her naked out of this apartment and throw her down four fucking flights of stairs.

Eyes narrowed, her face takes on a desperate, animalistic craving. He slips the pill between her lips, but she spits it back out at him. Her nails dig into his neck. Bewildered, waiting for Love to deliver him this instant from himself, he hits her in the mouth. Blood seeps between her teeth, fills the fold of her fat lower lip. This too she spits out. She sprays her blood all over the crotch of his jeans.

He rips open the front of her shirt, something he never wanted to do. Her breasts hang out, heavy and dark-nippled. Faint blue veins striate the skin. Below these breasts bulges a monstrous stomach, its button popped out like the knob to a door. And for the child behind this door, floating upside down in foul, contaminated juices, the Book says:

> *He is fully knowledgeable of you as He produced you from the earth, and since you were a foetus in your mother's womb. So do not assert your goodness.*

Tariq pushes down on her stomach. He has the sense that someone is watching him, but of course someone is watching him. Someone is always watching. He's crying. He can't believe it. Sobs clog his airway. He chews on the collar of his shirt. He gives up. He hates everything. Okay? He hates *everything.*

"You don't want to hurt me here," she says, trying to push his hands off her stomach. Tears leak out of her eyes, as if she just walked into a howling February wind. But her voice is steady. "Do you understand? You don't want to hurt me here."

He pushes down harder on her stomach. If he tried to penetrate her now, with this wilted dick of his, the head and shaft would double back on itself and flop down uselessly between his legs.

"You don't want to hurt him," she says. She whispers this, hisses it into his ear with the spirit of dizziness. "You want to hurt me. You want to hit my face. Do you understand? You want to make me as ugly as you are."

"Stop it."

"You're a faggot," she says. "You hear me? You're a pathetic faggot. Look at you. Look at how ugly you are. Who cut your cheek open? Your boyfriend? Your boyfriend cut your cheek open, you little fag?"

It takes three blows in the exact same spot—the bulging cheekbone, just below her right eye—before she cries out in pain. He backs away, trips over the air mattress. Something stirs inside of him. He takes a handful of pills off the carpet and gnashes them between his teeth. He watches her breathe.

She doesn't call out for help, but Jose does. Behind his closed door, spread out on the bed, or maybe crawling across the floor, burning his elbows on the carpet, Jose screams out the name of his wife.

He hurries to the bathroom—the apartment's smallest, calmest place—and on his way there, passing through the kitchen, he finds the trash can turned over. The black garbage bag has been ripped open, its contents spilled out across the floor. The dog gnaws on a chicken carcass. Tariq tries to pet him, but he moves away angrily. Too busy, too hungry. As the dog rips meat from bone, the carcass's jellied husk slides across the tiles.

The bathroom smells terrible. Tariq thinks that it's him, something foul and terrible oozing out of his body, but when he pulls back the shower curtain, he sees that the dog took a shit in the tub. One more mess to clean up. He pumps liquid hand soap on the pile of shit. While the bath runs, he sits on the edge of the tub and listens to the water rushing out of the faucet. He reads the label on the hand soap. *Lavender Blossom. Delicately scented. List of ingredients. Directions for use.* When he finishes reading the label, he starts over and reads it again.

When he gets out of the bathroom, he sees his mother standing at the kitchen counter. Keeping her back to him, she drops frozen sofrito cubes into a small pink hand towel. Down by her feet, the dog chews on a chicken bone in the midst of an entire day's worth of garbage: yellow grains of rice, batteries, a shampoo bottle, cucumber peels, coffee grounds, a water-damaged issue of *Entertainment Weekly,* a moldy tomato, bread crusts, crumpled Lotto tickets, sections of the *Post,* a

dented can of Goya beans, a near-full package of Oreo cookies. A brown liquid oozes out of the garbage bag and streams across the linoleum.

"I'm sorry, Mama. I'll fix this."

She twists off the top of the hand towel. With its belly sagged down with cubes, it looks like a pink Chinese dumpling. She carries it into what is now considered her room, where Isabel lies on the bottom bunk, her hair on the pillow, her face turned to the wall. She doesn't roll over when Lizette hands her the towel. Lizette whispers something in Spanish—something Tariq can't quite hear—and pulls the covers over Isabel's shoulders.

When his mother comes back out into the hallway, she seems to have trouble looking at him. She squints. Her sleep mask hangs from a ribbon around her neck. He wants to tell her, again, that he's sorry. He wants to ask her about mops and brooms and vacuums and paper towels and spray bottles of disinfectant.

"The dog's gonna choke on that bone," she says. "It'll shatter and get stuck in his throat."

She goes back into her room, closing the door behind her. Somewhere in this world there is a factory, Tariq thinks, and this factory only makes doors designed to be slammed in his face. The phone is ringing.

An hour later. Maybe more. The phone is ringing. His brother. He tells Tariq to come down to Papi's old store right away. Use the alleyways, he says. Come in through the bodega's back door. He speaks rudely, which is just like him. Unappreciative of the danger he's in. Tariq hangs up.

The phone is ringing. It rings and rings

and rings and rings. He snaps off the antenna. He pulls the cord from the wall.

12

Dogfight

Alfredo runs upstairs into the candy store, cops three cigars, runs back down into the basement, and, with a nervous grin, distributes those cigars, as if this were a dress rehearsal for Christian Louis's world premiere. Here. Take one. Take one. The cigars—cheap, thin, black—are called Dutch Masters and they should only cost $1.25, *maybe* $1.50, but Max, who's in an incredibly pissy mood tonight, has been selling them for two fucking dollars apiece. And Alfredo's been buying them anyway. What else is he gonna do? Dutch Masters come with an extra layer of skin, a tobacco leaf rolled around the stogie, which makes them harder to roll, which makes them the preferred apparatus of the weed-smoking connoisseurs down in this basement. He hands the cigars to K-Lo, Jossie, and Timmy P., the three nimble-fingered experts. Each one sticks the entire Dutch in his mouth and coats it with saliva, gets that tobacco dermis moist and removable. If Dutch Masters came with balls, these dudes would be fondling them, but no one makes that easy comparison, or at least no one says it out loud, because these dudes—like the Rembrandts and Vermeers from whom the cigar gets its name—are *artistes*. (Fancy-pants pronunciation preferred.) Besides, there ain't no reason to be thinking dirty thoughts. No reason to get all negative. There's weed to be smoked! Each expert peels off his tobacco leaf and hands it to somebody else—

Marc Franschetta, Jeff Hernandez, Billy Fitzgerald—apprentices who cup the leaf in their hands and breathe on it heavily, keeping it soft and pliable for the rewrap. Next up: splitting the stogies' spines. Penknives work nicely here, as do the tips of scissors, but K-Lo, Jossie, and Timmy P. all use their extra-long pinky nails. Tobacco guts get dumped onto the floor, which, Alfredo thinks, Max ain't gonna appreciate. Weed is broken up. Stems and seeds removed. Each expert stuffs their Dutch full of herb, rolls it tight, and—yo, let me get that skin back—wraps it back up. Now here's the hard part. K-Lo, Jossie, and Timmy P. start saying, *No, no, no, no* and *Hold up, hold up* because the men down here—Rick Sprinkle who sells perfume knockoffs on the street, Paulie Guns who sells heroin, Sean Lau who escorts escorts, Virgin Light whose real name no one remembers, Rhino who's recently come into some opium, Forest Hills David, Soft-Core Jonas, Lee who came all the way out here from Staten Island, Winston, Alex Hughes, Bam-Bam Hughes, the ghost of Curtis Hughes, even the apprentices Marc, Jeff, and Billy—all converge on the Dutch Masters. But the Dutches ain't ready. Still moist, if prematurely smoked, they would droop like wet noodles. Back up, people. Back up. Everybody's gonna have to be patient, an attribute—a virtue, if you ask Alfredo—that's been in short supply thus far.

"Yo, Alfredo. Where's this dog of yours at?"

"Yo, Alfredo. Where's your brother at?"

"Yo, Alfredo. What the fuck is up with them corny-ass shoes?"

Alex and Bam-Bam Hughes haven't punched Alfredo in the face yet, which he thinks is a pretty good indication that they either don't hold him responsible for Curtis's death or that Baka didn't tell them about the Vladimir mugging. Because when it comes to punching people in the face, Alex and Bam-Bam are not the type to bide their time. They huddle in the center of the basement, near the makeshift ring, arguing over which one of them should drag Diana upstairs. They worry that once the Dutches get sparked, the pooch might get blazed. It's not like anyone would slip a stogie between her drool-slicked jaws, but she could catch a contact high, could start giggling and craving Cheetos, rendered useless for her upcoming dogfight. A German shepherd with steeple-shaped ears, she needs to get taken out of stupefaction's way, and yet neither brother wants to miss his chance to get stupefied. They got brain cells to kill, shit to forget.

How do brothers fairly decide who has to go and who gets to stay? They start with the primary stratagem of intrafraternal diplomacy: rock-paper-scissors. When that doesn't work—each brother keeps throwing down rock—they turn to the primary creed of potheads around the world: *Ah, fuck it.* They'll both stay down here and get blazed. It'll be fine. They figure if there's one dog alive who's built up an immunity to THC, it's gotta be Diana.

Neck extended, snout in the air, she paces inside her ring like an uppity movie star, reluctant to sign autographs. The men down here watch her indifferently. Almost everyone plans to bet on Alfredo's dog because pit bulls carry more gangster cachet than German shepherds, because Diana seems too snooty for dogfighting, because, primarily, Alfredo's dog hasn't shown up yet and imaginations grow fat on the unseen. The guys down here have endowed the pit bull with four rows of fangs, a set of titanium nuts, a two-pack-a-day smoking habit, a rap sheet going back to juvie, a tail shaped like a swastika. Diana's tail? You kidding? It's fuzzy and droops off her ass. The bottom of it drags across the floor as she sniffs the cardboard boxes demarcating the ring's boundaries. Stacked waist high, the boxes are full of Max Marsh-mallow's heavier inventory—bottles of laundry detergent, cans of Goya beans—and Diana presses her nose to the cardboard, as if she can smell the frijoles negros inside.

Dry at last, the Dutch Masters get sparked. Paulie Guns pulls out a Zippo, for which he gets roundly mocked. You out of your mind, Paulie? The butane contaminates the flavor. Even the apprentices know that much. Three Dutches make their way through three separate ciphers. They pull beautifully. With a Dutch pinched between his fingers, Rick Sprinkle talks and talks and talks about some calling card scam until his boy Rhino yells at him to stop sleeping on that shit and pass it along. Chastened, Sprinkle takes two extra hits and the tip of his Dutch glows red like a pimple. He passes it on to Soft-Core Jonas, who intentionally coughs out the smoke, hoping to dilate his lungs.

"Don't be blowing that shit at the dog," Bam-Bam warns.

"Where else is it supposed to go?" Jonas says, and it is a fair enough point. Diana's ring is in the middle of a basement without windows or ventilation, and the haze—with no place to go but everywhere—spreads its fuzzy tentacles outward, drops down into all corners, wraps itself around the leg of a rickety card table, fills lungs, fills nostrils,

climbs the stairs into the candy store, and creeps up the rungs of a wooden ladder that leads to a pair of metal grate doors. These doors, the basement's only exit besides the stairs into the store, open up onto the sidewalk for deliveries; scattered around the borough, they are the kind of doors Isabel always makes Alfredo step around when they're walking together down the street.

A Dutch comes his way, but he passes it on, unsampled. Alfredo doesn't need weed softening his synapses, not with all the shit he has to juggle: the mounting impatience in this basement, Max Marshmallow's regret, the Impala full of cops parked across the street and waiting for Alfredo's go-ahead. But he can't give that go-ahead till the guest of honor arrives. And if Tariq doesn't come? If he never shows up? Then Alfredo will have gone to all this trouble, ass-fucked all his friends, for nothing. More important, if Tariq doesn't show up—these questions come straight from the Department of Worry in bold, fourteen-point font—then where the hell is he? And what's he doing? And where's Isabel in all this? It has been over an hour since Alfredo last heard from his brother. Alfredo called and called, and the phone rang and rang, until *something happened,* and all Alfredo could hear was the dead dial tone of his parents' line, a nasal sound, an auditory cousin to the G-flat hum of the Emergency Broadcast System, a sound of panic, of disaster, of terrorist attacks and nightmares come true.

The Dutch returns to Alfredo, smaller than before, and this time he does not pass it along. Not because he wants a toke—it's the last thing he needs—but because he's distracted. His eyes are closed, his ears cocked. He looks at the ceiling, and slowly, one by one, so does everyone else. Footsteps creak on the floorboards above their heads.

"About fucking time," Jossie says. "I'm not trying to wait around here all night."

The footsteps keep creaking. The men follow the sound blindly, their faces upturned toward the ceiling and its pink clouds of foam insulation. Stoned, their mouths hang open, as if they were watching an airplane descend toward LaGuardia.

Alfredo fights his way to the front of the crowd, but just as he feared, just as the pessimists expected, this isn't Tariq plodding down the stairs, but a poorly goateed white kid named AIDS.

When the groan goes up, AIDS puts his hands in the air and says,

"What'd I do?" He wasn't even going to come tonight, thinking his friends don't really like him (his nickname is *AIDS*, for chrissakes), but his mother doesn't want him spending his Saturday nights alone, playing Xbox, eating junk food, and so she hectored him out of the house. *Where are your friends, honey? What are they up to tonight?* When he got to the bodega, the lights were off and the sign in the window turned to CLOSED. He felt relieved to be able to go home, back to his room, back to his *Halo*, but just as he was about to turn around, an old man thrust his puffy-cheeked face out the door and asked what's what. AIDS froze. He assumed there was a secret password that (of course) no one had told him about. When he stammered something about a dogfight, the old man told him to go around to the back of the store. Which was just so cool! AIDS felt like a Prohibition gangster as he hopped over the fence into a dead-grass backyard. The old man swung open the back door and led him through a little railroad apartment and into the bodega and now here he is. Walking into a basement full of disappointment. "What'd I do?" he says. He doesn't know. He never does.

"Yo, Alfredo," says a voice from the haze. "When the fuck's this dog of yours gonna get here?"

Alfredo goes upstairs and buys beer at two times the regular cost. Olde E, Bud Light, Natty Ice, Modelo Especial.

"Thanks," says a different voice from the haze. "But when the fuck's this dog of yours gonna get here?"

He goes back upstairs and buys snacks for the stoned. Drake's cakes, Airheads, plantain chips, quarter waters.

"Thanks, but . . ."

He goes back upstairs—his calves starting to burn—and buys another Dutch, which he brings straight over to Rhino. He asks Rhino if he has any of that rumored opium on him, and if so, would he mind rolling a Dutch and sprinkling some of it over the herb. Opium is a rarity around here and Alfredo hopes the mere sight of it, the mere *smell* of it—in this windowless basement full of young men, cheap beer, and its flatulent aftereffects—will compel people to stick around, as the promise of crème brûlée might keep bored dinner guests in their chairs. Until, of course, the spoon scrapes the bottom of the dish. Until, of course, the O-laced Dutch gets smoked down to the quick.

"Sorry," Rhino says. If he has any opium, it's gonna stay in his

pocket, wrapped up in butcher's paper. "But yo, listen—why don't you just call your brother?"

"The phone's been disconnected."

"Then go fucking get him," Alex says.

Only three blocks separate the Batistas' apartment from Max's candy store, but Alfredo feels reluctant to traverse those streets at night. Look at the grief-puffed eyes of Alex and Bam-Bam Hughes. Check out how high their shoulders are hunched. It's a scary world out there.

"This is a *dogfight*," Alfredo whines. "Shit isn't *supposed* to start on time, know what I mean?"

No one knows what he means. None of the guys down here even *pretend* to have been to a dogfight, except for Jeff Hernandez, who pretends to have been to all sorts of things (he also claims to have invented the "Jingle Bells/Batman Smells" song). Before anyone arrived, Alfredo put a strip of duct tape in the center of the ring, dividing it in two. He isn't sure if that's protocol, but a basketball court has a center line, so maybe a dogfighting pit does too. Who knows? Should the ring be built over a tarp, to keep blood off the floor? What about referees, judges, a bell clapper? Is betting handicapped? Should there be an undercard, a pair of roosters pecking each other to death, a bikini-clad kitten parading a poster board with the number of the round? Nobody knows. But they do know there should be two dogs: it's the without-which-there-ain't-shit of dogfighting. The guys down here don't need rap videos or DMX lyrics to tell them that.

"This is fucking bullshit," says a voice from the haze. It becomes a refrain, a refrain that circles the room twice as fast as any herb-stuffed Dutch. It's fucking bullshit that Alfredo's dog ain't here yet, that they've all been standing for hours, that they work shitty jobs at RadioShack and Foot Locker, that the weekend's already half over, that no one brought cards for Spades, that no one brought dice for Cee-lo, that they still live with their mothers, that going to high school sucked, but not being in high school sucks worse, that the Mets missed Clemens, that the weatherman predicts rain, that there ain't any bitches down here except Diana pacing inside her ring, and, speaking of which, it's fucking bullshit that she's in there at all, getting mad comfortable, chilling in that cardboard arena before the fight starts, which probably gives her like a totally unfair advantage.

"Bullshit," Bam-Bam says.

Winston steps on Rhino's relatively new sneakers. Rhino bought them at a discount from David, who stole them from the Foot Locker he works at in Forest Hills, and now—would you look at this?—they've got a big black scuff on them. When Rhino starts bitching, Winston asks him what does he expect, walking around in white fucking shoes for crying out loud. After he says this, Winston's eyes bug out of his skull a little bit farther than usual, as if his mouthing off has surprised even himself. Maybe, Alfredo thinks, Winston is at long last growing some balls. Maybe with Mike Shifrin somewhere outside this basement Winston has got enough to worry about and doesn't need Rhino and his bitching on top of it—but that's impossible, Alfredo reminds himself, because he never told Winston about Baka's intelligence report. Alfredo didn't want to overburden his friend, didn't want more hair falling out of his head. Whatever the impetus behind Winston's newfound moxie, it doesn't seem to matter to Rhino. He knocks the beer out of Winston's hand, the can sprays what looks like bile all over Billy Fitz's jeans, and so Billy shoves Marc Franschetta, not because Marc did anything, but because Billy's Irish and Marc's Italian (third generation, but still: one keeps a shamrock in his wallet, the other drives a souped-up Camaro), and the both of them are convinced they're supposed to hate each other and administer headlocks whenever the opportunity presents itself, and because the opportunity has officially presented itself, there is more shoving, more screaming, more beers knocked out of more hands, which strikes Alfredo as a very good thing, since a fight—even one between people, not dogs—will at least keep his friends entertained. No such luck, Dito. Max Marshmallow appears on the stairs, wrinkling his nose. He wears his new gray sneakers, a pair of khaki pants clasped, in the manner of all old men, well above his waist, and a linen button-down shirt—Max all pimped out for his return to the world of shady goings-on, a return that has so far been less triumphant than dispiriting.

"I want everybody out of here," he tells Alfredo.

"Don't worry about a thing," Alfredo says. Guilt prevents him from looking Max in the face. Alfredo doesn't know what's going to happen tonight, doesn't know if Baka or Shifrin or Tariq are ever going to show up, but he does know that there are three DTs parked in an Impala across the street and they're busting in here, no matter what.

And once they do, it'll be trouble for Max. *Can't be running dogfights in your basement,* the law books say. Or something like that. He'll probably lose the store *and* the apartment behind it. The couch, the TV, the toilet with the handle that still sticks, the crystal dish overflowing with butterscotch candies—Alfredo worries that it'll all be corded off with yellow tape and then taken away. Auctioned off to law-abiding citizens, to fill the city's pockets. "You gotta trust me," he tells Max's chest. "I've got this all under control."

"Exactly *what* have you got under control?" Max says.

"Maybe I oughta buy some more Dutches off you. Get these guys to mellow out a bit."

"How much money you think I lost from closing the store tonight?" His Adam's apple protrudes violently. "All the shit I coulda sold, but didn't. How much money you think that is?"

"Let's go upstairs," Alfredo says. "You got any of those little apple pies? I'll buy them off you for three dollars apiece."

"I wanted a poker game," Max groans. What he has instead is a mob of thugs who expect violent entertainment and who have so far been denied. Like a leaky gas stove, these young men will be easily ignited. He sees his store, his home, his shingles-scarred body erupting in a giant, orange, billowing ball of fire. If only he would've gotten his poker game! There would've been cigar smoke instead of reefer smoke. He would've been able to kibitz in the purest sense of the word: sit just beyond the green-felt table and, with much tongue clucking and head wagging, offer his expertise on how best to bluff and false bluff, how to tease the pot, look at your cards, stack your chips, and time your bathroom breaks. "This," Max says as a do-ragged kid hocks up a loogie and *spits it onto his floor,* "is not what I had in mind."

"My brother could be upstairs right now," Alfredo says. He imagines Tariq in the fence-enclosed yard behind the store, banging on the screen door as if it were keeping secrets from him. If he gives up, if he goes to the front of the store with the dog on a leash, then he'll be seen by the police, who won't hesitate to nab him right then and there. Which isn't exactly ideal. Alfredo wants his brother cuffed up and sent back to Fishkill, sure, but he wants that shit to go down when he says it can go down. "While you're here messing with me," Alfredo says, "my brother could be upstairs trying to get in."

"I want them going out that way," Max says. He points to the

wooden ladder that leads up to the metal cellar doors. "Right now. Send them out that way. To the street. I don't want these animals tramping through my store. Send them out onto the fucking street."

"Ten minutes," Alfredo says. "Please. Just give me ten minutes. As a favor to our friendship." Max checks his watch, which Alfredo interprets as a positive sign. He knows he needs to talk whiter, show Max that the two of them are on the same side. "I'm asking for ten minutes, that's all, and if my brother isn't here by then, if we're not making money by then, I'll personally kick each of these assholes to the curb."

Across the street, Officer Lopez returns with bounty. Three sodas and three shish kebabs, purchased from the halal vendor around the corner. Whoever goes out and buys the food gets to sit shotgun. These are the rules. But when Lopez pulls on the door handle, it pulls back, locked from the inside. He shifts the food and drinks to one hand. He pulls on the handle again, and again it pulls back. Behind the car's tinted black windows, Sergeant Wright and Officer Hutchison are snickering. They're bullies, these two, and Lopez knows all about bullies. A couple of years earlier, when asked in his academy interview why he wanted to become a police officer, Lopez—who, to his detriment, has always been overly honest (cf. the Unnecessary Marital Confession of 1998)—said he'd been picked on as a kid. Only when the cap came off the interviewer's red pen did Lopez realize how badly he'd answered. Might as well have said, *I have some scores to settle. Can I get a gun now please?* But he managed to recover, talked some bullshit about how he knew what it was like to feel voiceless, what it was like to feel powerless, and what it was like to feel, uh, disenfranchised, a word he remembered from a John Jay criminal justice course. The interviewer recapped his pen. Ruben Lopez became Officer Lopez. And here he is, still surrounded by snickering bullies. But he doesn't need a gun, or even a nightstick, to handle these two, not when he has access to what his communication books call reward power, the ability to confer valued material goods.

He passes to the front of the car, where he will be most visible, and leans against the hood. Hot sauce dribbles down his wrist. On top of each wooden skewer a golden dinner roll sits speared. Lopez decrowns one of the kebabs and tosses the bread into the street. A gift for the

birds when they wake up tomorrow morning. Next he'll throw away the meat, sliding it off the skewer piece by piece. Needless to say, this particular shish kebab—extra hot sauce, extra BBQ sauce, extra lemon juice—belongs to Wright. The passenger's side door swings open.

Inside the car, Lopez distributes the bounty. Because Wright and Hutchison are Coca-Cola enthusiasts, and because Lopez can be a consummate ball-buster himself, he gives them each a can of Sunkist.

"Come on!" Hutchison says through a mouthful of meat. He is the heavier of the two bullies, and the less cruel. "Orange soda?"

"Yeah, sorry about that," Lopez says as he pops the tab on his Coke. "I woulda got you one of these, but the Afghani only had one left."

Orange, incidentally, is the color of the day.

Before the shish kebabs, Lopez, Hutchison, and Wright ate some slices (pepperoni, cheese, Sicilian) at Gianni's, and before the pizza they ate some arepas (cheese, cheese, cheese) from the arepa lady on Roosevelt Avenue, and before the arepas they risked cliché and went to Dunkin' Donuts (large coffee, Boston Kreme; large coffee, jelly; large coffee and that's it, Wright's alcoholism having long ago obliterated his sweet tooth). It was at Dunkin' Donuts that they ran into the skinny little Hispanic runt of a drug dealer from the night before. When he saw them approach, a grin broke across his face and Lopez couldn't shake the feeling that the kid had been there a long time, sitting at a table by the window, nursing a Coolatta and waiting for them to show up.

"Where's Ringo?" the kid said.

While his partners waited on line for coffee, Lopez sat down at the drug dealer's table. The kid carried some serious luggage under his eyes, pouches of skin that looked as if they concealed more pouches of skin, the way good suitcases have secret zippered compartments. Lopez put the kid in his late teens, long overdue for a growth spurt and already unfairly old; he was probably one of those babies who hit the delivery table looking exhausted, knowing full well the best sleep of his life was behind him, left in the womb. His face, shiny with oil, reflected the weak light of the donut shop. His legs shook under the table.

"Nice jersey," the kid said.

Lopez nodded, unsure if the kid was fucking with him. Earlier in the evening, Wright and Hutchison, both of whom wore Piazza jerseys, had taken umbrage with Lopez's outfit: a time-worn blue and

orange Knicks jersey from the mid-1990s. *You ain't wearing a Mets jersey?* they asked. *On today of all days?* Lopez didn't know what to tell them.

"What's the name on the back?" the kid asked.

"Starks."

"That's what I thought," he said. "That's what I was *hoping.* You know, I used to have a Starks poster up in my bedroom. The one where's he dunking on Jordan? A lot of people never forgave him— Starks, I mean—for that game seven in ninety-four. You know the one I'm talking about? Against the Rockets? Where he missed all them shots? But the thing that people forget was that he was so money in game six that we never would've even have gotten—"

"I'm sure," Lopez said, "that you've got other people you can talk basketball with. Right? People who care?"

The kid rolled his eyes. "Friendly as always," he said. "Shouldn't there be four of you? Where's the other guy at? The Habib. He in the car? No offense or nothing, but I wanted to talk to him."

Lopez wished he'd asked, *Talk about what?* But instead, his vanity easily punctured, he said, "You don't wanna talk to me?"

"Well, the Habib last night—he wasn't nice or anything. But he wasn't an asshole, you know?" He let that make its way across the table. He was probably the kind of kid who thought he got away with more than he actually did. Too loved as a child, parents trying to compensate for those heavy black bags under his eyes, no one around to call him on his shit.

"You wanna get paid?" Lopez said. "Is that it? You wanna get on the official CI list? Sing your song for cash?"

"Can you please keep your voice down?" The kid stared out the window into the parking lot. "Forget it. This was a mistake."

"Okay," Lopez said. "Let's start over." He put his hands flat on the table. He'd always been too aggressive, pushed too hard. Before joining the world's greatest police force, Lopez—who, like this kid, is a tad undersized—spent his mornings sucking down protein shakes, his Tuesday and Thursday nights in kung fu classes, his Saturdays out at a range on Long Island, firing thousands of rounds of ammo. Since becoming a police officer, however, faced with the day-to-day realities of the job, dismayed by the frequency (one might call it the eagerness) with which he unholstered his firearm, Lopez ditched the Wing Chun

and the target practice, met secretly with a department-sanctioned therapist, and, just as secretly, started reading communication books. (His favorite—*People Skills: How to Assert Yourself, Listen to Others, and Resolve Conflicts*—is sitting at the bottom of his gym bag, the book's cover wrapped up in brown paper.) He hoped the therapy and textbooks would make him a better, less gun-happy police officer, and not only has that proved true, but they've steadily strengthened his marriage as well. Sitting across from the drug dealer, Lopez tried what the textbooks call a reflective listening exercise. "Let me get this straight," he said, his voice stripped of all its hard, constabulary edges. "What I heard you say is that you've got something you want to talk to one of us about. Did I get that right?"

The kid scratched nervously at some dried-up custard on the table-top. "I've gotten myself into trouble."

"What kind of trouble?"

"The bad kind."

"Yeah, well," Lopez said. "That's the kind I see the most of."

"I'm fucked, man. Jesus fucking Christ, I am *fucked,*" and his hand flew to his forehead, his stomach, lengthwise across his chest, all four corners of the cross. He groaned, desperate and angry, as if he'd been up all night whipping his own back. Lopez sat up in his seat. He'd originally assumed the kid wanted to rat on somebody—most likely a rival drug dealer—but now things were looking significantly more promising. The kid didn't look like he was about to drop a dime on somebody else; he looked like he was about to drop a dime on *himself.* He had a confession to make. While the kid scratched at the tabletop, Lopez could almost see the Hughes homicide shimmering under the surface, golden scaled, ready to bite. Could almost see his long-coveted promotion to detective, his wife pouring him a congratulatory glass of Guinness when he got home, his mother's face when he called to tell her the news, the guys in the locker room whispering amongst them-selves: *You hear? Lopez collared the Hughes homicide. Lopez? Yeah, brought the guy in all by himself.* There it was, right in front of him, legs jiggling under the tabletop. Did the kid look like a killer? With the exception of his two young daughters, everyone as far as Lopez was concerned looked like a killer. If he just sat here, let silence work its interrogative magic, kept his line still in the water, then the kid would

come swimming toward him. Lopez put on his most neutral, most nonjudgmental face. A face designed to take on your burdens. To absolve all your sins. The kid frowned, as if he already had Lopez's hook caught fast in his mouth.

"The comedian drug dealer!" shouted Officer Hutchison. He stood over them, his round stomach hanging over the table's edge. "How long has it been? A whole day, maybe? Where's your boyfriend? He got you running errands? Jesus, kid, not to be critical or anything, but you look like shit. You're getting enough sleep, I hope."

Sergeant Wright, the skinnier and the meaner of the two bullies, sat down next to Lopez. He gave him a large coffee and a Boston Kreme, angling for shotgun privileges. Then he looked at the drug dealer and blew him a kiss.

Hutchison pointed under the table. "What the hell you got on your feet, kid?"

"Bowling shoes," Wright said without even having to look. Lopez dipped his head under the table to confirm; he hated that Wright had noticed this before he had.

"Bowling shoes?" Hutchison said.

"Don't you know anything about fashion?" Wright said. "Red pleather is the new shits."

"Let me ask you something," Hutchison said, but the drug dealer wouldn't even look at him. "Come Christmastime, my kid's gonna be begging me for a two-hundred-dollar pair of bowling shoes. But by then they'll be outta style, am I right? Save me some grief here. Six months down the line, what's gonna be the *new* shits? And don't tell me cowboy boots. I'd think you were messing with me."

"Kid tells me he's gotten into some kind of trouble," Lopez said.

"Tell him to call the police," Hutchison said. He took a bite of his donut, and like pus inside a zit, red jelly squirted all over his hand. "Number's nine-one-one. Think you can remember that?"

For the first time, the kid looked up at Hutchison. "You didn't want to get a whole box of donuts? Is that because you guys are undercover?"

"The comedian." Hutchison smiled. After he licked powdered sugar off his fingers, he took the kid's Coolatta and threw it in the trash.

Wright grabbed the baton. "If you're not eating or drinking any-

thing," he said. "If you're just sitting here, at an empty table, staring out the window—"

"Then that's loitering," Hutchison said, sounding almost sorry. "And loitering—"

"Is against the law," the kid said. He pushed himself out of his chair. "I get it. I understand."

Lopez followed him to the door. "Just tell me if this has anything to do with the Hughes homicide," he said softly. He felt the line about to snap, his future promotion about to dive back under the sea. "Just nod yes or no."

"This was a dumb idea," the kid said without turning around. "I didn't want to talk to *any* of you. I wanted to talk to the Habib."

Officer Ramsaran—the quartet's fourth, their Habib, their Ringo as the kid would have it—had taken the night off. He called the precinct, cashing in his emergency day, and then he called Lopez, providing the details. He'd been robbed. A humiliating experience for anyone, it is particularly hard on an officer of the law. *I would love to have caught 'em doing it,* he'd said, his voice shaking. He was taking the e-day, he explained, because he wanted to do some investigating himself, without departmental distractions or guidelines. He was going to ask the neighbors if they saw anything, ask pet store owners if they had any new customers, post some flyers on lampposts that would most likely be ripped off by tomorrow morning. *I'll do whatever you need,* Lopez promised. A Gulf War veteran with twelve years in the department, Officer Ramsaran was the kind of cop Lopez wanted to become: competent, well respected, an overall nice guy who was willing—and here's the big thing—to get ugly when he had to. Take for example an incident last year when, due to a contract dispute, the union delegate told all the men on the ground to go on strike. Nothing formal. No picket lines or hand-printed placards. Violent crimes were to be stopped— the union didn't want to *invite* chaos into the city—but the delegates did call for a moratorium on summons writing. There was to be no police work that generated revenue for the city. At least not until the contract dispute got settled. But an Egyptian officer named Kandil crossed that informal line and gave a woman a disorderly conduct ticket for calling him a pig. Everyone deferred to Ramsaran, Kandil's best friend on the force. And what did he do? In one heaping armful, he took everything out of Kandil's locker—sneakers, jeans, CD player,

family photographs, a gym bag that may have concealed some secret book wrapped up in brown paper—and he dumped it all into the hallway. It couldn't have been easy for Ramsaran—he didn't seem too happy doing it—but like Lopez tells his daughters when they complain about brushing their teeth or doing their arithmetic homework, *Hey, that's life. A series of crap you have to do, even if,* especially *if, you don't want to. That's what it's all about.* So if Ramsaran wanted Lopez to ask some questions, keep his ears open, turn over some rocks—then Lopez was going to do it. Even if it meant establishing a line of inquiry away from the Hughes homicide and toward a low-grade larceny. Even if it would never lead to a promotion, that much-coveted gold star pinned to the inside of his wallet.

"Hey, kid," Lopez said in the Dunkin' Donuts parking lot. "You know anything about a stolen pit bull?"

Lopez, Wright, and Hutchison are all plainclothes patrolmen who belong to the NYPD's Anti-Crime Unit, the department's version of chemotherapy, poisons injected onto diseased streets in order to kill deadlier, more dangerous poisons. They have the simplest job description—drive around and harass—and it's this watery vagueness that Lopez will miss least about the job if he ever makes detective. (*When* he makes detective. Power of positive thinking, Lopez.) Detectives have specific problems to solve, files to open and files to close; Anti-Crime drives the same streets night after night, harasses the same people, eats the same greasy food from the same greasy places. The lack of a concrete agenda can drive a man mad—it's driving Lopez mad—but it can also have its uses. With nothing to do, they can do anything they want. They can sit in a car outside a bodega and tear lamb meat off skewers and wait and wait and wait and wait and wait and wait for a skinny Puerto Rican to come out into the street with the thumbs-up, the green light, the A-okay.

"He ain't coming," Wright says.

"He's coming," Lopez says.

Originally the kid said he'd call them when Ramsaran's dog showed up. He said he didn't know where the dog was currently, but he knew where the dog would be: in the basement of a bodega in East Elmhurst. If they waited there, parked across the street, the kid would

call them as soon as the dog—and the thug who stole that dog—arrived. When he asked for the number to one of their cell phones, Hutchison laughed out loud. *Sure. You got a pen? My number's 1-917-GO-FUCKYOURSELF.* The new plan: as soon as the dog shows up, the kid will come out to the car, like a dinette waitress on roller skates, and deliver the message in person. Then Lopez & Co. swoop in and take back the pit bull. There's a couple of ways to go about this. They apply for a warrant, wait a couple of days, get it, storm into an empty bodega, make zero arrests, retrieve zero dogs, and finally explain to Ramsaran that they failed to retrieve his pit bull (which, most likely, would be dead by then) because they failed to react quickly enough; or they call up a judge, apply for an emergency warrant, drive over to the courthouse in Kew Gardens, pick up the warrant, drive back to East Elmhurst, storm into the bodega, make some arrests if anyone's still there, and scoop Ramsaran's dead dog off the ground; or they just go in and grab the motherfucker. After delivering the message, the kid's supposed to leave the door open. Because God forbid they're ever separated, Hutchison and Wright go in together. They enter through the front—under the pretense of grabbing a cup of coffee, because you don't need a warrant for *that,* do you?—and once inside the store, they hear some ruckus down in the basement and they decide to investigate. Lopez, working alone, will go around to the back and seal off the exit in case someone tries to sneak out the dogs. They'll even make some arrests for the overtime. And if they can't get prosecutions—any public defender able to find his own dick would use it to piss all over their probable cause and get the arrests thrown out of court—then so what? They will have pushed some ass-holes through the system. They will have harassed. They will have rescued the dog, which they will then deliver to a grateful Ramsaran, who doesn't even know they're out here, who will be so overwhelmed, so impressed, that—and this is Lopez's secret plan—when Ramsaran gets promoted to some elite investigative task force, he'll hand-select Lopez to be his partner. Why not? Why can't he think that way? Why can't he let his imagination go wherever it wants? All he's doing is sitting here and staring out the window and waiting for a fucking drug dealer, the world's scrawniest bouncer to lift the velvet rope and invite them inside.

"You know there ain't no way he's coming," Hutchison says. His skewer picked clean, he javelins it out the window. "You know we're just sitting here with our thumbs up our asses."

From the backseat Wright says, "He likes sitting with his thumb up his ass."

"Is it true?" Hutchison says.

"Hey, Lopez," Wright says. "Let me ask you something. You shave that space in the middle of your mustache? Or is that natural? How's that work, cause I've always been curious."

Lopez stares out the window, as if it renders him invisible. If he doesn't look at them, they can't see him. The bodega across the street is disconcertingly dark. Bodegas aren't *supposed* to be dark, Lopez thinks—not in this neighborhood, not at this time of night. He doesn't like it any more than he likes opening up his fridge at home and having the interior lightbulb stay dim. He blames the kid for some reason, as if the bodega's darkness were his fault, just as he always blames his wife for leaving the refrigerator door open too long. He adjusts his passenger-side mirror. Two figures have appeared in the glass: one a man-sized white guy, the other black and as big as a house. *They are closer than they appear,* the mirror warns.

"Hey, Lopez," Hutchison says. "You wanna stop them? Let's stop them. Ten bucks says they've got guns."

Wright sticks his head into the front seat, his face a few inches from Lopez's. "Let me guess," he says. "You think they're smuggling Chihuahuas in their pants. Is that right? For the big bad dogfight?"

"We gonna stop these guys, or what?" Hutchison says.

Lopez knows that both Hutchison and Wright have already assumed this night is going nowhere—no dog, no arrests, no overtime, no fun—and so they've put all quarterbacking responsibilities on him. The decisions are his to make, the fuckups will be his to bear. That way, when they go back to the 115th Precinct having done nothing all night but sit on their asses in a car without air-conditioning, Hutchison and Wright will be able to direct the full force of their prodigious ball-busting powers onto only one set of nuts.

At the entrance to the bodega, the two guys split up. The white guy continues down the block, while the big black guy goes around, as the others had done before him, to the back of the store. Neither holds

much interest for Lopez, because neither drags Ramsaran's dog on a leash.

"I'm almost sure those guys had guns," Hutchison says.

"Just so I got this straight," Wright says. "We're trying *not* to make collars tonight?"

"I want an empanada," Hutchison says. "Does anyone else want an empanada?"

"Hey, Lopez," Wright says. He rattles the headrest in front of him. Anti-Crime cops are not designed to be this still for this long. "Are you sleeping up there? Have you fallen *asleep*?"

"I'm awake," Lopez says.

"Oh thank God," Wright says. "Can you run the plan past me again? Because I'm confused. We wait here all night, yeah? That's the plan? We wait here and do nothing? Jesus fucking Christ, Lopez. Give up. Your little spic friend ain't coming back out."

"He'll come," Lopez says. He presses his tongue against the roof of his mouth to keep his teeth from grinding. "Any minute now."

The men in Max Marshmallow's basement look up. They hear a creaking, a groaning, the floorboards' lament, and like the basement dwellers in Samson's palace, each of these men fears the ceiling will come crashing down on top of their heads. Eyeballs nervously check exits. K-Lo, nearest the ladder, rests an uneasy hand on a rung. If anything happens, he'll climb up to the metal cellar doors, push them open, and escape out onto the sidewalk. Jossie and Paulie Guns and Virgin Light all retreat from the center of the basement and press their backs against the walls. The more paranoid—Alfredo among them—foresee rubble and rescue workers. The more dimwitted—Soft-Core Jonas among them—assume the sagging weight belongs to the Batistas' dog, a gargantuan, three-headed beast. Only Diana seems unaffected. As the ceiling groans, she paces inside her ring, her ears pressed neatly to the top of her head. She knows that whoever's coming down these stairs ain't got no quarrel with her.

"Look at all these beautiful faces," Baka says. He fills the stairway, poses as if someone were taking his picture. "What's going on? The big dogfight hasn't started yet? I'm not too late?"

"Not at all," Alfredo says as he picks his way through the people in front of him. This is his party and no matter who crashes the gate, he will act the gracious host. He wishes he had a Dutch to give him, fresh off the welcome wagon. He wishes Baka had a coat he could take and hang up on two hangers. "You're here just on time. We waited for you, matter of fact."

"How you doing? You doing good? Hanging in there?" Hands in pockets, Baka looks over Alfredo's head, scanning the room. "Where's your brother at?"

"You come all by yourself?" Alfredo says.

"You mean did I bring Pierre? Pierre of the busted grill? He's at home, thanks for asking. He's recuperating. He got himself hit—did I tell you this yet?—he got himself hit in the mouth with a bowling ball."

"Well," Alfredo says, "those things do happen." With a possessive, guiding hand, he steers Baka ringside, toward the cardboard boxes. A VIP view for a VIP guest. Not that there's much to see. A basement full of goons, smoking Dutches, drinking beers, eating candy bars, quoting from *The Big Lebowski,* and arguing, always arguing, about whatever binary they can think of: McDonald's/Burger King, Nas/Jay-Z, Shaq/Kobe, Marty/Dceve, Ron Jeremy/Peter North, the handball courts on Eighty-fifth vs. the handball courts at Travers Park. Alfredo looks around. K-Lo still lingers by the ladder, Sean Lau by the stairs. Lee, who came all the way out here from Staten Island, stands alone with his arms crossed in front of his chest. Rick Sprinkle tells a story no one is listening to; Forest Hills David picks up an empty shoebox off the card table and stares into it with a professional interest; Jonas looks like he's asleep on his feet. The only one who actually seems to be enjoying himself is Winston. The perfect cocktail party host, he works the room with a smile on his face, moving from clique to clique, making sure the awkward have fresh cans of beer to stare into. Since getting his own can knocked out of his hand, Winston has gotten another, which he seems to be spitting into instead of drinking from, as if every sip were being shown to Alfredo in reverse. That's weird. Alfredo looks into the ring to see if the dog is walking backward, growing younger— but nope, not at all. She's moving toward Baka. She trots over to his corner of the ring, where she deigns to sniff the fingers of his out-

stretched hand. Without a functioning adrenal system, Baka doesn't emit any fraidy-cat pheromones; there's no fear wafting off his considerable body, nothing that might antagonize the dog.

"A beautiful animal," Baka says, and Diana dips her head with false modesty.

"She sure is," Alfredo says. He watches jealously as Baka scratches behind her ears.

"And where's the pit bull at?" Baka says. "Or did this fine bitch eat him already?"

"Ha ha. No, no. Not yet, at least. The other dog's with my brother."

"Ah," Baka says. He frowns, looking more like a lion than ever. "And this is where I ask you again, like a fool, 'Where's your brother at?' And then you say, 'He's with the other dog.' And then I say, because I'm still such a fool, 'Okay, where's the dog at?' And then you say . . .'"

Alfredo is deciding how hard to laugh at this when he hears someone coming down the stairs behind him. He spins around, goes up on his tiptoes. But it's only Max, easing himself down by the handrail. Alfredo feels strangely disappointed. With Baka having just shown up, Alfredo hoped Mike Shifrin might follow, poisoned dagger in hand; it would confirm the ingenuity of his brother's plan, and by extension, just like the E-beeper, Alfredo's ingenuity in figuring it out. Fuck it. If Shifrin isn't going to show up on his own, then Alfredo will make him appear.

"Ha ha," Alfredo says as Baka continues to outline the Möbius strip of their hypothetical conversation. "You know what? Lemme borrow your phone and I'll call my brother up. See where he's at."

"What's wrong with *your* phone?"

"Juiceless," he says, patting his pocket. "I forgot to charge it last night."

Baka glowers at Alfredo, as if annoyed that he can't think of a good enough reason to turn down so simple a request. "Hurry that shit up," he says, handing Alfredo the phone. "I'm running low on minutes."

Alfredo hits the big green Talk button, and up pops a list of Baka's most recent outgoing calls. The screen is labeled History, as if this were a prime source document, yellowed at the edges. There are some names scattered in there—Amery, Jim, Pierre, Zach—but Alfredo isn't interested in any of them. Paranoid Baka would never enter a business associate's name into his cell, just as Paranoid Alfredo never saved

Baka's name to his own contact list. He scrolls through the list, looking for untagged numbers. Working quickly, he keeps the phone close to his chest, as if it were a half-decent poker hand. When he sees a number he likes the looks of—it's got a preponderance of fours, his father's lucky number—he dials it, knowing the call will never go through. Like a Podunk town in the Bible Belt, Baka's phone has no bars. The basement is a receptionless dead zone, but Alfredo presses the phone to his ear anyway. He's a pro at this by now. When, just as expected, the call fails to connect, Alfredo clicks the cell shut and hands it back to Baka.

"No dice?" Baka says.

"No service." Alfredo shrugs, as if to indicate he doesn't hold this against him. "You want something to drink? A Yoo-hoo or something?"

Instead of answering, Baka looks over Alfredo's shoulder, where a rumpus begins to take shape. Max Marshmallow is clawing at Forest Hills David's elbow, while David, his face contorted by a helpless smile, tries pulling his arm away. A marshmallow falls out of Max's mouth. It sits sticky and gooey on the basement floor, a white dented pillow. Mouth open, breathing heavy, Max grabs at David's wrist, and again David yanks his arm free. They play this game—clutch, release, clutch, release—all the way over to Alfredo.

"Yo, Dito," David says. "Tell this geezer to watch his hands."

"I caught him," Max says, his face red and pulsing. "I caught him. Going through boxes. Stealing."

"Check my pockets," David says. He spreads his arms out wide, pinned to the cross. "Check my fucking pockets *right now.*"

Thanks, but no thanks. Alfredo has already gotten into enough trouble going through other people's pockets—or unclipping beepers from belts as the case may be. He looks instead for Sean Lau, the escort's escort. He's probably got a hooker in the backseat of his car right now, and Alfredo wants to broker a deal. If he buys Max a handjob—he'll have to throw in a free Viagra, too—then maybe the old man will leave him alone for a few minutes. But Alfredo doesn't see Sean anywhere. He's gone back to work, it seems, snuck away without tendering regrets. Which is bad news for Alfredo's party. Like a barfly stumbling out of the men's room with toilet paper stuck to his shoe, Sean Lau has broken the seal. If anyone saw him go—*That dude's get-*

ting out of here, he's giving up on the dogfight?—then his exit will only be the first of many.

"You're out of time," Max says. He taps the face of his wristwatch. "Ten minutes later and I've got punk kids going through my merchandise."

"Man, fuck you," David says.

Max sighs, low and long-suffering. With only one marshmallow embedded in his cheek, his face seems lopsided, like a stroke victim's. He is an old man, and Alfredo, fifty years his junior, is jealous. Jealous of the wrinkles and liver spots, the red-rimmed eyes, the purple veins on the tops of his hands, the set of falsies he soaks in warm water at night. Oh, Alfredo thinks, to live so long that teeth turn to powder in your mouth!

Lee, who came all the way out here from Staten Island, claps Alfredo on the back and snaps him out of his reverie. "I think I'm gonna take off," Lee says.

"What? Already? Shit hasn't even started yet."

Lee shrugs, too polite to say he did not drag his ass all the way out to Queens to smoke Dutches and listen to Rick Sprinkle's stories. He came out here for the novelty of a dogfight, and that shit is looking increasingly improbable. If he leaves now and if he catches an E train right away, then he *might* make the 2:30 ferry back to Shaolin, *might* get home and be in bed before the sun comes up—Lee already swearing an oath, as many have sworn before, that never again will he make the trek out to Queens.

"Good," Max says. "Get out. Take your friends. You hear that, everybody? Dogfight's canceled!"

"Max," Alfredo says. "Please."

"Please my ass," Max whispers. "Don't make a jerk out of me. This is my store we're talking about. I *live* here. Understand what I mean? I'll call the police if I have to."

Alfredo wants to grab Max by the shoulders and scream in his face. Forget about yourself for a second. Consider Winston's safety. Consider Isabel, Christian Louis, the dry-bristled toothbrush waiting for me at home. Alfredo wants to duct-tape Max's mouth so he'll stop talking and Diana's mouth so she can't hurt anyone and the Hughes brothers' eyes so Alfredo doesn't have to look into them, and with any

leftover tape he wants to bind Lee's feet to keep him here, down in this basement, where Alfredo will whisper promises in his pink little ear. Sean left and now you're gonna leave and then everyone else is gonna leave, but you can't go, okay? I'm going to need you to listen to me very carefully: I'll do whatever it takes. Whatever it takes to keep you people down here. I'll tell jokes. I'll swallow fire. I'll spin plates, walk on my hands, juggle bowls full of goldfish.

"Just hold up," he tells Lee. "Stick around for a minute. I'll make this right."

As the weathermen predicted, the rain arrives. Fat drops *ping-ping* the metal cellar doors. Alfredo takes off his shirt and tosses it to the floor, as if this were a bathroom shower, not a meteorological one. With his jeans slung low, two inches of his lucky boxer shorts are visible. Made out of silk, with little teddy bears on them, the boxers were a gift from Isabel, paid for with her video store wages. Alfredo worries that these cuddly bears—especially the one in a bow tie, licking an ice cream cone—will draw some *ho snaps!* from the eighteen thugs, criminals, and tough guys crowding Max Marshmallow's basement, but on that score Alfredo is safe. No one looks at his boxers. They look instead at his bare-chested physique.

"Goddamn, Alfredo," Baka says. "You one outrageously skinny motherfucker." At three-hundred-plus pounds, Baka might be a less than credible source, but his judgment represents the consensus. Most of the guys down here have never seen Alfredo with his shirt off, and for those who have, like Winston, it's been a long, long time—circa tenth grade P.E. class. No one expected his ribs to jut out as much as they do. Nobody imagined his shoulders would be so narrow. "Do me a favor and turn sideways," Baka says. "I wanna see if you disappear."

"Yeah, yeah," Alfredo says.

The guys down here want to know if he's half Puerto Rican, half Ethiopian, if his nipples touch, if he needs to run around in the shower to get wet, if there's just one stripe on his pajamas, one belt loop on his pants. People do not usually play this game with Alfredo. He is too good at it, quick to snap back and unafraid of close-to-the-bone meanness. But tonight he ain't interested.

"Everyone get comfortable," Alfredo says. He walks over to the makeshift ring, where Diana lies flat and still on the floor, the base-

ment's cool cement under her belly. Sweat rolls down the bars of Alfredo's rib cage. He steps over a cardboard box, puts a tentative foot inside the ring. "I'm going to fight this dog."

"You're going to fight *our* dog?" Alex says.

Alfredo shrugs. "If that's okay with you."

Bam-Bam's eyebrows reach toward his hairline. On behalf of his brothers, both the living and the dead, he says, "Sure. Knock yourself out."

Diana stands up on wobbly legs. She yawns, and with her mouth swung open and her tongue uncurled, Alfredo can see deep inside her mouth, the dark corners, the fleshy punching bag at the back of her throat. He wishes he had his skull-crushing Timberlands instead of these tractionless bowling shoes. If he slips—it'll probably be on some blood, probably his own—he'll need to tuck his body into the fetal position, cover his neck with his fists, and wait for someone, anyone, to reach in and save him. Instead of looking at Alfredo, Diana watches the stairs, the way a jump shooter won't look at the hoop until the very last moment. Her ears pitch straight up into the air. Her body goes rigid, the tail hooked over her back like a scorpion's. Alfredo wants to call a time-out. He wants to step out of the ring, open up betting, buy himself a few extra minutes. He takes a peek behind him, plotting a possible escape route, and the dog charges. As she gallops toward him, he folds his body inward. He closes his eyes, covers his crotch with his hands, but Diana has already sailed past him. She claws at a cardboard box. She barks, again and again, and each time her head snaps forward and spit flies out of her mouth. The box tears open. Soup cans spill out all over Alfredo's shoes, a chicken noodle jailbreak. Diana retreats, then charges again, throws her irate body against another column of boxes. Her fangs are bared. She wants out of this ring; sensing this, everyone backs away, except for Alfredo, who stands paralyzed right next to her, close enough to feel the heat of her breath. His hands still cover his crotch. Through the fabric of his jeans, he pinches the head of his penis, to remind himself that it's still there. Diana's barking grows louder. She screams, *I'm down here you cunt, waiting for you, waiting all fucking night.*

Her challenge goes answered. No trick of acoustics. No thin echo down here. When Diana barks, she gets barks in return.

Tariq walks down the stairs, a leash snapped taut in his hand. Fight-

ing his way out of that leash is a dog, a pit bull, his eyes hot and enraged.

Lee slides his MetroCard back into his wallet.

Normally in an interrogation, or at least in the interrogations Alfredo's seen in the movies Isabel makes him watch, a long metal table separates the interrogator from the interrogee. Both parties sit in chairs, so that the interrogator, when frustrated, has something to throw against the wall. These chairs are usually cold and gray, in spirit if not in actuality. The room comes equipped with either a one-way mirror, streaked with grime, or a video camera, easily unplugged. These are the basics. Bonus features include blindfolds, polygraph needles, bright lights, tanks full of water, pinky-slicing shears, dental equipment, threats to one's family, interrogees dangling out of open windows, and games of Russian roulette in which the bullet has been discreetly palmed. Unfortunately for Alfredo, this basement has no chairs, no windows, no lie detector, no mirror, either one-way or two, and, for obvious reasons, he can't threaten Tariq's family. Alfredo can only ask questions, and hope to receive truthful answers.

"Where the fuck you been?"

The dog whips his head back and forth, those creepy human eyes of his straining to get out. Tariq holds him by the collar, even sits on his back as if riding a mythological beast, but the dog pulls him forward anyway. They inch closer to Alfredo, closer to the German shepherd on the other side of the room.

"Man oh man," Tariq says, admiring his dog. "Look at how strong he is."

"Where," Alfredo says, "have you been?"

"I'm sorry," Tariq says. "I can't hear you. Can you come a little closer?"

Alfredo stays where he's at. He shouts to be heard over the barking.

"Oh," Tariq says. "I got you now. Where have I *been*? I been at home. With the fam. Right where you left me."

"You been at home," Alfredo says. "This whole time."

"This whole time."

"And what have you been doing?"

"Praying!" he says, as if to say, *What else would I be doing?* His pupils

are dilated, as wide and dark as dirty old pennies. "I've been behind on my prayers today. All this running around."

"You start praying before or after you took some of that Ecstasy I gave you?"

"After," Tariq says. His face beams. "You are a terrific noticer, Dito. You are, excluding myself, the third-best noticer I know. Allah, of course, is the first. I took the drugs and *then* I prayed. Yes. Correct." He wraps a hand around the dog's mouth, and with only the German shepherd barking now, it becomes much easier for Alfredo to hear his brother. "It's against the rules. Drugs. It is strictly forbidden. The Book calls them intoxicants. The Book says they are a loathsome evil of Satan's doing."

"I bet," Alfredo says. "Did anyone outside see you come in here?"

"I used the alleyways to get to the back of the store. Just as you commanded. I found the key in the same spot Papi used to leave it in. Taped to the bottom of that potted plant. So his whores could sneak themselves in. You were probably too young for all that." He wears a faraway smile, as if recalling a party Alfredo hadn't been invited to. "Now let me ask *you* a question, Dito. How come you ain't wearing a shirt?"

Alfredo looks down at his chest, sees himself as his brother must see him. His ribs protrude as if he'd recently swallowed an open umbrella. His nipples are pink and embarrassingly small, set too close together on a chest that would belong more rightly to a prepubescent boy. There is no hair save for a thin trail that leads out of his boxer shorts and up to his belly button, an innie, unlike Isabel's, whom he desperately wants to ask about—*Is she okay? Was she asleep when you left?*— but he's afraid to say her name aloud. It'd give Tariq permission to say it, and the name would curdle in his mouth. Alfredo crosses his arms over his chest, to cover his exposed nipples, and maybe the dog interprets this as a sign of aggression, or maybe the dog's just mean, but either way, he throws Tariq off his back and flies at Alfredo's waist. Tariq pulls on the leash. The dog's teeth click against Alfredo's belt buckle.

"Look at how *strong* he is," Tariq says as he reels the dog in. "You gotta crouch down," he tells Alfredo. "You gotta get on his level. Show him your palms." Tariq cups his hands together, as if he were accepting

communion. Whole inches of the leash slacken. "Show a dog you've got no way to defend yourself and he'll love you forever."

"How much X did you take?"

"I been praying all night. Know what I figured out? Only Allah is perfect. Me? It's like I'm fighting on a crooked path, trying to get better, purer, but I just don't know . . . It's hard to explain." The leash bites into his hand, cutting off blood flow. His fingertips whiten. "It's like I'm either a work in progress, or it's already over for me. Like not in this lifetime. You know? Like maybe I'm broken. Maybe there's something wrong with me that can't get fixed. Maybe I *can't* get better."

"What did you do?"

"Crouch down," Tariq says. "Show this pup your palms and let's see how he reacts."

Baka approaches the brothers hunched over, legs splayed apart, fingers twitching above his hips as if he were a Wild West gunfighter. "Put 'em up," he orders Tariq. "Put 'em up, put 'em up—you dirty, dirty rat."

"You bring the Russian with you?" Tariq says.

"See?" Baka says. "This is what I'm talking about. No, 'Hey, Baka, my man! How's it hanging? How's tricks? That a real nice outfit you got on. Where I get me one of those?' Pleasantries, Jose, Tariq—whatever the fuck your name is. Pleasantries keep the world spinning. Separates us from animals." He pinches the nylon sleeve of his tracksuit. "Sports Authority, by the way. I buy them in bulk. Let me know if you want one. Hey, speaking of animals, and correct me if I'm wrong here, but I thought Muslims weren't allowed to keep dogs as pets."

"I don't know anything about that," Tariq says quickly. He seizes the dog's collar, as if to keep his hands from shaking to pieces. "I follow the Book, and the Book doesn't say anything about that."

"Whatever," Baka says. He turns to Alfredo. "Your clown posse is getting restless. They want to lay down some bets."

"There's nothing in the Book forbidding dogs," Tariq says. He runs his hands down the pit bull's front legs. "You think you know, but you don't know. I know. There's nothing about that at all."

"I'm not talking to you anymore," Baka says. "*Books?* Who gives a shit about books?" He pulls a money clip out of his pocket and waves

it under Alfredo's nose. "I'm talking about *bets,* Fredo. I've got some gambling to do. But if you delay this shit any further, people are either gonna leave or burn this place to the ground."

Alfredo can go to the police right now. *Stay right here,* he could tell everyone. *Be back in a hot minute.* He'll go up the stairs Tariq just came down. He'll take a deep breath, push through the front door, and run, head down, fists pumping like a good leadoff hitter, intent on beating the throw. In these lighter red and tan bowling shoes, he might get to the Impala before Mike Shifrin gets to him. If Shifrin is even out there. If the fucking cops are still out there! And if they are, if they haven't given up on him yet, then he'll stick his head through the Impala's open window and deliver the news. *The dog's here and he's all yours. Godspeed. Don't forget to make your arrests.* Maybe he'll ask one of the cops, the Hispanic one probably, to escort him back home. And then—if the cop wouldn't mind—to come back tomorrow and make sure he's okay. Hey, why stop there? Why not hire the cop as a twenty-four-hour bodyguard? He'll run alongside Alfredo's cabs, jump in front of the occasional bullet. While Alfredo can't actually pay this cop a salary, he'll at least buy him some official-looking sunglasses, some dark suits from the Salvation Army, maybe even one of those earpieces with the fusilli wiring. If they're not too expensive. Oh man, if he only had money. He wouldn't owe Winston anything, he wouldn't owe Baka anything, he wouldn't live with his parents, he wouldn't have stolen fifty-two pills of Ecstasy because he would've just gone out and *bought* fifty-two pills of Ecstasy. If he only had money, he wouldn't have kicked anyone in the throat. Curtis would be alive. And Alfredo would be home, in bed with Isabel, playing I Wish. It isn't fair. He brought out two hundred dollars tonight, but after all the marked-up Dutches and beers and candy bars and Drake's cakes and Little Debbies and plantain chips, he's only got a hundo left. And it's still more than he ever has on his person. And it's *still* less than what everyone else has got. In the pockets of the fuckers around him, Alfredo can see some fat-ass wallets. Where he can't see wallets, he assumes they've got money clips like Baka's, overburdened with bills. How is that fair? The cash in this basement could buy Christian Louis a birthday cake every year of his life, with enough left over for one big blowout bash: a rented-out movie theater, a rented-out roller skating rink, a party with a magician, a party with a clown, a party at McDonald's with their big-

ass ball pit, a trip to a petting zoo where a soft-tongued llama would lick grains out of Christian Louis's delighted little hand. Now we're talking. Worse comes to worst, at least there'd be that. Something happens to Alfredo, at least the little man would have cakes to tear into on his birthday.

Baka snaps his fingers in Alfredo's face. "Where'd you go?" he says. "Who am I supposed to talk to when you check out like that?" He tilts his head toward Tariq. "*Him?*"

Tariq smiles peacefully, and Alfredo knows that if Baka says one more word, Tariq will let go of the leash and that'll be it: pandemonium. Marc and Billy pushing each other over spilled beer and scuffed sneakers is one thing, but if Baka and Tariq go at each other? Forget about it. Alfredo needs to keep this place under *some* measure of control. If shit blows up, everyone will spill out of here, Tariq will never get arrested, the Mike Shifrin problem will go unsolved, and Alfredo will be right where he started. No way, man. Can't happen. He leads Baka away from his brother. They walk over to the card table with the shoebox on it, where Alfredo goes up on his tiptoes and sticks his hand into the haze.

"Single file, everybody. Let's get this shit started. Single file, please. *Single* file. Break out that cash mo, people. Make your wagers. Place your bets."

AIDS, the first man in line, bets twenty on the pit bull. When Alfredo tries to bully him into betting some real money, AIDS spreads open his wallet: ragged, empty, not even a cartoon moth. Because he never knows when to quit, he turns the wallet over and gives it a shake, and all his plastic cards—his Visa card, his Blockbuster card, his Queensboro Public Library card—slip out of their sleeves and fall to the floor. Alfredo places the poor kid's twenty in the shoebox. Next in line, Rick Sprinkle and Timmy P. step over AIDS to bet seventy-five dollars each on the pit bull. Rhino lays down a hundred.

"Ain't you gonna write that down?" he says.

"I don't have to," Alfredo says.

Max hovers behind him, his urge to kibitz stifled for way too long. "Write it down," he says.

"I got it all up here," Alfredo says, tapping his temple. "Locked away in the vault."

"Write it down," Max says.

While Winston goes upstairs to fetch paper and pen, Billy Fitzgerald bets this month's allowance ($140) on the pit bull. Marc bets $145 on Diana. Billy ups his bet to $150. Like an auctioneer, Alfredo points a finger at Marc, but that's all the money he's willing to wager. Billy puffs out his chest, already victorious. Paulie Guns bets last night's drug dealing profits ($64, most of that in five-dollar bills) on the Batistas' dog. *Gotta go with pit bulls,* he explains. Those with legal jobs—David, Foot Locker employee; Jossie, RadioShack employee; Virgin Light, barback at a gay nightclub in Manhattan; and Jonas, men's room attendant at Carnegie Hall—bet chunks of their paycheck, or, in Jonas's case, the $40 in tips dropped into his wicker basket last night. No one knows what Jeff Hernandez does for a living—he claims to be a theater actor, of all things—but he puts $200 on the pit bull. Alex and Bam-Bam bet $300 on their own dog. Wowser! Alfredo makes a show of counting out their money. K-Lo throws a fifty-dollar bill into the shoebox and then runs back to his perch by the ladder. Tariq doesn't bet. Neither does Max. But Baka does. Last on line, he puts $150 on the Batista brothers' dog.

"I thought for sure you'd bet against us," Alfredo says.

"So did I," Baka says.

Winston has yet to return with a pad of paper. Not that Alfredo needs it. Working from memory, he recites each wager aloud and receives head nods and *uh-huhs* and *that's rights* in return. When he's finished, he kicks off his bowling shoe and removes $100 from the bottom of his sock. He drops the money in the box. Purely for the sake of appearances. It's gotta seem like he's betting, right? Also for the sake of appearances—since he already knows the total—he counts up all the cash.

The men down in this basement bet $1,784. That's all together. They bet $1,064 on the pit bull, $720 on Diana. As per gambling custom, the house keeps 10 percent. Alfredo counts out $178 and lays it in Max Marshmallow's palm. (*You're kidding me,* Max says.) Alfredo tells the crowd there will be no handicapping, no odds. Wagers are straight up. If you put $100 into the shoebox and your dog wins, you win $190. There's your 10 percent. Here's the irony, which Alfredo keeps to himself: if Diana, the nominative underdog, wins the fight, then the house makes $310, the difference between what was bet (minus 10 percent)

on Diana vs. what was bet (minus 10 percent) on the pit bull. If the pit bull, the nominative favorite, wins the fight, then the house *loses* $310 because they won't have enough cash in the box to pay out the winners. The money in Max's palm will get taken away. And that still won't cover it all. They'll be $132 short, but really they'll be only $42 short because it's not like Alfredo would collect on his winnings. But still: they'll have to go into Max's old-fashioned cash register and pull out a couple of twenties, essentially taxing the guy for the pleasure of watching people hock up loogies on his basement floor. Like so much else, it doesn't seem fair. But then again, it ain't gonna happen. Diana can't win this dogfight because Alfredo has no intention of ever letting it begin.

"I'm going upstairs," he announces. With the shoebox tucked under his arm, he gives Max what is meant to be a reassuring nod. "I gotta lock up the cash."

Even though AIDS has the least amount of money in the box, he is, of course, the first to object. "Hold on," he says. "*Where* you going?"

"For the duration of the dogfight," Alfredo says, as if reading off a rule book no one else has access to, "the wagered money is supposed to be locked up in a safe place. This is procedure."

"Yeah," AIDS says, stroking his theoretical goatee. "But *why*?"

"Why the fuck you think people lock up money?" Alfredo says. He hopes that if he punishes AIDS enough, then no one else will question him. "I know you don't know shit about nothing, AIDS, but this is procedure. This ain't no dogfighting video game, okay? We lock up the money so we can all enjoy the fight without worrying about somebody sneaking off with the cash."

"Come on," Rick Sprinkle says. "You think someone down here would steal the money?"

Max says, "I'd be surprised if someone *didn't* try to steal the money."

"Is that supposed to be directed at me?" David asks.

Alfredo turns to Max. "You got a safe up there I can use?"

"You know I don't have a safe," Max says.

"Okay. I'll lock it up in the cash register."

"This is ridiculous," Bam-Bam says. "Nobody's gonna steal the money."

"Spoken like a true criminal," Alfredo says.

Baka laughs. He's been watching all this with a smile on his face, as if he were eager to see how it'll all play out. In a gesture halfway between admiration and affection, he wags his finger at Alfredo.

"I'm tired," Alfredo says, and it feels like the first true thing to come out of his mouth in hours. "I'm going up now. Any of you badasses and tough guys wanna keep an eye on me, then please—follow me up. Be my fucking guest." And with that, he heads for the stairs.

He finds Winston in an aisle stocked full of disposable goods: paper plates, plastic cups, paper towels, paper napkins, rolls of toilet paper individually priced. Winston is shaking his head, as if overwhelmed by the number of choices. He holds a can of beer in his hand. A small blue pencil—the kind used to fill out Lotto cards—hangs from his lips. He looks lost, an oversized child trapped in the dark. When he sees Alfredo, he opens his mouth to speak and the pencil falls to the floor.

"I can't find a pad of paper *anywhere*," he cries.

He stoops over to pick up the pencil, and Alfredo grabs him, pulls him toward the front of the store. Winston doesn't protest. As always, he's along for the ride. The two of them move quickly down the darkened aisles. Alfredo knows he's pushing his luck here—he could get Tariq arrested *right now*—but there is almost eighteen hundred dollars in this shoebox and that is too much cash to ignore. He carries it cradled like a baby. As he runs, the bills bounce off the sides of the box, in tune with the thumping in his chest. Cold fingers of sweat tighten across his scalp. His lungs shrivel like fists. As if he's been submerged underwater and is just now breaking the surface, air jumps down his throat, quicker and quicker. He's got to get rid of this shoebox. He puts it up on the counter, next to Max's cash register, and wouldn't you know: his chest unclenches. Able to breathe normally, unburdened of all that cash, he glides to the front door, where, under the eaves of his hands, he peers out into the street, looking for Russian gangsters and Chevy Impalas. The rain falls sideways like flashing needles of light.

"Unbelievable," Winston says, breathing heavily. The top of his beer can has been pushed into itself, making the hole much wider, a mouth caught in mid-yawn. Into this hole, Winston spits a ribbon of brown goo. "A big store like this, and not one goddamned pad of paper."

"What are you doing?"

"You mean this?" He pulls down his lower lip to reveal, tucked into the fold, a black-brown knot of chewing tobacco. His teeth are already stained. "It's called dipping."

"I know what it's called," Alfredo says, although, in truth, he did not. "You play the ukulele now, too?"

"I like it," he says. "It makes me feel mad dizzy."

Alfredo watches Winston drop another ribbon into the can, amazed that they've been here long enough for his best friend to cultivate brand-new addictions.

"Can I borrow your phone?" Alfredo asks. "Mine's dead."

"Seriously," Winston says. "What would you do without me?"

He tosses Alfredo his phone, and because Alfredo is worried about other things—because he's not thinking about catching it—he catches it. He flips it open and sees that Winston's usual background image, an orange-duned desert, has been replaced by a generic picture of an open highway. This annoys Alfredo. He doesn't give a shit about highways or deserts, but he finds it unbelievable that while he was plotting to keep them alive, Winston was sucking down pharmaceutical cocktails, experimenting with this dipping garbage, fiddling with his cell phone's preset wallpaper images. *Seriously? Does anyone out there have any fucking idea of the pressure I'm under?* With his jaw clenched, he scrolls through Winston's phone, past Contacts, past Settings and Tools until he gets to Messaging. He selects Compose New Message, and his thumbs go to work on the keypad.

> *my phone's out of service.*
> *alfredo got bit by a dog. he'll*
> *be coming out the back of*
> *the store. hurry! xo, baka*

The *xo* might be too much—hugs and kisses? really?—but Alfredo can think of no other way to approximate Baka's verbal flamboyance. He closes his eyes, sees the black backdrop of his lids. Summoned, the untagged numbers in Baka's call history float down. Green sevens locking into place next to orange fours. Alfredo enters all the numbers in the text message's address book. In a moment, in pockets scattered around New York City, phones are going to start ringing and beeping and vibrating. Baka's business associates—people Alfredo's never

247

met—are going to read a message he wrote, a message they won't understand from a number they don't recognize. That's okay. Alfredo is tossing a fistful of darts and needs only one bull's-eye. The odds seem decent to good. But those tireless fucks in the Department of Worry want to know what if Mike Shifrin's phone doesn't have text messaging capabilities. Oh please. Alfredo tears that particular thought down the middle and feeds both halves to the shredder. What kind of twenty-first-century drug dealer can't receive texts? He hits Send.

"What shitty weather, huh?" Winston says, looking out the front door. His breath leaves circles of fog on the glass. "Least it held off for the Mets game, I guess."

Alfredo takes the shoebox off the counter and brings it to Winston as fast as he can. He trades him, as they used to trade Marvel cards: the box for the beer can.

"Wait here five minutes," Alfredo says. "Then go across the street. Run across the street, actually." Five minutes should give Mike Shifrin, if he's even out there, enough time to check his phone, read a text message, cross the street, turn the corner, duck into the alley, and head toward the back of the candy store. Five minutes should be *plenty* of time. "Go over to that parked Impala," Alfredo says, tapping a finger on the glass of the door. "There are three DTs inside. Tell them the dog's here. Okay? And that they should make moves ASAP. Tell them to go around to the back of the store. The *back* of the store. You got it? Okay? Repeat all that back to me."

"There are three DTs across the street?" Winston says.

"They're here for my brother."

"Oh," Winston says. For the first time he looks down at the box in his hands. "Wow. Okay. And you want me to give them this money?"

Alfredo's head sags. It is only by an extraordinary effort of will that he keeps it from falling off his neck and rolling, eyes open, down Max Marshmallow's shiny linoleum floor.

"I want you to wait here for five minutes," Alfredo says. "Tell the police to come to the back of the store. The back. Then I want you to take that money and run home. Hide it under your bed." He tries to smile. "Stash it next to your dirty DVDs."

"This is our friends' money."

"What's the matter?" His hand sinks into the soft dough of Winston's shoulder. "You don't trust me?"

"I don't want to get into trouble."

"Winston, you'll be in trouble if you stay."

"That's not what I mean." He stares into the shoebox, frowning. "I *can't* hold this down. You know what I mean? I'll spend it all on drugs."

"You're quitting tomorrow," Alfredo says gently.

"I'll kill myself. I appreciate your faith in me. I really do. But you give me this money and I will die. Straight up. I'll spend every cent. I'll keep going till my heart bursts."

"All I need you to do is hold it down for twenty-four hours," Alfredo says. He considers the last twenty-four hours, how much can change in so short a time. "If you haven't heard from me by tomorrow, go over to my parents' place. Give the whole box to Isabel."

Max calls out Alfredo's name. He moves toward them through the dark, his voice terribly frayed, warbled at the edges.

"Change of plans," Alfredo whispers. He stands so close to Winston that the shoebox is pressed against both of their stomachs. "Tell the DTs the dog ain't here yet. *They* need to wait five minutes. Understand what I mean? Go now and tell them. They wait five minutes and then they come around to the back."

That should still work. As long as the cops catch Shifrin in the yard, Alfredo should be okay. If Shifrin has a gun on him—and why wouldn't he, if he's the O.G. Baka claims?—then he'll get collared on illegal possession of a firearm. Three and a half years, minimum. One problem solved. Then the cops go down into the basement and arrest everyone else, including Alfredo. Cost of doing business, as Baka might say. Everyone will spend a night, maybe two, in lockup, and then they'll all be back on the street. Except Tariq, who will have violated his parole—*I will not behave in such manner as to violate the provisions of any law to which I am subject, which provide for a penalty of imprisonment.* Problem number two: solved. Of course there might be complications—Max might lose his store, Shifrin might open fire on the police, Alex and Bam-Bam might miss Curtis's funeral, Jose Sr. might not get a Father's Day present—but no plan is perfect. This is as good as Alfredo can do. By Monday night at the latest, he'll be home with Isabel, kissing her ears, telling her, *I got rid of him, I took care of it,*

I did it all for you. Plus they'll have a nice $1,800 for the Christian Louis birthday fund.

"Please don't make me do this," Winston says.

"Hello?" Max cries out. "Alfredo?"

"Coming!" Alfredo says. He takes off Winston's cap and puts it on his own head. The Saturday night outfit he never expected to wear: stolen bowling shoes, yesterday's jeans, silk teddy bear boxer shorts, no shirt, a Spider-Man cap that falls down to his eyes. "How do I look?" he asks.

"You look stupid," Winston says. He runs his hand through the alopecia quilt of his scalp, as he does whenever his head is exposed.

"Imagine how stupid *you* look in this thing."

When Winston reaches for the hat, Alfredo pulls his head back.

"I need it," Winston says. "It's raining."

"You'll be running so fast, you can't get wet."

"It's my trademark," he says.

"I know, but not tonight, okay?" He turns Winston around so he faces the door. Across the street, there might be a man who wants to kill Winston as badly as he wants to kill Alfredo. In an ideal world, Alfredo gives this man his five minutes to go around to the back of the candy store. But with Max Marshmallow's voice getting closer, coming up the aisle behind them, Alfredo does not have that kind of time. This is not an ideal world. This is this world, and in this world Alfredo pushes Winston out the door and into the street.

"Run," Alfredo whispers.

Maybe Winston can't hear him. He hugs the box to his chest. He pokes his head out from under the awning and looks both ways down the street. Toward Manhattan, toward Flushing. Alfredo punches the glass door with the side of his fist, and Winston takes off. Or at least tries to. He runs with the out-of-water coordination of a seal, the shoebox tucked under his jiggling fin. From high school, from P.E. classes, from relay races demarcated by orange cones, Alfredo knows what's coming and already he feels a bodily unease. Winston runs into the street. With the rain coming down hard, he splashes through puddles, his head on a swivel. He looks discombobulated, as if he's been dropped off in a foreign country hostile to his own. He snags his foot on an invisible tripwire, and his free arm shoots out for balance. Here

we go. Tangled feet. Windmilling arms. Alfredo presses his face to the door, the glass cool against his forehead. He watches Winston crash into Marc Franschetta's souped-up Camaro, parked three cars behind the DT's Impala. The alarm goes off. The *honk-honk-honk, oo-woo-oo-woo* that Alfredo, and every other New Yorker, knows by heart. The Camaro's blue headlights flash in rhythm to the alarm, the car a dance party all to itself. Alfredo can't be sure about this—it's hard to see—but it looks like the cops have slumped down in their seats, as if they were uncomfortable being on the other end of these lights and this siren. Despite his fall, Winston has held on to the box. But he looks terribly vulnerable out there, marooned in the middle of the street.

"Alfredo!" Max calls out.

Alfredo turns away from the door and meets Max halfway down the beer aisle, where forties and six-packs sit befogged in humming, buzzing refrigerators. The fridges are backlit, the beers individually glowing. It is the only light in the store—except for the red eye of the smoke detector—and both Max and Alfredo draw near it.

"Let me hold on to the key," Max says.

"The key?"

"The key," Max says. In his agitation, he grabs hold of the closest thing—the refrigerator door handle—for support. "The little yellow register key on the counter. Next to the till."

"Right," Alfredo says.

"Well, let me get it."

Alfredo wants to press his face against this old man's chest. Even with his shirt off, bare-chested, exposed, Alfredo feels comfortable in front of Max. He is a good twenty years older than Jose Sr., but in a different life, a life in which Alfredo was born Jewish and white in, say, 1962, then this old geezer could've been Alfredo's father. Alfredo's name would be Saul, or something like that. He'd live in an alternate New York, where the Mets beat the Yankees in 2000, where Estes plunked Clemens, where the Twin Towers still stand, if not both then maybe one. As Alfredo nears the crisis of his life, he can't help but think of these hypothetical worlds, existing somewhere in some corner of the universe. He never kicked Vladimir in the throat. Jose Sr. never sold the store. Alfredo never brought this trouble into Max's basement.

"If you leave now, you can say we broke in. You can say you never knew anything, you were never even here. I'll back that up."

"You made a jerk out of me," Max says, his mouth emptied out. Alfredo imagines he swallowed the last marshmallow, and it slid all gooey down his old turkey throat. "You made a jerk out of me in my own store."

"You wanted to play gangster," Alfredo says softly.

"Excuse me?"

"You wanted to play gangster," Alfredo says, the reservoir of his sympathy containing only so much. "You wanted to play gangster—this is what you get."

"I'll call the police if I have to."

Alfredo puts the beer can in one of Max's hands, the Spider-Man cap in the other. "I'd let you use my phone," he says, stepping around him. "But the battery's dead."

Misha Shifrin jogs toward the back of the bodega. He is smiling, pleased to have all this rain pouring out of the sky. Water splatters the pavement, drips off the brim of his hat. Black, straight-billed, the hat belongs to Vladimir, and Misha wears it tonight, as he did last night, for good luck. As he nears the fence-enclosed yard, he pulls on a pair of rubber gloves. He isn't worried about leaving behind fingerprints—the rain will wash everything away—no, what Misha's worried about is gunpowder particles staining his hands. The police can test for that kind of thing, and while there's some debate as to whether or not it's admissible, it is certainly incriminating. With the gloves snapped tight around his wrists, Misha hops over the fence. Lands in the yard with a muddy squish.

The moon reveals only half its face. It hangs suspended at last quarter, and in its weak light the grass looks more yellow than green, dying if not already dead. Misha squats down in a corner of the yard, where a garden hose lies snaked between paint cans. There are no trees. No room for ball playing. A chipped ceramic pot has filled up with water. This is, he thinks, as good a place as any. From his corner of the yard, he watches the door, his grip tight on a Baby Glock 26.

He squats there long enough for his calves to cramp and for his brown leather oxfords to sink into the mud. Five hundred dollars these

shoes cost him. He put them on this morning without thinking, distracted by phone calls and emails and the *Today* show and the kettle screaming on the stovetop. When he shifts his weight, the ground sucks at his feet. He'll have to incinerate the shoes when he gets home, along with the gloves. Unbelievable. Five hundred fucking dollars. He fishes a protein bar from his pants pocket, and, reluctant to loosen his grip on the gun, he opens the packaging with his teeth. A bit of wrapper comes loose in his mouth and he spits it into the grass. The protein bar smells like peanut butter and maple syrup and disappears in three bites. He smacks his lips. He is thirsty now but not at all tempted to open his mouth and let the rain fall onto his tongue. Too much acidic content. Particulates. Carcinogens. Toothy tumors eager to congregate on the underside of his lungs.

With his free hand, he searches the grass in front of him. Looking for that tiny bit of wrapper. Stupid. He imagines police investigators finding it, looking up dental records, matching the marks on the wrapper to the teeth in his head. Not that he has any dental records in the States—but still, it isn't worth the risk to leave the wrapper behind, just as it wasn't worth the risk for that gorilla Baka to have sent him a text message. An electronic record of conspiracy. Stored forever in some AT&T supercomputer. Misha considers it his own fault for dealing with those kinds of people in the first place.

Less than a block away, a car alarm goes off. Misha keeps his head down. Tries to make himself as small as possible. With that car alarm blaring, lights might turn on in the houses around him. Faces might come to windows. Someone—unlikely, but possible—might call the police. Misha takes his hand off the gun, tries to wipe his gloves dry against the front of his pants. He considers getting out of here right now, taking a cab to the Okeanos bathhouse in Midtown, trying again tomorrow—but there will always be car alarms, Misha, there will always be bad, sinking feelings, and as your deadbeat alky father used to say, *Kto ne riskuyet tot ne pyot shampanskoe,* or, poorly translated, *Who doesn't make risks doesn't drink the champagne.*

The car alarm changes registers, the horn blaring now, *ank-ank-ank-ank,* growing louder, more insistent, and maybe that's why Misha doesn't hear the Spanish kid running up the alleyway until it's almost too late.

The kid vaults over the fence. Where Misha had landed on both

feet, the kid slips. He falls hard to the ground. Mud splatters his cheap-looking Knicks jersey.

Misha comes out of his crouch. He needs to get close. He'll have one shot before neighbors reach for phones, and then he'll have to take off running. He got lucky with the rain, but he can't expect a peal of thunder to cover the gunshot. The kid is rubbing his hip where he fell. He looks surprised to see Misha coming toward him, just as Vlad must've looked surprised when this coward kicked him in the throat. Misha stands over him, close enough to read the name on his jersey—"Starks"—and now that he's this close, he realizes that the kid is not a kid at all, but a grown man, which is surprising, sure, but it'll make all of this easier. Misha raises his gun, ready to blow the jaw off this cock-sucker's face.

Misha is shot through the chest. His mouth fills up with something warm and watery and without taste. He hears more gunshots. Maybe two. Maybe one plus its echo. He doesn't remember firing. The gun is still in his hand, he thinks, but he can't be sure because he can't lift his head off the ground to check. His feet feel like wax. Rain strikes the rusted-over lids of paint cans, and it sounds like a wooden finger tapping on wood. Drenched, the hat constricts around his head. He wants to wiggle out from under it, but he can't get anything to move. He wants to spit out whatever liquid is filling his mouth, but he can't remember how.

Earlier. Alfredo is walking down the stairs, having just given Max the Spider-Man hat and the beer can. He takes the steps one at a time, his hand on the wooden railing. The basement's light swallows him up to his waist. He needs to delay this dogfight till the DTs show up, which—knuckles rapping on the railing—should just be a little bit longer. This is what he'll do: he'll tell the goons down in the basement that before the fight can begin, the dogs need to be wiped down with towels and water. To make sure their coats haven't been covered in poisons. *Procedure,* he'll say. Hey—that's not bad. That should work. Alfredo is feeling good, feeling the intoxicating brew of manipulating all the players, but when he comes off the last step and enters the basement, his stomach lurches. Of course. How foolish of him. No one ever waits. No one's ever patient. The show has started without him.

Inside the ring, the older brothers—Alex Hughes, Tariq Batista—heat up their dogs. The soup cans have been collected and stacked neatly off to the side. Alex holds Diana by the scruff of her neck. She drags him toward the center line, that silver strip of duct tape, and if his sneakers squeak, it goes unheard, swallowed by the barking of the dogs, which is louder than ever. Too loud, Alfredo thinks. Noise trips up the stairs, up the ladder, slips through the cellar doors and runs down the sidewalk. The cops, if they have ears on their heads, will surely be able to hear the barking. And if not the barking, the cheering. Alfredo needs to stop this. He has a deal with the cops. More important: *this is not part of his plan.* But what can he do? His body won't allow him to step into the ring—all collars and leashes have been removed—and there isn't an inch of space in the crowd in front of him. Alfredo's friends and half friends surround the ring, closing around it like a noose. He goes up on his tiptoes to see his brother gripping the dog by the sleek engine of its neck. Tariq moves his lips quickly and purposefully, as if working some kind of enchantment. Sweat drips from his chin, and Alfredo, unthinkingly sympathetic, wipes at his own. Tariq kisses his dog on the top of his head, between the ears—and like an irritated teenager, the dog struggles to get away. They inch closer to the center line. The pit leans forward on powerful legs, lips peeled back from gums. On the other side of the line, Diana tries to bite at his face. The crowd constricts even tighter, which Alfredo didn't think possible. As he takes a step forward, so do the dogs. Right up to the center line. Their noses almost touching. Alex and Tariq struggle to pull them apart and drag them into their respective corners. It is in this moment, with the magnetism between the animals at its strongest, that the handlers let go.

Afterward, when thinking back on this night, everyone down here will remember the crack of initial contact. The way the dogs, both of them airborne, collided in the center of the ring. The way the bone of one dog's skull smashed into the bone of the other dog's skull.

The pit bull's head hangs at an awkward angle to the rest of his body. As if he wants to get a good look at his tail but can't muster the energy. *This isn't fair,* Alfredo wants to shout. He looks to his brother, who stands outside the ring, one foot on a box, arms folded in front of his chest. *This is not fair!* When the dogs collided in midair, the pit bull snapped something in his spine. Look at his neck. Look at how he can't

defend himself as Diana bites into his face. Blood slides down his freckled nose. Thick black drops drip onto Max's floor. When Alfredo imagined this happening, he imagined the dogs barking and the crowd hushed, but it is the other way around. Everyone is screaming; the dogs are silent. Diana hoists her front legs over the pit bull's head. He escapes the clinch, goes low, his body turned sideways, his ribs protruding, his head dragging across the floor. She goes high, tears a chunk from the tip of his ear. She bites his face again. His lower lip swings loose from his mouth. It looks chewed on. It looks like it's been tied up with butcher string. Diana splits his nose. She mauls his face, which turns pink and red, with a little yellow between the eyes. When he limps away into a corner of the ring, toward Tariq, she follows. Without a yelp or a whimper, he sinks down onto his back. He shows her the white of his stomach, the animal kingdom's universal signal of submission. She bends her face to his stomach and disembowels him.

Tariq turns away from the ring, his face drained of color. He holds the leash in his hands and he's fidgeting with it, wrapping it around one palm and then the other, snapping it tight. His lips are moving. He staggers backward, and Alfredo races toward him. He doesn't know what's happening, but his brother is coming apart in a way Alfredo's never seen before. It seems as if he's stopped breathing, and Alfredo needs to get to him, needs to blow air into his mouth. All bodily instinct, he pushes his way through the crowd, throws his elbows when necessary. Tariq jumps when Alfredo grabs hold of his shoulders. His vacant, dilated eyes stare into Alfredo's face as if he no longer recognizes him.

"This is twisted," Tariq says. "This is all upside down."

Alfredo can barely hear him. The noise has exploded: Diana, victorious, crows inside the ring, while everyone else is pulsing, calling for a mop, a garbage bag, a bucket of soapy water, anything, anything at all to clean up this mess. Tariq's eyelids are fluttering. His knees dip, and Alfredo needs to hold him upright. Tariq is shaking his head, moving his lips, but Alfredo can't hear him. He grabs Tariq by the hand and pulls him through the crowd, toward the stairs, where it is quieter, and while at first Tariq resists, dragging his feet, soon Alfredo is not pulling his brother but getting pushed. Tariq puts his head down and forces Alfredo against the wall.

Tariq grabs him by the waist. He squeezes hard, leaves purple finger

bruises on the skin. Alfredo wants to tell him to stop, you're hurting me, but he's not sure he'd be heard. Tariq whimpers. His head snaps forward, smashes into Alfredo's chin—an accident maybe, but Alfredo's teeth click together so hard his ears pop. Tariq squeezes Alfredo's arms, prods at his torso, and it occurs to Alfredo that his brother's roving hands might be looking for an opening—something like an appendix scar—that he can split open and crawl into. He wants rights of possession, Alfredo thinks. He wants to take up residence. He wants to inhabit a body that never went to prison, never got cut up, never lost a girlfriend or a dog, a body without cause for grief.

"You win," Tariq says. His hands drop down to his sides. "Okay? You win. I give up. I'm crashing. You understand?"

No, Alfredo does not. He does not understand. He tries to push his brother away, but he can't extend his arms. Tariq's in too close. He smells like Barbasol and Irish Spring. He hooks his chin over Alfredo's shoulder, his bald head smooth and cool against Alfredo's cheek. And there it is: the indent on the back of his brother's neck. It opens up right in front of Alfredo, that soft pocket he's always been tempted to fill. Maybe—who knows?—Alfredo has one too. How could he be sure he doesn't? It'd be on the back of his neck, which he can't see on his own, and he never thought to ask anyone else to look out for it. It could be a thing he carries with him all the time, a thing Isabel's noticed but never mentioned.

"The police are coming," Alfredo whispers. He is unsure if what he's doing is right, but he cannot help himself. He clinches his arms behind his brother's back. "Go home, okay? Go upstairs into the store and leave out the front door. You'll be safe, you understand? But you gotta go now. You gotta get out of here."

Blood trickles from Tariq's nose. It is bright red, impressively so. Either he snorted some of that X, or he's getting one of the stress-induced nosebleeds he was prone to as a child. Alfredo tries wiping at the blood with his thumb, but he ends up just smearing it across Tariq's upper lip.

"Pinch your nose," Alfredo says. "Tilt your head back." He wipes his bloody thumb off on Tariq's shirt, before remembering that it's actually his shirt. "Aw, shit."

"What's the matter?"

"Tilt your head back."

"What's the matter?"

"It's okay. Tilt your head back. You're bleeding."

"No," Tariq says. "That isn't my blood." He takes a step back and spreads his hands over the front of his jeans, where the denim looks discolored, almost rusted. "You're an excellent noticer, but no, that's not my blood. That's Isabel's."

"Jose," Alfredo says softly.

"She spit onto my crotch. It's her blood. It isn't mine. It isn't mine at all."

Alfredo takes Tariq's shirt in his fists. He tries to push him, but Tariq has him pinned against the wall.

"And it's dark down here," he says. "And you *still* noticed. That's real impressive, Dito."

"Is she alive?" It is the most miserable question he's ever asked. He bites down on the insides of his cheeks, but it doesn't work. He has burst into tears. He is afraid to breathe, afraid that if he opens his mouth any wider he will crack the world in two. "Jose? Is she alive?"

"She's at home," he says. "In bed. With Mama, believe it or not."

"And are they *alive*?"

"You think I'd kill my own mother?" he says. When Alfredo doesn't answer, Tariq's shoulders start trembling. He giggles. His eyes are bright and shining, his mood swinging toward elation. Alfredo understands that this shift in mood has nothing to do with the pills his brother swallowed. It is the violence brewing in his chest. "I don't blame you," Tariq says.

People are looking at them now, if they haven't been already.

"It's a disgusting thought," Tariq says with a smile. "But I don't blame you for thinking it. I hurt everything I love, right? I love Allah, I hurt Him. Took all those pills, that loathsome evil. I love Isabel, and then—"

A strangled, desperate moan sweeps through Alfredo's body. Backed up against the wall, he starts quivering. He hates himself. He needs to get away, run home through the streets. Tears drip off his glasses.

"Stop that," Tariq warns. "Stop crying right now."

Alfredo nods. He tries holding his breath. If he had a shirt on, he could dry his face. Instead, he bites into his cheeks again, harder this time.

"I loved that dog," Tariq says. He inches closer, so that there's no space between them. "I loved that dog and now look at it. Look at this *disaster*." He shakes his head, amused. "It's like you're the only one I haven't hurt. What's that supposed to mean? You're so fucking smart—you tell me. What's it mean? Because *I* don't know. I can't understand it, Dito." He shoves a finger in Alfredo's face. "You're the one who broke the rules."

The blood above Tariq's lip has hardened into a brown crusty streak. His breathing deepens. He is smiling, panting, and for Alfredo the potential advantages of being backed up against this wall—it'd protect his kidneys, keep him up on his feet—have all been obliterated. He needs to get away. But there's no room for Alfredo to make a run for it, just as there's no room for him to rear back and deliver a blow. An elbow to the chin might work, if Alfredo could get enough strength behind it. Or he could use his keys. That might work. He could take one of his keys and have it jutting out of his fist. But he can't imagine himself doing it, not properly, not for real. He feels too weak. Blood surges to his temples.

"Isabel broke the rules, too," Tariq says. "But I had always been prepared to forgive her. That was the plan. The straight path. Isabel I had never intended to punish."

Alfredo sinks his fingers into the warm festering wound on his brother's cheek. He hits bone, hits nerves. Tariq's eyes widen in surprise. Lurching away, he screams. Loud enough to silence the dog in the corner. One long sustained head-clearing bell clap. He is bent over, one hand on his cheek, the other punching his thigh. When he turns back to the wall, Alfredo is gone.

The haze has thickened. By now every one of Alfredo's friends has turned away from the ring, away from the pit bull with its bowels coiled and steaming on the floor. They clot the center of the basement, these men. A dark mass of bodies, they seem to be standing one on top of the other, up to the ceiling and all of them shouting.

Alfredo runs toward them, hoping to disappear. He bangs off one body and into another: a pile of flesh, heavily cologned. Baka. Has to be. Alfredo wants to ask him if he has that .38 on him, tucked into his waistband, but there isn't any time. He hears his brother coming behind him. Of course. They're working on Tariq's terms now. This is what he has always wanted: a fight. Alfredo reaches into his pockets for

his keys, a weapon, pulling out loose change, dimes and nickels, a cell phone that goes skittering across the floor. His brother. His brother has the keys. Alfredo runs toward the pyramid of soup cans stacked neatly to the side of the ring. He grabs one off the top. It fits perfectly, as if made for his hand. When he turns around, he sees his brother sprinting toward him, his powerful arms swinging, his face dark and distorted.

The thing to do is wait. If Alfredo throws the can, he'll miss. He knows that. Impressive velocity, unfortunate aim. The thing to do is wait till Tariq gets close enough and then drive the can down into his face. Open up his forehead. Let the blood run into his eyes. But what Alfredo really wants to do, given the events of the last twenty-four hours, given that *he was the one* who failed Isabel, failed her a thousand times over, failed to not only protect her, his one responsibility in life, but actually facilitated her abuse, dropped Tariq off at home, on the doorstep, instead of at Budd's Bar or Gianni's Pizzeria or BQE Billiards or any one of the dozens of strip clubs on Queens Boulevard, volunteered his keys, neglected to call the house and warn her, left her exposed, shattered the life they imagined for themselves during round after round of late-night I Wish . . . because now nothing can ever be the same, not with this horrible thing between them, her mouth filling up with blood, his brother's hands, Christian Louis cowering in the womb . . . given all that, what Alfredo really wants to do is take this can and smash himself in the face. His arms are shaking. He feels helpless and dizzy, drowning as always under a collision of self-berating thoughts and images and fantasies and reveries, and he needs to stop thinking, yes yes yes, he needs to stop thinking and listen to his body because while Alfredo wants to hurt his brother and hurt himself, all his body wants to do is go home. That's all. Isabel is spitting up blood and Alfredo's body wants to hold a cool glass of water to her lips.

He runs. Turns his back to his brother and runs, a body in motion, in flight. Wind fills his ears. It comes up from nothing, this wind, comes leaping out of the smoke and stale air of the basement. The faster he runs, the louder it howls. He turns toward the mouth of the stairs. Gripping the soup can tightly—it's part of his body now, no time to throw it away—he bounds up the steps three at a time. His brother comes storming behind him. It's Tariq who's howling, not the wind. He sounds close. Sounds exhilarated. Their feet pound the

planks of the stairway, Tariq in sneakers, Alfredo in these horrible traction-less bowling shoes.

Three steps from the top, he trips. He braces his fall with his arms out in front of him and the soup can explodes on impact, sprays chicken broth, a mini geyser, into his face. It goes up his nose, into his mouth. His jeans rip open at the knees.

The men down in the basement cry out. Alfredo has fallen and his friends raise a collective groan—*Oh!*—their voices wincing with sympathy. But that's all they'll do. Facedown on the stairs, Alfredo knows there ain't nobody coming to save him. The cries of the men down in the basement are shot through with pleasure. These men are spectators, not participants, and they have been waiting a long time for this reckoning.

Tariq grabs Alfredo by the ankles and yanks him down the stairs. No place to go, no one to save him. Steps dig into Alfredo's cheek, his ribs, the plastic temple of his eyeglasses. Tariq is humming. His hands radiate heat as they rub circles on Alfredo's back, on the hunt for just the right spot. He punches Alfredo hard in the kidney. Stay quiet, stay still. An acknowledgment of pain will only frenzy Tariq, and besides, Alfredo's afraid that if he opens his mouth to cry out, his brother will try to curb him: force him to bite down on a step before kicking in the back of his head. Tariq's breath smells sweet, like chocolate. He hits Alfredo again in the kidney, scoops the air from his chest. Again Alfredo doesn't cry out. He focuses on a cross-grained knot of wood in the step above him. When he's hit a third time, his bladder fills up with blood, he feels a sticky warmth in his crotch, feels all the cords of his neck tightening, but he does not cry out. Tariq's humming grows louder, darker. He grabs hold of Alfredo's hair, hoists him up by the waist of his jeans, and this is the chance. Alfredo kicks out behind him, hits—what? The step underneath him? His brother's knee? He doesn't know. He kicks out and hits something hard and pushes off of it. Tariq's hands claw at his back, at the twin nubs of his shoulder blades, but there's no shirt to grab on to, and Alfredo rises up to his feet, up all the stairs, and he is a body again and he accelerates and he runs runs and oh Alfredo oh Alfredo, you sick bastard, you have gotten away.

Light-headed, giddy with panic, he looks over his shoulder and smiles.

Up in the store now, he flies down an aisle full of cleaning supplies,

the shelves deep with detergent, disinfectants, bottles of bleach, three-packs of sponges. It's dark. Alfredo's shoes slap linoleum—level ground at last, a relief after the trip up the stairs. The men down in the basement can surely hear him rumbling above their heads, but they may as well not exist, there's no sense thinking about them, there's no sense thinking at all. How natural this feels! Running through a darkened store he's known his whole life, his brother behind him. Alfredo craves to turn around again and look over his shoulder, but the heat on his neck tells him he shouldn't.

At the end of this aisle, he will have a choice of two exits. Two different ways out of here. He can either keep going straight, to an employees-only door—which will take him through Max's railroad apartment, to a screen door in the back, to the tiny yard enclosed by a waist-high fence, which Alfredo will have to leap over just to get into an alleyway—or he can make an easy left out of this aisle and head toward the entrance at the front of the bodega. It's no choice at all. The front doors will take him to the street. Three blocks from home. Closer to Isabel.

Alfredo plants a hard foot to the right and turns left. Tariq's momentum carries him forward. Bigger, stronger, he has a harder time slowing down. His body caroms off the beer fridge, spiders the glass. Alfredo considers waving good-bye, a little finger flutter off his hip, but it'd slow him down, the last thing he wants. Gotta get home. Out of the aisle and into a clearing, he dashes toward the front doors. This is it. If he makes it to the street, he'll be gone. Impossible to catch. He'll have backyards, the Alleyway, gypsy cabs, the Q32 bus. At intersections, he'll have his choice of four different directions. And he'll never get tired. Even with his kidney burning, he'll fly all the way home.

Bells jingle as the door opens up. Alfredo is still a few feet away and for a crazy half second he wonders if he's done this with his mind. Maybe he's so in tune with his body, he can manipulate the external world, telepathically swing open doors. No. Two men enter the store on a run, come barreling toward Alfredo and Tariq. With one man right behind the other, they even look like Alfredo and Tariq, except white and taller, with sports jerseys on, blue Mets and black Mets, Piazza and Piazza. The heavier of the two men, the one in the blue jersey, doesn't seem to understand what's happening yet. He runs behind his partner, as Tariq runs behind Alfredo, and realization reaches these

stragglers on a delay. But the skinny white cop sees Alfredo at the same time as Alfredo sees him. Right away. His face tightens. His arm swings up to point a gun at Alfredo's chest.

"Hold it!" he shouts. "Stop right there!"

Both cops are still far enough away that they might not recognize Alfredo as the kid from the donut shop. From across the darkened store, he wants to tell them not to worry, that they're on the same side. But of course they are not on the same side. Alfredo doesn't slow down. He runs right at the skinnier of the two cops, the one whose face is a gun barrel only. A toothless mouth. Alfredo goes low as he turns around, uses his hand on the floor to pivot. Three fingers streaking through dirt, as if he were caught on the base paths, between second and third. If the cops are far enough away that they might not recognize him, then they're far enough away that they might miss. And it's not like they can shoot a suspect in the back, right? As he turns, Tariq wraps an arm around his waist, but Alfredo is too slippery, too fast and too free. He runs away from the cops and away from his brother, toward the employees-only door waiting for him behind the counter. Both policemen now, two voices, shouting, warning. Hold it right there! Stop right there! He runs past the deli case with its tubes of meat. Leaps over a stack of today's papers, tied up in twine, their mastheads removed. He is afraid. He can't swallow. He tastes the broth on his tongue. The section of the counter in front of him works on a hinge, lifts up for easy access. Alfredo slides under it. The doorknob turns nicely in his hand.

When Alfredo accelerates, to tear through Max's railroad apartment, he loses track of the cops. He can't hear them anymore. The may be too slow, way behind, or they may have decided not to chase him, choosing instead to go down the stairs into the basement. But Alfredo *can* hear his brother. Tariq is panting, close behind. The apartment they sprint through is as narrow as a subway car, and dark too, darker than the inside of the store. Both men know where they're going. They've been here before. It is any summer night in the late 1980s and Papi stands behind the counter in the store selling Lotto tickets and Mama pan-fries pork chops in the kitchen and because of some mischief—a water gun filled with urine, a mix-tape deribboned— Jose Jr. chases Alfredito under the plush wings of parrots, through a hallway, into the living room, and now the boys are everywhere at

once, it is 1987, it is 1988, it is 1989, and the two dark-haired brothers are running, are asleep on the sofa bed, are playing War on the carpet, are eating single-sliced cheese straight out of the cellophane, are sitting in front of the television plastering He-Man stickers all over its screen. Alfredo wants to warn them—when Papi sees this he's gonna bring the belt to your asses—but the children have already started to shimmer and fade.

A gunshot deadens the air. Blasts the wind from his ears. Confused, he hears beeping. Two more gunshots, and he can't tell if they're coming from in front or behind, they're so explosively loud. He thinks of Isabel and feels something inside of him plummet. He runs faster, panicked. The door upcoming is actually two doors: a wooden door, interior to the apartment, swung all the way open, and an outer door, a screen door, latched closed to the rain. Is Tariq still behind him? Alfredo is too frightened to look. He can't stop. At the end of the couch, in the dark, Max sits with a cordless phone in his hands. It's the phone that's beeping, left off the hook for too long. Max looks small and afraid. He extends his arms out in front of him, palms up, as if bestowing a gift. Almost too late, Alfredo sees what's coming. With his hands rising instinctively to cover his face, he crashes through the screen door, takes it right off its hinges.

"Gun!" he shouts. His arm has punched through the wire meshing of the door, tearing it into flaps. He falls face forward into the yard, into the mud, and as he falls he shouts, "Gun! Gun!"

When he hits the ground his glasses go flying. Everything fuzzes over, loses edges, definition. Less than five feet away, a blurry-faced police officer, the Latino, kneels next to a body on the ground. The cop looks stricken. He turns to Alfredo with a bovine stare, the skin twitching around his mouth. Mike Shifrin—who else could it be?—lies motionless in the grass. Amazing. That Shifrin is here. That he exists. He must've had the drop on the police officer, must've gotten to the yard first, and yet he's the one on his back, his feet crossed peacefully at the ankles, his white shirt bunched up around blood-blooming holes. And the cop is the one who's still alive. All that academy training. Or maybe his policeman's trigger just squeezes more easily. The air smells of smoke. Shifrin looks like he's been shot three times in the chest, maybe more. It's hard to tell. Alfredo can't see as well as he'd like—the rain doesn't help—but he is thinking quickly and clearly, rejuvenated

from the bodily sprint through the store. Splayed out on the grass, his elbows in the mud, Alfredo feels as if he exists inside of time and it is a small safe world enclosed on all sides.

Tariq comes running through what used to be the back door. When he sees what's in front of him—the dead body, the cop, Alfredo low to the ground—he closes his eyes.

"Gun," Alfredo is shouting. "He has a gun! He has a gun!"

Tariq tries to slow down. Alfredo can see it in the way he tilts his head back, the way his hands lift on their own, which is truly the worst thing he could've done, those hands rising, and with a whipcrack of thunder, the first bullet hits him. It rips through his forearm and enters his shoulder, exploding it into fragments of muscle and bone. He is shot two more times in the chest. It spins him. Turning, he sinks down to one knee and slides forward in a crumple, an ear pressed to the ground.

The cop speaks into the silence that follows. "Where is it?" he says. He comes out of his crouch and runs over to Tariq's body. "I don't see it. Where is it?"

Alfredo doesn't know how to answer. He sits in the grass, his head bent, and he paws at the ground in front of him, searching for his eyeglasses. An earthworm gropes blindly out of the soil. It is light red and shiny, almost translucent, and when it slithers across Alfredo's knuckles, he recoils. He feels sick.

"Where is it?" the cop cries. There is blood in his voice, the threat of more violence. "Where the fuck is the gun?"

When Alfredo doesn't say anything, the cop slips his boot into Tariq's open hand. Alfredo wants to tell him to stop—*please don't touch him*—but he is afraid to give orders. He feels like he's waking up from a nightmare, but has still not come all the way out. Something else, something bad, is coming. He picks up off the ground a green piece of paper, a flyer of some sort, blown off a windshield and into the yard. Soaked all the way through, the paper's numbers and letters run together. Nothing makes sense. Rain drums into his eyes. It falls heavily, this rain. Makes music against the busted screen door, fills the open mouth of Mike Shifrin. A gun lies in the grass, close to Shifrin's body. If it's a snub-nosed .38, Alfredo can't tell. He can't see that far, nor does he know what a .38 looks like. The cop seems distracted. He stares into the house, ready—as Alfredo is—for the next bad thing.

The other two cops must be all the way downstairs by now, trying to convince a basement of angry young men to press their palms to the walls. The gun winks at Alfredo. He could crawl squishing through the mud, could grab it so easily. He could make sure. He allows himself to look over at Tariq, who kneels slumped over in the grass, his legs twisted under him, that ear to the ground as if he were straining to hear whispered, underworld voices.

"Don't," the cop says. The pistol he points at Alfredo shakes in his adrenaline-surged hand. "Don't you fucking move."

"No," Alfredo says. His own hands, clenched into fists, hang uselessly at his sides. "Please, no."

With his gun straight out in front of him, the cop circles behind Alfredo. He kicks him hard between the shoulder blades. Alfredo falls forward. Mud fills his ear. The cop digs his knees into Alfredo's back, presses down on his already battered kidney.

"Your friend's dog died," Alfredo says. Facedown in the mud, he doesn't know if he can be heard, but he wants all the facts known. "I'm sorry. I'm sorry about that dog. I never meant for that to happen."

His arms are pulled behind him. With a *click-click-click,* the cop cuffs Alfredo's hands behind his back. Alfredo prays. He prays that Isabel's mouth will heal, that Christian Louis will never know. That his parents, after hearing the news, will not close their hearts to him. The mud gives way under Tariq's head and he slides all the way down onto his stomach, revealing for a flashing moment the indent at the base of his neck. He is dead, and Alfredo has no words of his own to meet that. Silently, to himself, with his thin wrists cuffed so tightly that metal digs into bone, Alfredo recites the Lord's Prayer. He gets halfway through before stopping at daily bread. He does not ask to be forgiven. Why bother? Alfredo's hunger for forgiveness exceeds the world's capacity to dole it out.

Part Three

13

From the New York City Department of Records

1. FULL NAME OF CHILD	First Name **Christian**		Middle Name **Louis**	Last Name **Batista**	
3. SEX **male**	3a. NUMBER DELIVERED of this pregnancy **1** 3b. If more than one, number of this child in order of delivery		4a. DATE OF CHILD'S BIRTH (Month) (Day) (Year) **August 14, 2002**		4b. HOUR **7:07 PM**
5a. PLACE OF BIRTH	5a. NEW YORK CITY BOROUGH OF **Queens**		5b. Name of Facility (if not in institution, street address) **Elmhurst Hospital Center**		5c. TYPE OF PLACE **Hospital**
6a. MOTHER'S FULL MAIDEN NAME **Isabel Maritza Guerrero**		6b. MOTHER'S DATE OF BIRTH (Month) (Day) (Year) **October 18, 1982**		6c. MOTHER'S BIRTHPLACE City & State or foreign country **Queens, NY**	
7. MOTHER'S USUAL RESIDENCE a. State b. County **NY Queens**	7c. City, town, or location **Corona**		7d. Street and house number Zip **34-51 107th Street 11368**		7e. Inside city limits of 7c **Yes**
8a. FATHER'S FULL NAME **Alfredo Victor Batista**		8b. FATHER'S DATE OF BIRTH (Month) (Day) (Year) **January 14, 1983**		8c. FATHER'S BIRTHPLACE City & State or foreign country **Queens, NY**	

9a. NAME OF ATTENDANT AT DELIVERY **V. Mukherjee, M.D.**	9b. I CERTIFY THAT THIS CHILD WAS BORN ALIVE AT THE PLACE, DATE, AND TIME GIVEN
information added or amended _____ (Reason) _____ _____ (Date) (City Registrar)	Signed _~Bridget Goodman~_ Name of Signer **Bridget Goodman** Address **79-01 Broadway, Elmhurst, NY 11373** Date Signed _August 18, 2002_

VITAL RECORDS   DEPARTMENT OF HEALTH AND MENTAL HYGIENE   THE CITY OF NEW YORK

14

The Birthday Party

Isabel opens the cupboard and checks on the one. To make sure it's still there. For what must be the zillionth time today. She checks on the one compulsively, the way a traveler checks pockets and fanny packs, searching for the four familiar corners of a passport. As was the case ten minutes ago, the one glitters in its packaging, hidden behind the pancake mix. It hasn't moved. Despite the sweltering conditions inside the apartment, it hasn't melted. It is a good one. Sturdy base, long Victorian neck, little black wick poking out the top. The one looks as if it's been dipped in vanilla frosting and dotted with rainbow sprinkles. It looks edible, dangerously so. After Isabel sets it on fire, she'll have to make sure Christian Louis doesn't grab it and stick it in his mouth. God knows, he'll try.

When Isabel bought the one, the lady behind the cash register said, "Oh Lord, how exciting. Can you believe how fast time flies?"

Isabel asked Alfredo that very question this morning. She was lying on the air mattress with the baby—check that: with the toddler—while Alfredo stood in front of the mirror, getting ready for work.

"Can you believe how fast time flies?"

By way of answer, Alfredo slapped the wall behind her head. His hand came away with blood on it, the wall smeared with a red crescent moon.

"Don't do that ish on the walls," Isabel said.

"You wanna get bit up by mosquitoes all day, be my f-ing guest."

Christian Louis grabbed hold of Isabel's hair and stuck the ends in his mouth. On his cheek, a wine stain birthmark seemed to pulse with redness, as it always does in the early mornings. "A year already," Isabel said, looking at her son. "I can't believe it. Can you believe it?"

"No," Alfredo said. He folded his lime-green tie and buried it in his pocket. It was a clip-on, part of his everyday uniform, and Alfredo would rather have cut off his hands than be seen wearing it on the subway. He adjusted the cuffs of his shirt, hitched up his polyester pants. "I can't. I can't believe it."

"You look nice," Isabel said.

While she looks at the one, Christian Louis tries to get under the sink. He slides his head between his mama's legs and rattles the cupboard doors, the handles of which are bound by duct tape. When Isabel needs to get at her poisonous cleaning supplies—which is always, what with Christian Louis's table manners and Alfredo's mosquito vendetta—she has to slit the tape with a knife and then rebind it, every single time. Which is not *that* big a deal. The vice president said go out and cop mad duct tape, and so they bought plenty of rolls. They got duct tape coming out their asses. They got duct tape covering the baseboard power outlets. They used to have duct tape sealing the windows shut, a necessity with a moves-making baby in a sixth-floor studio, but it got too f-ing hot to be keeping the windows closed—ninety-one miserable degrees— and so Isabel went out and bought those heavy-duty black metal safety bars. Charged them to the card and installed them herself.

While Christian Louis wiggles between her ankles, Isabel slips the one behind the pancake mix. She could check in the freezer to see if the ice cream cake (Oreo crumb!) is still there, but it doesn't seem necessary. Where's a cake gonna go? She slides Christian Louis across the kitchen floor and deposits him in front of a different cupboard, one without any poisons. But because the handles aren't bound, he expresses little interest. He's like his father in this way: if it ain't forbidden, he ain't interested. He sits still in front of the cupboard, a skeptical expression on his face. But Mama knows best. When she bends over and opens the doors, revealing its bounty, he laughs. He's a great one for laughing. He reaches into the cupboard and pulls down all the

pots and pans. She puts a wooden spoon on the floor in front of him, and he picks it up, because he can do this now. *He can pick things up.* And holy ish, can he make noise. Spoon in hand, pots in front of him, he goes to work, bang-bang-banging away.

If Alfredo were home, he'd say, "Little man's gonna be a drummer like that guy in the Roots. Gonna make us a *fortune.*"

While her baby bangs pots, Isabel sits down in the kitchen chair and blows balloons. They smell nasty, like unlubricated condoms, and after the first dozen she goes a little cross-eyed. The tip of her finger turns purple from tying off the ends. Sweat blots the back of her tank top, but that might have less to do with the effort of balloon blowing and more to do with the throat-tightening humidity inside this apartment. Feeling light-headed, she tosses a balloon toward the drummer boy, and it bounces off his face. He laughs. She tosses another, and this time he swings at it with the spoon. He doesn't make contact—*sawing and a miss!*—but if Alfredo were here, he'd compliment the effort, say something like, "Little man's gonna be a slugger like Piazza. Gonna make us mad millions." And Isabel would say, as she always does, "Little man's gonna be whatever he wants."

One hopes.

She rubs a balloon against the top of his head. His soft dark hair sticks up like he just stuck a fork in an electric outlet. Scratch that. Too frightening an image. His soft dark hair sticks up as if he were . . . as if he were . . . as if he were the world's smallest mad scientist. How would she feel about that? Being the ma dukes of a future corpse reanimator? Sounds great. He could bring her back to life after she dies. They could go on teleportation trips together, celebrate his hundredth birthday on Jupiter. She presses the balloon to the wall, where it clings in place. She wishes she could explain how static electricity works—she'll look it up on one of the library computers—but the lack of an explanation doesn't seem to matter to Christian Louis, future scientist, future target of torch-wielding mobs. He stares at the balloon and slaps his forehead. Still laughing, beyond delighted, he grabs another balloon and sticks the tied-off end in his mouth.

Isabel jumps out of her chair and yanks the balloon away. She remembers something her mother the puta once told her about a cousin, a little girl back in Puerto Rico who swallowed a deflated balloon, choked on it, and died. Isabel's heart is racing. Christian Louis

watches her carry the balloon away from him, his arms straining, his fists grasping at air. If there's one thing she's learned in this past year it's that her baby boy is surprisingly difficult to break, and yet, *better safe than sorry,* the motto of mamas the world over. With a needle plucked from a tomato pincushion, she pops the balloon. It makes a loud, sudden sound, louder than Christian Louis's drumming. Eyebrows crossed, he opens his mouth as if to deliver a particularly abusive diatribe, and then he bursts into tears.

Two dozen more balloons lie scattered around the apartment, the party's first awkward guests. She pinches off each of their necks, slides her needle through. There are no bangs this time, no pops. Air trickles out of the balloons in a slow, painless hiss. She quarantines them all in the sink, where the sight of their wizened husks has her chewing her lip. Great. *Now* what is she supposed to do for decorations? Tomorrow the well-meaning, one-upping Abuela Lizette gets her shot—she's probably already rented out a declawed bear who brings his own unicycle—but tonight is for the three of them, Alfredo, Isabel, and Christian Louis, their own party in their own home, with balloons, there are supposed to be *balloons,* and an Oreo crumb ice cream cake, and a super elegant birthday candle. The one! Isabel checks on it to make sure it's still there—okay, okay, to make herself feel better—and there it is, tucked behind the pancake mix. It is a good one, but it is not the only game in town. As Christian Louis had done earlier, Isabel eyeballs the cupboard under the sink. When they moved into this Corona apartment she bought close to fifty candles—pillar candles, floating candles, tea-light candles, votive candles, lavender-scented heart-shaped candles—and she keeps them under the sink, behind duct-taped handles, saving them for a day that never seems to come, a day when she can slip into a warm bath for an hour, close her eyes, masturbate, and relax. She wants to hold all these candles in her arms, wants to hear their whispered promises.

Christian Louis is still crying. He reaches out for his mother, the balloon popper, the betrayer, and she lifts him up off the kitchen floor. She bounces him in her arms. She is a plane hitting turbulence, and he her only passenger. She flies him to the closet, where behind the door, wrapped up, waits his first birthday present. It is a Fisher-Price musical learning table, but she doesn't tell him that. It's a surprise.

"*Seventy* bucks," Alfredo had said when he saw the receipt. "For a table? Our parents never bought us anything that cost *seventy* bucks."

"Exactly," Isabel had said.

The table is an interactive toy, she explained. It helps kids learn their numbers and ABCs. It has fifteen sing-along songs—nursery rhymes and lullabies—and Isabel feels confident she'll know every single one.

"Does it come with volume control?" Alfredo had asked.

She could check right now, but the table's already been gift-wrapped. She yanks open the closet door, asking the baby in her arms if he can say *birthday present, birthday present.* Before he can gurgle out an answer, she slams the door shut. He gets a peek, that's it. When the sneaky little bastard reaches for the doorknob, she whirls him away.

She's going to tell Alfredo tonight. She'll wait till after the birthday cake, after Christian Louis has opened his present. She'll wait for the very peak of Alfredo's happiness, and then she will pounce. Her timing needs to be perfect, as it must be whenever she does anything: initiate sex, bring up their credit card bill, open her mouth at all. He's been poisonously moody these last few months. Last few months? He's been moody since last June. Worse than moody—she could live with moody—he's been withdrawn. He works as an elevator boy in a deluxe Manhattan apartment building, shepherding the rich from the lobby to their apartments, and from their apartments to the lobby, a never-ending north-south circuit; his boss, Ms. Webb, tells him he'd get promoted to doorman (an escalation in salary and, it seems, in masculinity) if he'd only engage the residents in some chit-chat as they rise and descend, if he'd talk to them about, oh you know, the weather, the Yankees, the latest Broadway shows. *But I don't feel like talking,* he complains to Isabel. *I understand,* she says. *I do. But maybe it's time to reopen that big fat mouth of yours and start yapping again.*

He usually shrugs when she says this. Or closes the bathroom door on her. Or rolls over in bed. Or crushes a blood-fat mosquito against the wall.

So tonight she'll have to wait till his shell shows a crack. Maybe he'll say a joke or laugh at one of hers. Maybe he'll smear ice cream cake on Christian Louis's nose. Sing the itsy-bitsy spider. Look at Isabel kindly, ignoring for once the thin white scar engraved under her eye. He'll be smiling at her with unguarded, soft-faced affection, and right then, in

that moment, she'll drop the news. Another one's coming, she'll say. We're pregnant again.

At around 3:30 in the afternoon, Alfredo staggers into the apartment. Legs quivering, he bangs into the doorframe. His keys slip out of his hand. He is home an hour later than expected, which would normally elicit from Isabel a certain set of questions, but she finds herself distracted by the sweat pouring off his reddened face. He carries—or attempts to carry—an enormous cardboard box. A stack of today's mail slides across the top of the box, and when Alfredo's knees buckle, an envelope corner stabs him in the throat.

"Oh my God," Isabel says. She holds Christian Louis's hands in the air, while he, with the grace of a stringed puppet, puts one foot in front of the other. He tries to get at his father, and Isabel follows. "Tell me that's not a birthday present," she says.

"It's not a birthday present," he says.

"Well, what the H is it?"

"What's H mean?"

"*Hell,*" she whispers.

"We can't say 'hell' in front of him?" he asks, setting the box down on the floor. "It's in the Bible."

"Alfredo," she says. "What's in the box?"

Seemingly too eager to go looking for the scissors, Alfredo uses his keys to slit the packing tape. When he gets the cardboard flaps open, he gives a chunk of Styrofoam to Christian Louis, who sticks it right in his mouth. Alfredo reaches into the box and pulls out—tada!— another box. This second box doesn't look like it conceals more boxes. It is a self-contained animal, made out of plastic and metal, with a three-pronged plug for a tail and a pair of accordion wings.

"An air conditioner?" Isabel says.

"An air conditioner," Alfredo says triumphantly. "I figure, what kind of environment do mosquitoes love the most? Hot and humid, yeah? I figure, where does heat go in a six-story apartment building? To the top, right? To *our* floor."

Isabel checks the box for dents, to see if it fell off the back of a truck.

"How much?" she says.

"Don't worry about it."

"I worry about it. How much? Where'd you get the money?"

"It was mad cheap. It's *August*. Ain't no one buying air conditioners in *August*."

"Well," she says, pulling the Styrofoam out of Christian Louis's mouth, "I hope you got a real smart place to put it, because it ain't fitting in them windows."

Alfredo looks up at the windows, tilts his head to the side.

"It'll fit," he says.

He grabs a magazine from the stack of today's mail and carries it with him to the futon. Leaving behind him, in his wake, bits of cardboard and torn-up tape and plastic wrapping and Styrofoam blocks and Styrofoam crumbs and the air conditioner itself, all over Isabel's floor, expecting, as he always expects, someone else to clean up his messes. Christian Louis, whose disloyalty knows no bounds, toddles over to his father. Alfredo picks him up, holds him in his lap with an arm wrapped around his belly, with a soft and easy tenderness. For not the first time in this past year, Isabel feels jealous of her own son. The baby books warned her that this happens to *fathers*—they look at the nine-month tenancy, they look at the breastfeeding, they look at the close bond between mama and child, and the resentment wheels start a-churning—but Isabel didn't read anything about *mothers* envying their children. You kidding? Good luck trying to find "maternal resentment" in a baby book index. But why shouldn't she feel jealous? When Alfredo holds Isabel it is stiffly, at a distance, as if he had a cold he didn't want to give her.

She has repeatedly told him—most often in bed, in the dark, when it is easiest for her to say these kinds of things—that she does not blame him for the incident, for what happened to her. The man who was responsible was responsible. She cannot say it any clearer than that. But there are moments, moments like right now, when Christian Louis is literally out of her hands and her mind can go to work on attacking itself, and she starts wondering if she's got it all backward. What if Alfredo isn't worried about Isabel blaming him? What if it's the other way around? His brother is dead and he blames *her*. What can she say to that?

In his father's lap, Christian Louis rips pages out of the magazine. Alfredo looks on indulgently, which annoys not only Isabel, but also, it seems, the white guy on the cover, a cartoon soldier whose face is

frozen in teeth-gritted frustration. A video game character probably. The magazine is called *GamePro,* and according to Alfredo he needs to subscribe because there isn't anyplace in Corona where a guy can just walk in and buy a magazine. He didn't explain, however, why a guy who doesn't own, much less play, a single video game would want the magazine in the first place. But Isabel has some ideas.

Alfredo wrestles a torn-out page from Christian Louis and holds it above his head. The baby—sorry, the toddler—strains to get at it. Forget the Fisher-Price musical learning table, forget the Styrofoam. This page is the only thing he wants. He climbs Alfredo's chest, grabs at his hair, but Papi lifts the page higher. He's reading it, and Isabel figures it must be the one page in the magazine devoted to tournament news. Alfredo, she assumes, is looking for Winston's name. For reasons mysterious to her, Winston and Alfredo haven't talked in over a year. When male best friends break up—is there a better way to put it?—it's either over a woman, which can't be the case here since Isabel would be that woman and God knows Winston's terrified of her, or it's over money, a more likely explanation. But not necessarily the correct one. Maybe Alfredo just got tired of trying to convince Winston to quit drugs. Maybe Winston is a pair of concrete boots, and Alfredo felt he had to leave him behind when he left his old lifestyle behind. Maybe Alfredo couldn't look at Winston without feeling corrosively guilty. (Maybe Isabel is projecting here.) She doesn't know. She doesn't know what happened between those two, just as she doesn't know how much the air conditioner cost, or where he bought it, or how he carried it home, or where he got the money to pay for it. She does know, however, that the more she asks, the less likely he'll be to provide answers. She watches him crumple the magazine page and toss it onto the floor.

"And who's cleaning that up?" she says.

"Give me a minute."

"And the box in the middle of my floor? Maybe you haven't heard, but I've got a birthday party to throw."

"Where's the balloons at?" he says, grinning. "I thought there was supposed to be balloons."

"Are you crazy?" she asks. "Don't you know they're a choking hazard? I had a cousin once who—"

"No balloons?" Alfredo says. "No balloons on his *birthday*?" He

spins Christian Louis around, so that he faces his mother. "Lookit," Alfredo says. "Lookit how sad he is not to have any balloons."

Spit bubbles up between his lips. He reaches toward her—that's right, that's right, he ain't playing Daddy's dirty little games—and Isabel tries to take him away, tries to lift him into the air, but Alfredo has hold of his foot.

"Where's the screwdriver at?" he says. "I'm gonna take the bars out of one of them windows and put in the AC."

"It's not gonna fit."

"It'll fit."

It fits. While Alfredo muscles it into the window frame, Isabel worries the AC's droopy ass will slip out of his hands and pancake some poor soul on the street. But he read the instructions for once. As he puts in the mounting brackets, he almost looks like he knows what he's doing. He uses the window to anchor the unit, and while that doesn't exactly seem sturdy enough, Isabel is past the point of doubting his competence. Isabel, as a matter of fact, is officially impressed. Alfredo spreads the accordion wings an inch in each direction—this is a *tight* fit—and secures them to the window frame. He takes a step back and slaps the top of the AC. It doesn't budge.

"Not bad, huh?"

"Not bad," she says.

"Don't go all gushy on me," he says, and his thin lips smile. Because she hasn't asked in a while, because it seems as if she's no longer interested, he says, "I charged it to the Visa."

"Okay," she says. With the monthly bills getting fatter and fatter, she and Alfredo had agreed to put a freeze on their credit card spending, but she chooses not to reprimand him here because (1) that he paid with the card means that he did not pay with cash, which means that he did not go out and do something stupid to get that cash; (2) Isabel has made some recent credit card purchases of her own, including, but not limited to, the birthday balloons that are currently hiding at the bottom of the trash can, the birthday cake, the birthday candle, and the musical table birthday present; (3) as he paces in front of his successfully installed air conditioner, Alfredo looks happier than he has in weeks, maybe months, and Isabel needs his good mood to snowball.

"Well what you waiting for?" she says. "Plug it in."

The machine grumbles to life. Isabel and Alfredo lean toward it, as if welcoming a friendly visitor into their home. In his mama's arms, Christian Louis struggles to get at this strange new beast, to touch its buttons and flashing green lights, to slide his fingers into its upturned vents.

"Shouldn't the air be cooler?" she says.

"It needs to warm up."

"It needs to warm up to get cold?"

Alfredo hooks the hem of his work shirt over the vents. The air impregnates him, swells his shirt so that the buttons seem to be straining. He chuckles, a deep *ho ho ho,* as if this is what's expected of all men who've been suddenly, stupendously potbellied.

"Get out the way," Isabel says. "You're blocking the air."

"Thought it wasn't cool enough for you."

"Move it," she says.

Alfredo comes close to her, to steal Christian Louis's nose. "Can you say no more mosquitoes?" he asks. "Can you say no more sweaty balls?"

This is the moment to be terrific, she thinks. With the AC humming. With Christian Louis straining between them, in Mama's arms but reaching for the thumb in Papi's fist. This is the moment to tell him everything. May not get a better chance all night.

"It isn't very cold though, is it?" he says.

"It's fine," she says. Like any longtime couple, in order to practice their craft they sometimes switch positions in an argument. "It just needs time," she says.

"Maybe something's wrong with the filter."

"It's fine," she says. "Leave it alone."

Stooped over, squinting, he hits some of the beep-beep buttons on the AC's console.

"It's *fine,*" she says.

He adjusts the temperature. He switches the settings from cool to fan to money saver, and back again to cool. The AC groans with impatience. Alfredo turns it off, stares at it with his hands on his hips. He gives it a light slap, a warning to get its act together, and when he turns it back on, the AC sputters, clears its throat, and then shuts down completely. Just like that. At the same time, the living room light goes out. At the same time, the kitchen light goes out. At the exact same time—

when the AC shuts down, and when the kitchen and living room lights go out—the refrigerator stops humming. And the coffeemaker clicks off. And the microwave clock goes dark. And the sound of all the power in the apartment going dead seems somehow louder than the sound of all the power in the apartment alive.

"Goddamnit," Alfredo says.

"I told—"

"Don't," he says. He closes his eyes. "Don't say a word."

What do they do first? They do what everyone does first. They try flipping the light switches. With blank expressions on their faces, they flip the switches up and down, well past the point of where it might actually start working. They go hunting for the circuit breaker box—why is it so f-ing hard to locate the circuit breaker in a *studio apartment*?—and, oh hello, they find it in the cupboard with the pancake mix and the number one birthday candle. How about that? The main circuit breaker is big and black and serious-looking, the mother of all light switches, and it turns over with a satisfyingly loud click. But it doesn't do any good. The power stays off. They open the fridge and immediately regret opening the fridge, allowing all that cool fog to escape. They take the AC's fat-headed plug and slide its three prongs into a surge protector, then they take that surge protector and plug it into the wall. They try turning on the AC. Nothing. They try flipping the light switches again.

Outside, cars are honking their horns. Alfredo opens a window and hot air jumps into the apartment. The honking grows louder, angrier. The building across the street is dark, each of its apartments without light, but that might not mean anything. It's early still, not even five o'clock, and most people haven't come home from work yet. To get a better look out the window, Alfredo leans forward and bangs his head.

"I can't fucking—"

"Hey!" Isabel tilts her chin toward Christian Louis, who sits on the carpet and plays with the Styrofoam. "Language please."

"I can't get my f-ing head," Alfredo says, "through that f-ing window with them bars in the way."

"Well," Isabel says. "That's kind of the idea."

He presses his cheek against the bars. "I think I can maybe see the

street corner. Wow. I think the traffic lights are out. This is crazy. Hey—you wanna go outside?"

She comes up behind him, puts her chin on his shoulder. "What if it's terrorists?" she says.

"In *Queens*?"

With Isabel still hovering over his shoulder, Alfredo tries calling his parents. The cell phone screen flashes Connecting . . . Connecting . . . Connecting, a promise it eventually breaks with Signal Lost. Alfredo redials and gets the same runaround. A call continuously pushed up a mountain, a signal that's never found. When Alfredo tries again without success, Isabel volunteers her own phone. It was a gift from Alfredo, given to her last June after the incident, and it has only five numbers saved in its memory: Alfredo's (duh); the video store where she still works part-time; Pizza Sam's; Peking Kitchen; and the Batista residence, which Alfredo is dialing right now, and which, in a moment of bored rebellion, Isabel labeled "Babysitters R Us." When the words flash across the screen, Alfredo smirks.

The call goes through. Sort of. It seems to connect—Isabel thinks she might even hear a ring—but then an automated female voice tells them that the network is busy. Whatever that means. Sounding almost bored, almost distracted, as if she were washing her robot hair, the automated voice tells Alfredo to call back later.

He taps the phone against his chin, stares distantly over the top of Isabel's head. She knows that look. He has officially checked out, transported himself into some past or future self. He walks into the kitchen, and, as Christian Louis had done hours earlier, he rattles the doors to the cupboard under the sink. He asks where the scissors are, so he can cut the duct tape on the handles, and it unfortunately falls to Isabel to tell him that the good scissors are, well, they're inside the cupboard under the sink.

"Where are the *bad* scissors?" Alfredo says. "Or do I not want to know?"

"You can use a knife," she says.

"That's why all the knives are dull?"

"The knives aren't dull," she says. "What you want in there anyway?"

A direct question. How foolish of her. She sits on the futon, watches Alfredo saw at the duct tape with his massive wad of house keys. He has his back to her, his shoulders hunched near his ears, and while Isabel can't see his face, she's pretty sure his tongue is clamped down

between his teeth. He throws open the cupboard doors. He pulls out all the candles—all the pillars and floaters and votives and tea-lights—and stuffs them into a blue plastic grocery bag.

"What the fuck?" she says.

"Language!" he says, sounding delighted to have scored so easy a point.

"Those are mine," she says.

"Don't worry," he says without turning around. "I'm gonna leave some here."

"Those are my candles."

"Don't be selfish, all right? I'm taking them to my parents. Remember them? You used to live in their house for a year?"

"You can't be serious," she says. "You're *leaving*?"

"My parents are old, Izzy. The power has gone out. I'm going to go over to their apartment, see if they're okay." He fills a second bag with Isabel's candles. "I'm not being a bad guy here."

She picks Christian Louis up off the floor and pulls him into her lap. "We're coming with you."

"You can't, I'll be going way too fast." He snaps his fingers. "I'm going to *run* over there."

"But it'll be dark soon."

"Exactly," he says. "Exactly my point."

"But," she says, and Christian Louis grabs at her mouth, as if he wants to shut her up, keep her from saying something she can't take back. She bites down on his fingers, softly, then not so softly. "We have to sing 'Happy Birthday,' " she says. "We have to open presents. We have to eat the cake before it melts."

Alfredo comes out of the kitchen to stand over them. His stomach grumbles; the bags hang heavy in his hands. Isabel won't say anything, and he won't look at her. He stares down at the carpet, afraid, she thinks, to see the chastising scar zigzagged under her eye. In the movie version of her life . . . no, no, no, no, no, no, no . . . she promised herself that she'd leave that line of thinking behind. She doesn't live up on the screen, she lives in *this life*, in a hot, powerless studio apartment in Corona, Queens. She seizes Christian Louis's wrists. She can't have him reaching toward his father. Alfredo needs to know he's leaving not two people but one unit, united against him. She jiggles the baby on her knee. She shoves her nose in his hair, smells the sweet soft crown of his head. Baby powder. Ripe apricots. No-tears shampoo. When Alfredo

walks away, the glass of the votive candles clinks together, as if they were toasting to someone's health, as if they were wishing the world's travelers a hearty bon voyage.

"Be right back," Alfredo says, but Isabel's heard that shit before.

At first Alfredo thought it might only be his block that lost power—wouldn't that be just his luck?—but as he walks through Corona he sees one defunct traffic light after another. The one-family homes are dark. The three-family homes are dark. The churrascarias, the botáni-cas, the farmacias, the eyebrow threaders, the pizza parlors, the liquor stores, the auto body shops, the Seoul Glass Emporium—they've all gone dark. In every storefront window, neon signs have turned gray, veins without blood. The whole neighborhood's been knocked out. Who knows? Maybe the whole borough. Alfredo feels surrounded not by buildings but by the molted skin of buildings. Queens, for the first time in his life, looks exhausted.

He stops at the corner of Northern and Junction boulevards. His arms are tired. His boxers stick to his thighs. It is here, at this intersec-tion, that his new home, Corona, becomes his old home, Jackson Heights. Out in the street, halfway between those two worlds, a silver-haired black guy directs traffic. He wears an ill-fitting marine uniform and blows on a cheap plastic whistle. Instead of a baton, he wields an empty water bottle, and yet the cars respond, braking when he tells them to brake, speeding up when he lets them. He blows his whistle at Alfredo, invites him across the street.

Without any red lights, Alfredo could drive for miles and miles, his foot on the gas the entire time. He could drive clean out of New York and into a new life in a new state, a state with electricity. Not that he has a car. Or even knows how to drive.

As he crosses the street, he gets close enough to the ex-marine to see the gravy spotting his sleeve. He asks the guy what's going on—*What's the story?*—and the guy's answer is simple.

"End of the world."

Alfredo walks into Jackson Heights. The people he passes—the dog walkers, the butchers outside their shops, the Dominican dudes on milk crates—they all smile and nod, as if to say, *Here we go again.* For a little under two years, they've been waiting for something like this.

And now that it's here, in the form of a blackout, snipping their reading lamps, cutting off their telenovelas and subway lines, New Yorkers resort to one of their oldest fail-safes: aggressive indifference. A shrug of the shoulders. A smile and a nod. When the apocalypse arrives, when a door opens in the sky and God's throne appears sparkling like jasper, and the seven angels blow seven trumpets, and fire devours the armies of Satan, the good people of New York will stick their heads out their windows and say, *Eh*.

"You better drink plenty of water," an old white lady tells him. She's coming out of the supermarket, pushing her own cart, smelling strongly of vinegar. She wraps her dry hand around his wrist. "This kind of heat?" she says, shaking her head sadly. "You better stay *hydrated*."

"Do you know what's going on?" he asks.

"What's going on?" she says.

"No, I'm asking. What's going on? What happened to the power?"

"I haven't got the foggiest," she says. She jerks her head behind her, toward Manhattan. "But I know it's out. Everywhere. Even in the City. And you better drink plenty of water."

"I will," Alfredo says. "I promise." He loves this old lady a little bit, wants to escort her home, make sure she gets there in one piece, but he knows if he offered, he'd just end up spooking her. He keeps walking. He thinks of that poor bastard Brian Schwartz, the college boy whose shift started when Alfredo's ended. If that old lady is right, if the power went out in Manhattan, then Brian's probably stuck in the elevator, his hands pressed to the walls. Man oh man, like being buried alive.

Alfredo misses his brother. It sneaks up on him sometimes, all the time, Brian Schwartz in an elevator, Jose Batista Jr., in the Cavalry Cemetery, and the grief of it, the weight of it, sits on Alfredo's chest like a brick. He can't stop it from coming. Despite everything, Alfredo misses his brother and he does not know what kind of man that makes him.

But, strangely, the farther he walks into his old neighborhood, their old neighborhood, the less he thinks about it. He knows of course that thinking about not thinking about it is a kind of thinking about it, but Jackson Heights, even blacked out, hums with distractions.

Up ahead, a mob of purple-shirted day campers encircle a fire hydrant. It is the most tempting hydrant for miles around. Without any arms, without even the thalidomide stumps of your average fireplug, the hydrant looks particularly defenseless, naked almost, and yet it is kept

safe, perpetually closed, unfairly benefiting from the Mafioso-like protection of a red-bricked firehouse one block away. The children's shirts are soaked through from some earlier, easier escapade. Their hair is wet, their sneakers squishy. One of the boys crouches down in front of the hydrant and fondles its lone breast. If he has a wrench, Alfredo can't see it. But maybe kids these days don't need the brute instruments of Alfredo's youth. Maybe this kid has charm, maybe he can sweet-talk the water out of the pump. The boy is watched, but everyone on this block, on all these blocks, is watched. Behind him, in sidewalk beach chairs outside a travel agency, dark-skinned men mumble words of encouragement. It feels good, Alfredo thinks, to be back in Jackson Heights. Purple, shiny, huddled close together, the children look like a cluster of grapes, and rather than puncture their group, Alfredo steps into the street and goes around. In a parked car, with the windows rolled up, an Indian family of four shares a bucket of fried chicken. You won't see that in Corona. Things seem more alive here, more colorful. Although that might not be fair. It's possible that Alfredo, in his new neighborhood, hasn't been looking hard enough. He hasn't been to the Lemon Ice King of Corona, for instance, hasn't even gone to Flushing Meadows Park to check out the Unisphere. But are the pigeons' eyes in Corona this red? Does the Corona air smell of baked bread, of melted cheese?

Alfredo finds himself, midreverie, on a problematic stretch of sidewalk. Set halfway down this row of stores, like a decaying tooth, lurks Gianni's Pizza. At this time of day, it's probably full of Alfredo's old friends, some of whom spent time with him in lockup last June before the PDs got everyone's cases thrown out of court. *Warrantless search, Your Honor!* Alfredo wants to see those guys, and he doesn't want to see those guys. As he slows down, he catches his reflection in a ninety-nine-cent store. He hates turning around in the middle of the street— it always makes him feel like an asshole—but what else can he do? For the benefit of those who might be looking, he comes to a complete stop, makes a *tsk* sound and throws his head back with exaggerated frustration, as if he forgot to turn the oven off, the iron off, as if he left an important piece of classified microfilm in the wrong titanium suitcase. He spins around on his heel. Goes the way he came. As he passes the Indian family, he keeps his head down, makes a left on Northern

Boulevard. By doing so, he travels, as he always meant to travel, in the opposite direction of his parents' place.

He sets up shop in front of the Alleyway. The Laundromat has closed its doors for the night, but the nail salon stays open. Whether this is the Rapture or Osama bin Laden, some ladies still be needing their manis and pedis. Across the street the Koreans who bought the candy store struggle to pull down their security gate. Worried about looters, and rightfully so. Alfredo, who is feeling good, happy to be here, hollers at the Koreans. Tells them the security gate is electricity powered and won't be budging anytime soon. They throw their hands up, as if swatting at flies, and then go back to pulling on their gate. Whatever. That's their business. They're trying to close, but Alfredo's just getting started. Opportunity's knocked. Alfredo spreads the candles in a half circle around his feet, as if he were warding off evil spirits. He positions pillars with pillars, votives with votives. Like the Statue of Liberty, he hoists a torch in the air.

"Get 'em while you still can, folks. Gonna be dark for a hot minute. Get your candles. Blackout special. Five-dollar candles. Get your candles here. Bring home some light. To your husbands and wives. Five dollars a candle. Five dollars apiece. Buy four, get one free. Five dollars, five dollars, five dollars. Need all the light you can get, folks. Gonna get bad tonight. Terrorists coming to kill us. What do you say? Five dollars. Get your light right here. Queens prices. Can't beat 'em. Five dollars apiece. Get your light. Gonna need some light. Selling it here. Stay out of the dark. Everybody needs some light. Five dollars apiece. Talking about light, folks. Light for sale. Light!"

A few hours later, with the sun turning orange behind her head, Isabel finally tracks down her man. She shifts the baby in her arms, checks his diaper for softness. When Alfredo sees them walking toward him, he laces his hands behind his head, probably thinking it makes him look casual, like an awfully cool dude lounging on a beach blanket, but really he looks like a man preparing himself to be arrested.

"How much for the whole thing?" Isabel says.

"That's a lot of candles," he says.

"I thought maybe I'd get a family discount." Christian Louis yanks

on her ponytail, as if he were ringing a bell. "I thought maybe since they were my fucking candles—"

"Hey!" Alfredo says, and tilts his head toward the baby.

"Are you serious?" she says. "Are you *seriously* telling me what I can and cannot say?"

Alfredo watches a taper candle roll away from him, all on its own, and get stuck in the space between sidewalk panels.

"You see my parents?" he says.

She did. She tried waiting at home, lasted a full ninety minutes, but when the apartment shadows thickened, she scooped up Christian Louis and bolted out the door. When they got to Babysitters R Us, Lizette clapped her hands together, squealed with abuela delight. She had birthday presents, she had noisemakers, she had party hats, she had some nice ripe bananas she could fry up . . . but what she did not have, what she hadn't even seen today, was a five-foot six-inch flat-assed Puerto Rican pendejo. To get out of the house, Isabel practically had to peel Lizette's fingers off Christian Louis. She begged them not to go. Talked about the blackout of seventy-seven. Said it wasn't safe for a mother and her young child to be out on the streets when the sun went down. But Isabel—how stupid of her—thought Alfredo might be in some kind of trouble.

"I want to say I'm surprised," she says. "I want to *be* surprised. But you know what?"

"I was gonna replace all the candles I sold," he says. He sounds excited. "But that's not all I was gonna do. I was gonna buy Christian Louis a chair for his new table. The sickest chair they had. I was gonna take you out for a romantic dinner, just me and you. Do it right, you know. Get us back on track. I was gonna pay off some of the Visa bill."

"And how many candles you sell so far?"

He shrugs, deflated. "It's not the busiest block."

"Maybe you're not the best salesman," she says.

Christian Louis turns red. His birthmark glows. He's been up for too long, overstimulated, feeding off Mama's fury, and now he squirms in her arms, moments away from a crankfest explosion. She didn't bring the stroller because she wanted Christian Louis up against her chest, wanted to feel, through his skin, the thump-thump of his heartbeat. She's regretting her sentimentality. She gives him her house keys, which

he sticks under his tongue. Happy birthday! Face soured, he chucks the keys into the street, and then, of course, unavoidably: the wrath.

"Shh," Alfredo says. He comes closer to rub Christian Louis's back. "You see him toss them keys?" Alfredo asks softly. "Little man's gonna be a strikeout king."

"You can't be leaving us anymore," she says. The baby still wails between them, mouth open, his enraged face tilted toward the red-slatted rooftops. Birds bend the branches of a tree. They perch themselves on streetlamps and telephone poles, under air conditioners and awnings, their bright avian eyes turned to the street. "You hear me?" Isabel says.

"I'm out here for *us*," Alfredo says.

"You want to do us a favor? Stop leaving."

"A guy came up to me," Alfredo says, looking her in the face. "White guy. I tried to sell him a candle, and he called me a piece of trash. Got in my space. Said I was exploiting something or another, you know? I thought he was going to kill me. A big guy. Then I thought that maybe he'd been sent to kill me, you know? Someone my brother knew. Someone Shifrin knew. I think about this shit all the time. This guy's in my face and I'm like this is it. Here we go."

"And did he?"

"Did he kill me?" Alfredo says. He looks down at his work shoes, his work pants, his work shirt, as if he wants to make certain before he answers. "No," he says.

"There you are," Isabel says.

"Here I am."

"So I'm pregnant," she says. She looks up at the sky. "You think we'll see stars tonight?"

Alfredo leans against the brick wall behind him. He doesn't collapse against the wall or fall against it as if he'd been punched in the chest. He does it calmly, bends his body to the bricks. He puts his hands deep down into his pockets.

"I think it's a boy," she says. She's not certain. This new baby hasn't started whispering secrets in her ear yet, but she feels inside of her a decidedly masculine presence. She imagines him—a quarter of an inch long, half the size of her pinky nail—stretching his legs out in front of him, hands plunged in pockets, trying to look casual as the uterine walls around him expand. "You want a little brother?" she asks Christian Louis. "You want a little bro to boss around?"

"I don't think I can handle this," Alfredo says.

She misunderstands him. When Alfredo says he can't handle this, he means he feels unqualified to handle this in a moral sense. He considers himself a corrupt human being—the things he's done, the things he thinks—a man unfit to raise one boy, much less two. In the last year, each folder in his intracranial filing cabinet has been tagged with the ass-reaming rebuke *And you're supposed to be a father?* He can't face more stickers on his files, stickers emblazoned with this unborn baby's name.

But Isabel thinks he's talking about money. She thinks he means they can't raise two children on his elevator boy's salary. And so when he says he can't handle this, she says, "Sure we can." She has him hold the baby, positions his arms so that they provide an acceptable sling of support. She asks, "How much you selling these candles for?"

"Five dollars," he says.

She rolls her eyes. She stoops over to pick up her house keys and the candle that fell between sidewalk panels.

"I'm keeping this one," she says, and slips the candle into her back pocket. "This one came to me."

Christian Louis seizes his father's finger and clamps down hard. Isabel turns away from them. She walks to the lip of the curb, where the sidewalk meets the street. People come and go, fanning themselves with takeout menus. Right around here, just up the block in fact, her mother the puta is probably in her recliner, halfway through a pre-evening nap, a white tube sock draped over her eyes. In just a moment Isabel will start hawking candles—the finest candles in Queens—for the low low blackout special price of ten bucks apiece. And eventually, when night falls and the streets darken, her voice will begin to falter. And when that happens, Alfredo will put their child in her arms, and the two of them will stand close together and take turns calling out prices. But first, before all that, while her voice is still strong, Isabel is going to scream. Her mother is sleeping and Isabel wants to wake that bitch up. She wants to see pigeons scatter and curtains flutter, wants glass to break, wants to drown out her baby's crying, wants to knock butterflies out of the air and ice cream out of cones and buttons off of shirts, wants ears to bleed and buildings to crumble, wants to feel the tingle, the rattle, the streets catching fire. Get ready. She takes a deep breath, cups her hands to her mouth.